Soils

Preface

Soils of the world are important primarily because they support plants. Plants feed the animals; and man lives by eating both plants and animals. Aside from fish, man and his animals are entirely dependent upon products from the soil.

If the soil is low in phosphorus, plants growing there will also be low in phosphorus, and man and his animals will have deficient teeth and inferior bones. For we obtain essential minerals only from plants and animals that get them from the soil. Our primary source of essential minerals is the growing plant; hence, this book on soils and plant growth.

The objectives of this book are:

1. To help the student to develop intellectual curiosity leading toward an understanding of the basic principles underlying soil science.

2. To assist the reader in organizing, evaluating, and applying scientific information about soils.

3. To convey an appreciation of the dynamic character of soil and soil research.

4. To try to instill into the student a scientific attitude by stressing the need for continually weighing new findings in terms of past observations and experiences.

5. To discourage the tendency to accept established practices and published information without subjecting them to critical study.

6. To provide the student with a practical approach to typical present-day soil problems.

7. To help the reader to enjoy a study of the soil and to appreciate the importance of soils to all human activity.

The author has gardened, farmed, studied agriculture, or taught soils to farmers, farm youth, and college students in Texas, Mississippi, Kansas, Illinois, Michigan, New York, and New Hampshire. In addition, he has been on special agricultural assignments in Brazil and Greece. It is hoped that this background has "flavored" this book, not with "regionalism," but with universalism. The author does not have any prejudice either for or against any region. On the contrary, it is the author's opinion that the principles of soils and plant growth are universal and that these principles can readily be adapted for solving practical problems anywhere in the world.

Roy L. Donahue

Acknowledgment

The sources of the facts presented in *Soils—An Introduction to Soils and Plant Growth* are given in the footnotes and in references at the end of each chapter. The *interpretations* of these facts are my own. I say "my own," but actually nothing is mine alone. My ideas have been strongly influenced by my past and present associates and by my students at Michigan State University, Cornell University, the University of New Hampshire, Texas A. & M. College, and Mississippi State College. Associates who have greatly influenced my opinions include Jethro Otto Veatch, Professor Emeritus of Soil Science, Michigan State University; the late Dr. C. E. Millar, formerly Head of the Department of Soil Science, Michigan State University; Dr. H. O. Buckman, Professor Emeritus of Soil Technology, Cornell University; Dr. Richard Bradfield, Professor of Agronomy, Cornell University; Dr. Carl Ferguson, formerly of the Department of Agronomy, Texas A. & M. College; Dr. Robert F. Chandler, Jr., Rockefeller Foundation, New York; Dr. Ide P. Trotter, Dean of the Graduate School, Texas A. & M. College; the late T. C. Richardson, Texas Editor, Farmer-Stockman, Dallas, Texas; Mr. Ferdie Deering, Editor, Farmer-Stockman, Oklahoma City; Mr. E. C. Martin, Administrative Assistant, Texas Extension Service, College Station; Sam Whitlow, Editor, Farmer-Stockman, Dallas, Texas; and Dr. Herbert E. Hampton, Professor of Agronomy, Texas A. & M. College.

Thanks are due my wife, Lola, who was happy to see the yard neglected and the garden weedy so that this book could be completed on time. Our children, Roger, Julian, and Jane, did extra work so that "Dad could work on his book."

To Anita Collind I owe a debt of gratitude for taking a personal interest in typing the manuscript.

Dr. Everett F. Evans, consultant in conservation education and curriculum, and co-author with me on *Our South: Its Resources and Their Use, The Range and Pasture Book,* and *Exploring Agriculture,* gave freely of his time to make *Soils—An Introduction to Soils and Plant Growth* more readable, more accurate, and more consistent. I can never repay him for this good work.

R. L. D.

Courtesy of North Carolina Agricultural Experiment Station, U. S. Department of Agriculture, American Potash Institute, and National Plant Food Institute

Plate 1. Left, severe nitrogen deficiency. Note yellowing begins at tip of lower leaves and proceeds up the midrib, giving a V-shaped pattern. Center, symptoms of extreme drought. As distinguished from nitrogen deficiency, drought affects upper as well as lower leaves. Severe potassium deficiency shows up in the plant on the right as a marginal scorch.

Courtesy of North Carolina Agricultural Experiment Station, U. S. Department of Agriculture, and National Plant Food Institute

Plate 2. Nitrogen made the difference! Nitrogen at the rate of 180 pounds per acre was applied to the corn on the left. The corn on the right received no added nitrogen. The yields were 110.3 and 24.4 bushels per acre, respectively.

Courtesy of U. S. Department of Agriculture and National Plant Food Institute

Plate 3. Potato plants, showing phosphorus-deficiency symptoms. Left, critical stage resulting from extremely low phosphorus supply. Terminal growth has stopped; plant did not recover when phosphorus supply was increased. Right, incipient stage showing stunted growth, dark green foliage, and cupping of lower leaves with some tip-burn. This plant recovered when phosphorus supply was increased.

Courtesy of Maine Agricultural Experiment Station and National Plant Food Institute

Plate 4. Left, normal growth of potatoes that received 2,000 pounds of 4-8-8 fertilizer. Right, potatoes showing phosphorus-deficiency symptoms; they received the same amounts of nitrogen and potash, but no phosphoric acid. These plants are darker green in color and stunted in growth, the foliage is crinkly, and the leaflets fail to expand normally. Growth continues beyond the normal time of maturity.

ROY L. DONAHUE

Professor of Agronomy on the
Kansas State College-International Cooperation Administration-India Team

SOILS

an Introduction
to Soils
and
Plant Growth

Englewood Cliffs, N. J.
PRENTICE-HALL, INC., 1958

© 1958, BY

PRENTICE-HALL, INC.

ENGLEWOOD CLIFFS, N. J.

LIBRARY OF CONGRESS
CATALOG CARD No.: 58-5075

PRINTED IN THE UNITED STATES OF AMERICA

82185

DEDICATION

This book is humbly and affectionately
dedicated to my college professor

JETHRO OTTO VEATCH

Professor Emeritus of Soil Science
Michigan State University

who did not tell me to major in soils, but through
his counsel led me to make the decision for myself.

Contents

PART I: FUNDAMENTALS OF SOIL SCIENCE

1   Soils and Plant Growth   3

Soil Factors Influencing Plant Growth   4
Early Concepts   5
A Modern Concept   6
Soil Fertility and Native Vegetation   8
Areas of Mineral Deficiency and Toxicity   9
Summary   10

2   Physical Properties   16

Mechanical Analysis   16
Soil Separates   18
Soil Texture   19
Coarse Fragments   22
Organic Soils   22
Particle Density   22
Bulk Density   24
Pore Space   24
Soil Structure   25
Summary   27

3   Parent Materials of Soils   29

Classification of Parent Materials   29
Residual Materials (Minerals and Rocks)   30
Materials Transported by Water   32
Materials Transported by Wind   33
Materials Transported by Ice   33
Materials Transported by Gravity   34
Cumulose Materials (Peat and Muck)   34
Physical Weathering (Disintegration)   35
Chemical Weathering (Decomposition) and Chemical
   Transformation   35
Summary   36

4 Soil Formation and Classification   **38**

Climate and Soil Formation   38
Parent Material and Soil Formation   42
Relief and Soil Formation   43
Biosphere and Soil Formation   43
Time and Soil Formation   43
Zonal Soils   48
Intrazonal Soils   50
Azonal Soils   52
Summary   53

5 Soil Survey   **54**

The Use of Soil Surveys   55
The National Co-operative Soil Survey   57
Soil Series, Types, and Phases   57
The Soil Profile   60
Soil Profile Description   60
The Soil Survey Report   61
Land-Capability Classification   62
Productivity Ratings   64
Forest Site Classification   65
Soil Maps as an Aid to Engineering   65
Nutritional Predictions   65
Land Classification for Irrigation   66
Land Classification for Drainage   67
Other Uses of Soil Surveys   67
Summary   67

6 Chemical and Colloidal Properties   **69**

Colloidal Clay (Clay Crystals)   69
Organic Soil Colloids (Humus)   71
Cationic Exchange   71
Soil Texture and Exchange Capacity   72
Organic Matter and Exchange Capacity   73
Adsorption and Exchange of Anions   73
Soil pH   74
The Fixation of Potassium   76
Phosphorus Fixation and Chelation   77
Summary   77

7 Life in the Soil   **79**

Soil Microflora and Soil Structure 79
Plant Roots 81
Soil-Inhabiting Mammals 83
Earthworms 85
Arthropods and Gastropods 87
Protozoa and Nematodes 87
Distribution of Soil Microflora 88
Physiological Classification of Bacteria 88
Autotrophic Bacteria 89
Heterotrophic Bacteria Classified 89
Symbiotic (Legume) Bacteria 90
Nonsymbiotic Nitrogen-Fixing Bacteria 92
Nonnitrogen-Fixing Heterotrophic Bacteria 93
Fungi 93
Actinomycetes 94
Algae 94
Summary 95

8 Organic Matter   **97**

Functions of Organic Matter 97
Chemical Properties 98
Biological Properties 100
Maintaining Soil Organic Matter in Humid Regions 101
Maintaining Soil Organic Matter in Semiarid Regions 103
Summary 104

9 Soil Water   **106**

Infiltration 106
Permeability 108
Soil Water Classified 109
Measuring Soil Moisture 110
Available Water 112
Percolation 113
Leaching Losses of Nutrients 115
Summary 116

10 Plant Nutrition   **119**

Elements Essential for Plants and Animals 119
Forms in Which Nutrients Are Taken in by Plants 119

10 Plant Nutrition (Cont.):

The Mechanism of Nutrient Uptake 120
Foliar Nutrition of Plants 122
Soil Physical Conditions and Plant Nutrition 124
Nitrogen 125
Phosphorus 126
Potassium 127
Calcium 127
Magnesium 128
Sulfur 128
Micronutrients 128
Summary 129

PART II: APPLIED SOIL SCIENCE

11 Lime and Liming Practices   132

Why Soils Are Acid 133
What Lime Does in the Soil 134
Crop Response to Lime 135
Liming Materials 136
Chemical Guarantees of Lime 138
Physical Guarantees of Lime 139
Lime Requirement of Crops 140
Effect of Lime on Soil pH 140
Soil pH and Nutrient Availability 141
Methods of Applying Lime 142
Overliming 143
The Lime Balance Sheet 144
Summary 144

12 Fertilizers and Their Characteristics   146

The Fertilizer Industry 146
Solid Nitrogen Materials 150
Ammonia 152
Ammoniation 153
Nitrogen Solutions 153
Material Supplying Phosphorus 154
Materials Supplying Potassium 155
Secondary and Minor Elements 156
Formulation of Mixed Fertilizers 157

12 Fertilizers and Their Characteristics (Cont.):

Examples of Open Formulas 158
Problems of Manufacturing Mixed Fertilizers 161
Acidity or Basicity of Fertilizers 161
Summary 162

13 Use of Fertilizers 164

Fertilizer Consumption 164
Nutrients Removed by Crops 166
Time of Applying Fertilizers 166
Fertilizer Placement 168
Crop Increases from Fertilization 169
Profit from Using Fertilizer 169
Fertilizers and Soil Moisture Efficiency 171
Summary 173

14 Tillage 177

Tillage and Plant Growth 178
Deep Tillage 181
Tillage to Control Insects 183
Tillage and Organic Matter 183
Soil Moisture and Tillage 183
Kinds of Pan Formations 183
Tractor-Tire Compaction 185
Plow Pans and Infiltration Rates 186
Cropping Systems and Soil Structure 187
Factors Restricting Root Growth in Compact Horizons 188
Summary 189

15 Water Conservation 191

The Hydrologic Cycle 191
Precipitation 194
Runoff 195
Storage of Water in the Soil 196
Terracing for Water Conservation 196
Contour Tillage to Conserve Water 198
Forests and Water Conservation 199
Plants as Luxury Consumers of Water 201
Land-Use to Conserve Water 203
Problems of Frozen Soils 205
Summary 208

16 Soil Conservation 210

The Nature of Water Erosion   211
Rainfall and Erosion   213
Water Erosion a Selective Process   213
Depth of Topsoil and Crop Yield   214
Cropping Systems to Reduce Soil Losses   215
Terracing to Control Erosion   216
The Problem of Wind Erosion   217
Wind Erosion a Selective Process   218
Controlling Wind Erosion   219
Summary   221

17 Irrigation Practices 223

Water Quality   224
Consumptive Use of Water   226
Water-Holding Capacity of Soils   228
Normal Irrigation Depth for Crops   228
Amount and Frequency of Irrigations   228
Sprinkler Irrigation   230
Furrow Irrigation   231
Corrugation Irrigation   233
Border Irrigation   234
Summary   235

18 Drainage Systems 237

Drainage in the United States   237
Benefits from Drainage   239
Soils That Require Drainage   239
Drainage Capacity of Soils   242
Surface Drainage   243
Tile Drainage   245
Summary   246

19 Manure, Compost, Sewage Sludge, and Sawdust 247

Composition of Cow Manure   247
The Care of Manure   248
Reinforcing Manure   250
Nutrients in Feed and Manure   251
Poultry Manure   252

19   Manure, Compost, Sewage Sludge, and Sawdust (Cont.):

Rabbit Manure   253
Manure as a Mulch on Corn   253
Manure and Available Water   253
Manure and Crop Yields   254
Dollar Value of Manure   254
Organic Matter and Soil Structure   255
Compost   255
Sewage Sludge   256
Sawdust   256
Summary   259

20   Management of Mineral Soils in Humid Regions   261

Cropping Systems and Soil Conditions   262
Cropping Systems and Losses of Nitrogen   264
Legumes in Rotation   264
Fertilizer and Lime Needs of Potato Soils   265
Long-Time Fertility Trends   267
Summary   269

21   Management of Peat and Muck Soils   271

Origin of Peats and Mucks   271
Classification of Peat   272
Organic Soils of the Florida Everglades   272
The Uses of Peat   273
Adapted Crops   274
Fertilization and Liming   275
Water Control   275
Subsidence   275
Tillage Compaction   276
Special Problems of Management   277
Summary   278

22   Management of Soils in Arid and Semiarid Regions   280

Soils in Arid and Semiarid Regions   281
Reclamation of Saline and Alkali Soils   282
Plants as Indicators of Saline and Alkali Soils   286
Greasewood—An Accumulator of Salt   287
Salt Tolerance of Crops   288

22   Management of Soils in Arid and Semiarid Regions (Cont.):

Soil Moisture and Crop Response   290
Cropping Systems   293
Fallow   294
Summary   297

23   Soil and Plant Diagnosis   **299**

How to Obtain a Soil Sample for Chemical Testing   299
Soil Testing   301
Plant-Tissue Tests   301
Deficiency Symptoms in Corn   302
Deficiency Symptoms in Small Grains   304
Deficiency Symptoms in Cotton   304
Deficiency Symptoms in Legumes   305
Deficiency Symptoms in Truck Crops   306
Plant Symptoms on Saline and Alkali Soils   307
Correlation of Soil Tests, Plant-Tissue Tests, and Plant-
   Deficiency Symptoms   309
Portable Soil-Testing Kits   309
Summary   311

Appendix A (Glossary)   **314**

Appendix B (Conversion Factors)   **337**

**Appendix C (Atomic Weight and Valence of
   Common Elements)**   **338**

Author Index   **339**

Subject Index   **343**

PART I

Fundamentals of Soil Science

1

Soils and Plant Growth

Soils supply nutrients for growing plants, and plants furnish feed for animals and food and fiber for us.

Some soils are naturally productive and support luxuriant crops of great value with very little human effort, while other soils are so unproductive that they support almost no useful plant life regardless of what is done to them. Between these two extremes lie the majority of soils, which must be limed, fertilized, drained, or irrigated to make them desirably productive.

Productive soils are ones which contain adequate amounts of all essential elements in forms readily available to plants, are in a good physical condition to support plants, and contain just the right amount of water and air for desirable root growth. Not only must the soil contain the essential elements, be in good tilth for plant support, and contain the proper amounts of air and water, but also it must supply these essentials *every day* in the life of the plant.

Too little calcium even for a day may reduce crop yields. And if the soil is hard and crusty so that it is too wet after a rain and too dry a few days later, plant growth is stunted. To be more specific, all crop plants need the same kinds of elements as well as water and air, but plants differ in the relative amounts of their requirements of these essentials. For example, blueberries, alfalfa, and rice all require the same elements, as well as air and water. But blueberries grow on soils very low in both available nutrients and water, while alfalfa requires a very fertile soil which is constantly moist. On the other hand, alfalfa and rice both have a high water requirement, but alfalfa must have plenty of air mixed with the water, whereas rice does well when the soil is flooded.

3

FIG. 1.1. Soils are important primarily because plants grow in them.
Courtesy Allan B. Prince, New Hampshire Agricultural Experiment Station.

Soil Factors Influencing Plant Growth

From the soil, plant roots receive mechanical support, essential elements, water, and oxygen.

Some soils are in such a physical and chemical condition as to encourage plant roots to grow deeply and to extend long distances laterally. These soils are ideal because the plants growing in them will be windfirm, drought-resistant, and capable of absorbing nutrients from a large volume of soil. Plant roots may be restricted by naturally or artificially compacted layers, infertile horizons, too much or too little soil moisture, or soluble salts in toxic quantities.

At present 16 elements are known to be essential for the growth of crop plants. They are carbon, hydrogen, and oxygen from air and water; phosphorus, potassium, sulfur, calcium, iron, magnesium, boron, manganese, copper, zinc, molybdenum, and chlorine from the soil; and nitrogen from both soil and air.

Water and air occupy pore spaces in the soil. Following a heavy and prolonged rain, the soil pores may be almost completely filled for a few hours. After a day or two, some water will have moved downward in response to gravity, and the larger pores will be emptied of their water but filled with air. With a further loss of water by evaporation or transpiration, air will replace more of the water. The next soaking rain will repeat this process.

The important part of this air-water relationship is that there must be enough total pore space and that the pore spaces must be of the proper size ranges to hold enough air and water to satisfy plant roots between cycles of rainfall or irrigation.

Early Concepts

Xenophon, a Greek historian (430-355 B.C.), is credited with first recording the value of green-manuring crops when he wrote:

"But then whatever weeds are upon the ground, being turned into the earth, enrich the soil as much as dung."

Cato (234-149 B.C.) wrote a practical handbook in which he recommended intensive cultivation, crop rotations, the use of legumes for soil improvements, and the value of manure in a system of livestock farming. Cato was also the first to classify land according to its relative value for specific crops. His classification included:

1. Land for vineyards (grapes)
2. Land for gardens
3. Willow land
4. Land for olive trees
5. Meadow land
6. Corn land
7. Timber land
8. Land for small trees
9. Land for oak trees

The usefulness of turnips for soil improvement was emphasized by Columella about A.D. 45. Liberal amounts of manure were recommended for turnips, and the turnips were to be plowed under and the land planted to corn. Also advocated by Columella were land drainage, and the use of ashes, marl, clover, and alfalfa to make the soil more productive.

Then the barbarians of the north conquered Rome. Scientific agriculture and other forms of art and culture were arrested until nearly 1600.

A classical experiment was performed by Van Helmont (1577-1644) in Holland. He put a five-pound willow tree in 200 pounds of soil (oven-dry basis). The tree received only water for five years. At the end of this period, the soil weighed only two ounces less than 200 pounds, but the willow tree weighed 169 pounds and three ounces. Since the tree was given only water, Van Helmont reasoned that water was the "principle" of vegetation.

While Van Helmont's experiment was advanced for the times, his reasoning was later proved false on two counts:

1. The loss of two ounces of soil, which he ignored, consisted of minerals such as calcium, potassium, and phosphorus, that were absorbed by the tree. If Van Helmont had burned the willow tree at the end of the experiment, he could have recovered his two ounces of soil minerals.

2. The willow tree consisted of carbon from the carbon dioxide of the atmosphere, and oxygen from the atmosphere. The occurrence of carbon and oxygen from air as constituents of the willow tree refute Van Helmont's conclusion that water is the "principle" of vegetation.

In 1731 Jethro Tull, of Oxford, concluded that cultivation was one of the prime essentials of growing plants, and that nitre, water, air, fire, and earth all contributed to increases in plant growth. Liebig, a German chemist, in 1840 published "Chemistry in its Application to Agriculture and Physiology." His thesis was that carbon for plant nutrition came from carbon dioxide of the atmosphere, hydrogen and oxygen from air and water, and nitrogen from ammonia. Phosphates were stated to be necessary for seed production and potassium for the development of grasses and cereals.

In 1843, the oldest agricultural experiment station in the world was established by J. B. Lawes and J. H. Gilbert at Rothamsted, England, a few miles from London. This experiment station laid the groundwork for modern research techniques in soils and plant growth.

A Modern Concept

A close look at a handful of fresh, moist, productive loam soil will reveal much information that has not yet appeared in books. The soil is composed of lumps which are held together by fine roots. Upon closer examination with a 10-power hand lens and a 100-power microscope, these lumps of soil are also observed to be held together by fungal hyphae and the vegetative parts of actinomycetes. Shiny streaks on the soil lumps were probably made by the slimy secretions of earthworms. This slime, as well as the gums and resins remaining as temporary end-products of organic decomposition, are good cementing agents that help plant roots, fungi, and actinomycetes to glue the individual particles into desirable lumps.

Now imagine that you plant a seed in the handful of soil. Soon root hairs permeate the entire soil mass, following mainly along the crooked paths left by previous plant roots, earthworms, ants, fungal hyphae, and the vegetable parts of actinomycetes.

FIG. 1.2. A close look at the soil will show that it is composed of lumps of varying sizes that are held together by fine roots. *Courtesy Henry Corrow, New Hampshire Extension Service.*

The root hairs obtain nutrients by an exchange of cations and anions between the surface of the roots and the surfaces of clay and humus particles. There is also a similar exchange between the root surface and the soil solution. The root uptake of calcium, for example, is accomplished by the release of two hydrogen ions from the root to either the soil solution or the surfaces of clay or humus, in exchange for a calcium ion from these sources to the root. Similarly, the plant root appears to exchange OH ions for nitrates, sulfates, phosphates, and other anions. One difference in the plant uptake of cations and anions is the fact that most cations are on the surfaces of clay and humus, whereas most anions are in the soil solution.

FIG. 1.3. The slime secreted by earthworms aids in cementing the soil aggregates into desirable sizes for greater plant growth. *Courtesy Soil Conservation Service.*

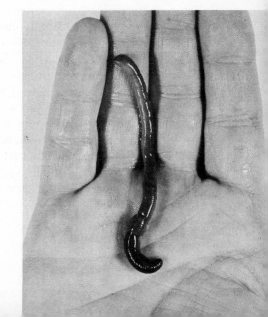

1.4. Hilgard observed that after clearing longleaf pine forests and cropping the land to corn, fertilizers were necessary after two or three years to insure good yields.
Courtesy Florida Forest Service.

Soil Fertility and Native Vegetation

Contrary to popular belief, many soils, even when virgin, were never plentifully supplied with all essential elements. Before the common use of lime and fertilizers, farmers would adjust to differences in native fertility by choosing the best virgin land, farming it until crop yields declined, then clearing other virgin land. This is the common practice even today in many underdeveloped countries where lime and fertilizers are not readily available.

Hilgard, one of our best early American soil scientists, in his book first copyrighted in 1906, made a shrewd observation on the relationships between native vegetation and soil fertility in the South when he wrote:

"Thus in the long-leaf pine uplands of the Cotton States, the scattered settlements have fully demonstrated that after two or three years cropping with corn, ranging from as much as 25 bushels per acre the first year to ten and less the third, fertilization is absolutely necessary to further paying cultivation. Should the short-leaved pine mingle with the long-leaved, production may hold out for from five to seven years. If oaks and hickory are super-added, as many as twelve years of good production without fertilization may be looked for by the farmer; and should the long-leaved pine disappear altogether, the mingled growth of oaks and short-leaved pine will encourage him to hope for from twelve to fifteen years of fair production without fertilization." *

In the Northeast and in the Lake States, tulip poplar, basswood, elm, ash, and white oak usually grow on soils that are naturally more fertile than is indicated by the growth of red pine, hemlock, beech, red oak, and the spruces.

* E. W. Hilgard, *Soils*. New York: The Macmillan Co., 1911.

Fig. 1.5. Hilgard further observed that if oaks and hickories grew with long-leaf or shortleaf pine, the soil stayed productive without fertilizer for as many as 12 years.
Courtesy Arkansas Division of Forests and Parks.

Areas of Mineral Deficiency and Toxicity

Plants are capable of taking from the soil only that which is available. It is often true that nutrients may be adequate for normal plant growth but not in sufficient concentration for adequate livestock nutrition. Likewise, a plant can absorb certain elements which it may or may not need and which do no harm to the plant but are toxic to livestock.

The forage growing in many soils in the following states does not contain sufficient phosphorus for adequate livestock nutrition:

Oregon	Texas	Tennessee
Nevada	North Dakota	Florida
Idaho	Minnesota	South Carolina
Montana	Michigan	North Carolina
New Mexico	Kentucky	Virginia
	Maryland	New York

Cobalt has not yet been added to the list of elements essential for plants, but animals require it in their nutrition. Cobalt deficiency has been reported in livestock in these and other states because the soils and forage plants do not contain sufficient cobalt:

Oregon	Virginia
Michigan	Maryland
Louisiana	Massachusetts
Florida	Vermont
South Carolina	New Hampshire
North Carolina	Wisconsin

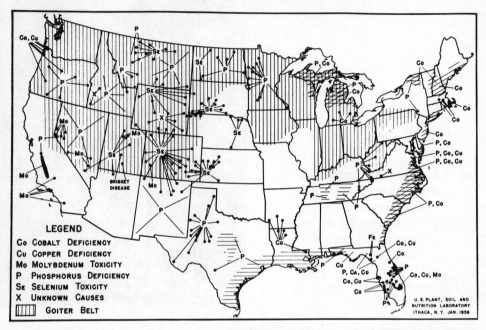

FIG. 1.6. Deficiency and toxicity symptoms in livestock have been officially reported as shown on the map.

Courtesy Kenneth Beeson, U. S. Plant, Soil, and Nutrition Laboratory, U. S. D. A.

Copper deficiency in livestock due to inadequate copper in the soil has been reported in:

Oregon	Florida	Maryland	Virginia

Molybdenum toxicity has been officially observed in livestock in:

California	Nevada	Utah	Florida

Selenium toxicity in livestock has been known in several western states since 1857, but the cause was understood first in 1928. Soils containing as little as one part of selenium per million may produce vegetation that is poisonous. Although selenium is not necessary for plants, many plants accumulate enough of it to be toxic to livestock in these states:

Utah	Kansas	South Dakota	Montana
Colorado	Wyoming	Nebraska	North Dakota

Summary

Soil is the original source of nutrients and food for all plant and animal life. Most soils need lime, fertilizers, drainage, or irrigation to produce satisfactory crops. Crops receive from the soil mechanical sup-

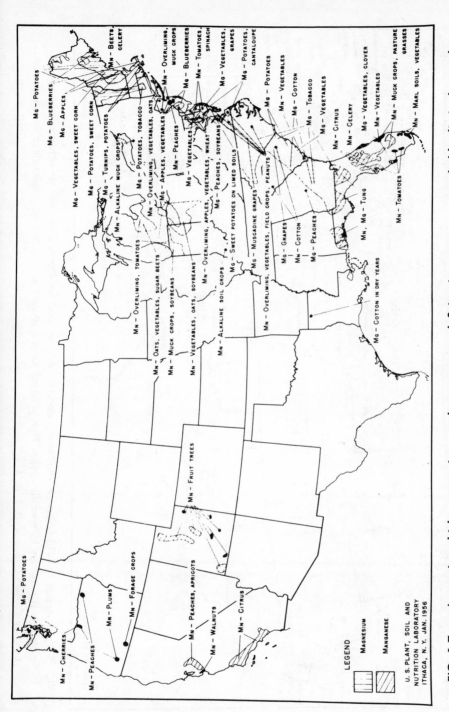

FIG. 1.7a. Areas in which magnesium and manganese deficiencies occur, as revealed by limited growth or other symptoms of nutritional troubles in specific crops. The general areas shown are actually intermittent in character.   *Courtesy Kenneth C. Beeson, U. S. D. A.*

11

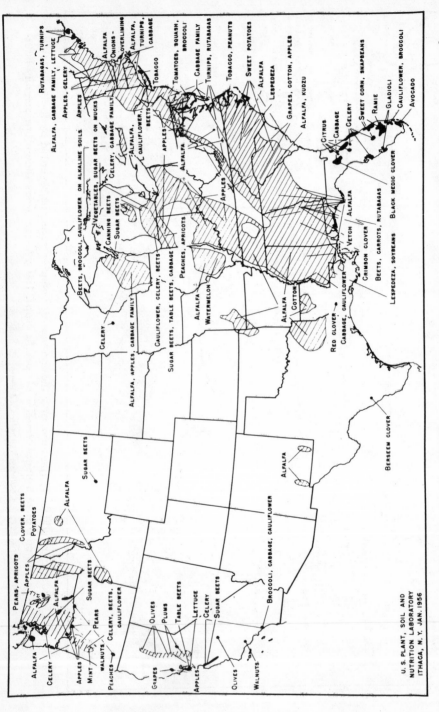

FIG. 1.7b. Areas in which boron deficiency occurs, as revealed by limited growth or other symptoms of nutritional troubles in specific crops. The general areas shown are actually intermittent in character.

Courtesy Kenneth C. Beeson, U. S. D. A.

U. S. PLANT, SOIL AND
NUTRITION LABORATORY
ITHACA, N. Y. JAN. 1956

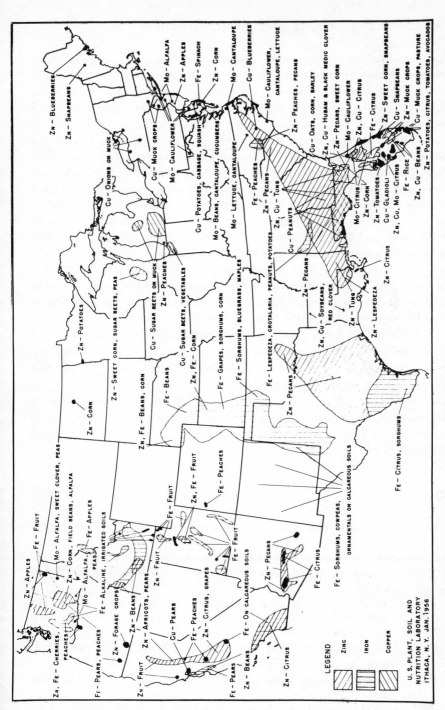

FIG. 1.7c. Areas in which copper, iron, molybdenum, and zinc deficiencies occur, as revealed by limited growth or other symptoms of nutritional troubles in specific crops. The general areas shown are actually intermittent in character.   *Courtesy Kenneth C. Beeson, U. S. D. A.*

13

port, essential elements, water, and oxygen. There are at present 16 elements known to be essential for the growth of crop plants. Water and air in the soil occupy the same pore spaces; after a rain most of the pores contain water, but in a few days air gradually replaces some of the water.

The value of manure, cover crops, and legumes was recognized before the time of Christ. Early scientists and philosophers looked for the "principle" of vegetation, but centuries later scientists concluded that there were **many** "principles." Liebig in 1840 was among the first of the scientists to explain plant nutrition in a manner somewhat similar to the way it is known today. Then the Rothamsted Experiment Station was established in 1843 near London, England, and field plot techniques as a scientific instrument came into being.

Soil granules are held together by plant roots, the vegetative parts of fungi and actinomycetes, slimes from such animal life as earthworms, and waxes and resins from the partial decomposition of bacterial bodies and the remains of higher plants.

Plant roots take in nutrients by an exchange of cations and anions from the soil solution and the surfaces of clay and humus particles. There is a good correlation between the general fertility level and the growth of native vegetation.

Forages in various parts of the United States have been reported deficient for livestock in phosphorus, cobalt, and copper. In certain areas forages have also been shown to contain toxic amounts of molybdenum and selenium.

Questions

1. Compare and contrast the soil requirements for blueberries, alfalfa, and rice.
2. Name the essential elements that come only from the soil.
3. What were some of the recommended soil improvement practices before the Christian era?
4. Calculate the percentage of soil minerals in the live willow tree in Van Helmont's experiment.
5. What was Liebig's thesis?
6. What happened in 1843 that is of interest to scientific agriculture?
7. Explain the uptake of plant nutrients.
8. Give a specific example of the relationship between soil fertility and native vegetation.
9. Compare the areas where phosphorus and cobalt are deficient in forages for livestock.
10. Which is more widespread, selenium or molybdenum toxicity?

References

Beeson, Kenneth C., *The Mineral Composition of Crops with Particular Reference to the Soil in Which They Were Grown.* U.S.D.A. Misc. Pub. 369, 1941.

Donahue, Roy L., and M. K. Thornton, *The Story of the Soil.* The Texas A. & M. College System, College Station, Texas, 1953.

Hilgard, E. W., *Soils.* The Macmillan Company, New York, 1911.

Russell, E. John, and E. Walter Russell, *Soil Conditions and Plant Growth.* Longmans, Green and Co., New York, 8th ed., 1950.

Soils and Men, The 1938 Yearbook of Agriculture. United States Department of Agriculture.

Thompson, Louis M., *Soils and Soil Fertility,* Second Edition, 1957, McGraw-Hill Book Co., Inc., New York.

Weir, W. W., *Soil Science, Its Principles and Practices.* J. B. Lippincott Co., Philadelphia, 1949.

2

Physical Properties

The soil is a complex mechanical system. For a soil to be in good physical condition for plant growth, the air, water, and solid particles must be in the right proportions at all times. Every cubic inch of soil that is expected to support plant life must be:

1. Open enough to permit the right amount of rainwater or irrigation water to enter the soil, but not so open as to allow excessive loss of water and plant nutrients by deep percolation.

2. Sufficiently retentive of moisture to supply roots with all needed water, but not so retentive as to create undesirable suspended water tables.

3. Well enough aerated to permit all plant root cells to obtain oxygen at all times, but not excessively aerated to the point of preventing a continuous contact of roots with moist soil particles.

To understand how an engine functions, it is necessary to take the engine apart and study each separate piece. The same is true with a soil. When a soil is taken apart and each part studied, the process is called a *mechanical analysis*.

Mechanical Analysis

When scientists take a soil sample apart, they usually find that it is composed of:

1. Large pebbles and stones
2. Coarse sand
3. Fine sand
4. Something resembling flour (silt)

5. Lumps or clods of varying sizes which consist of clusters of soil particles (mostly clay)

6. Plant roots

7. A dark substance spread throughout the soil mass which most people call *humus*

8. Dead leaves and twigs

9. Ants, earthworms, and other forms of animal life.

Not all of these substances are properly a part of the mechanical analysis of the soil. Only the mineral matter which is less than two millimeters in diameter is to be considered soil. This means that, before a mechanical analysis is made, the soil sample must be screened through a two-millimeter sieve. All of the rocks, pebbles, leaves, and plant roots that do not go through the two-millimeter screen are discarded.

In like manner, the humus is not a part of an official mechanical analysis. If the humus percentage is fairly large, it must be destroyed before the determinations are made. Treatment with hydrogen peroxide will destroy most of the humus.

After the soil sample has been screened through a two-millimeter sieve and, if necessary, the humus destroyed, a particle size-distribution analysis can be made. The purpose of a mechanical analysis is to determine the amounts of *individual* soil grains of the various sizes. To get an accurate estimate of the percentages of each group of individual (primary) soil particles, it is necessary to completely disperse all lumps or aggregates so that they can be separated into their primary groups. If complete dispersion were not obtained, a small lump of clay the same size as a sand grain would be reported as sand in the results of the mechanical analysis.

There are several methods of mechanical analysis, but only two have wide acceptance: the *Pipette Method* and the *Bouyoucos Hydrometer Method.** Both methods are based upon the differential rate of settling of soil particles in water, and the accuracy of the methods depends upon these conditions or assumptions:

1. Complete dispersion of the soil in water

2. A dilute suspension of soil in water so that the soil grains can settle without bumping into or otherwise influencing each other

3. All soil particles settle as if they were smooth and rigid spheres

4. The rate of settling of the particles is assumed not to be influenced by the walls of the settling vessel.

5. A constant and known temperature of the soil-water suspension.

6. All soil particles are of the same density.

* For other current methods of mechanical analyses consult: V. J. Kilmer and L. T. Alexander, "Methods of Making Mechanical Analysis of Soils," *Soil Science* 68:15-24, 1949.

FIG. 2.1. Students in an introductory soils laboratory making a mechanical analysis of a soil by the Bouyoucos hydrometer method.
Courtesy Agronomy Department, University of New Hampshire.

Soil Separates

A mechanical analysis reports the percentages of different size groups of particles. From coarse to fine, these size groups (soil separates) and their diameter ranges, according to the system of the U. S. Department of Agriculture, are given in Table 2.1. For convenience in memorizing the size ranges, a comparison is shown of the diameter range of the soil separates with the United States monetary system.

TABLE 2.1. The Soil Separates and Their Diameter Range, Compared with the U. S. Monetary System

Soil Separate	Diameter Range (Millimeters)	U. S. Monetary System (Dollars)
Very coarse sand *	2.0 —1.0	2.00—1.00
Coarse sand	1.0 —0.5	1.00—0.50
Medium sand	0.5 —0.25	0.50—0.25
Fine sand	0.25—0.10	0.25—0.10
Very fine sand	0.10—0.05	0.10—0.05
Silt	0.05—0.002	0.05— —
Clay	Less than 0.002	— — —

* Before 1947 this soil separate was known as *fine gravel*. When comparing recent mechanical analysis data with that made before Jan. 1, 1938, it should be noted that before 1938, *silt* was defined as particles between 0.05—0.005 mm in diameter, *clay* as less than 0.005 mm; and particles less than 0.002 mm in diameter were called *colloid*.

Natural field soils are always mixtures of soil separates. The relative percentages of the seven soil separates in a field soil are almost infinite in possible combinations. Soils may contain from less than one per cent to almost 100 per cent of any soil separate. To bring order to this apparently chaotic situation, the United States Department of Agriculture has established limits of variations among the soil separates and assigned a textural name to each group. For example, soils containing a large amount of sand are *sandy,* those with a high content of silt are *silty,* and soils containing a high percentage of clay are *clayey.* When the soil does not exhibit the properties of either sand, silt, or clay, it is called a *loam.* The limitations in the range of each textural name were established upon significant differences in the physical properties of each textural class.

Soil Texture

"Soil texture" refers to the relative percentages of sand, silt, and clay in a soil. The size of the sand grains further modifies the textural name. The more common soil textural names, listed in order of increasing fineness, are: *

Sand	Silt loam	Silty clay loam
Loamy sand	Silt	Sandy clay
Sandy loam	Sandy clay loam	Silty clay
Loam	Clay loam	Clay

For convenience in determining the textural name of a soil from the mechanical analysis, an equilateral triangle has been adapted for this purpose. Figure 2.1 is a guide for a textural classification. The left angle represents 100 per cent sand, the right 100 per cent silt, and the top angle, 100 per cent clay.

The textural name of a soil may be obtained from the results of a mechanical analysis in this way. Assume that the mechanical analysis of a soil is as follows:

Sand	*Silt*	*Clay*
40%	40%	20%

To find the textural name of this soil, locate the 40 along the bottom of the triangle, then proceed upward and to the left along the heavy line. All points along this 40 line are 40 per cent sand. To locate the 40 per cent silt line, look along the right side of the triangle labeled *per cent silt,* until you come to 40. Follow down and to the right along the heavy line until this line intersects the 40 per cent line of the sand. Now check this point of intersection by locating the 20 per cent point along the left side

* The terms "clay," "silt," "very fine sand," "fine sand," and "coarse sand" are used as names for soil separates as well as for specific soil textures.

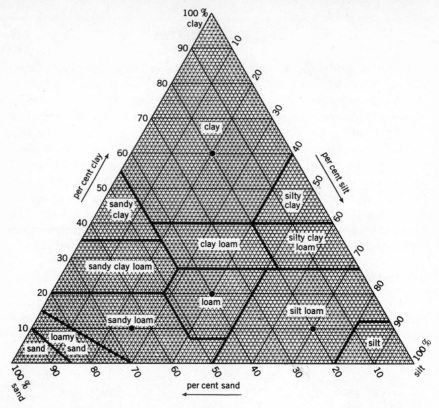

FIG. 2.2. Guide for textural classification as of May 1, 1950. (Source: U. S. Department of Agriculture, Bureau of Plant Industry, Soils, and Agricultural Engineering.)

of the triangle (per cent clay). Follow this 20 per cent line to the right; it should intersect at the same point where the 40 per cent sand line and the 40 per cent silt line intersected. This point is the midpoint of the textural name *loam*.

Follow the same instructions and find the textural name of soils with the following mechanical analyses:

Soil	Sand	Silt	Clay
No.	%	%	%
1. Sandy loam	65	25	10
2. Clay	20	20	60
3. Silt loam	20	70	10

Because of the small scale of the chart, it is not possible to show all recognized soil textures in the sandy range. For this purpose it is necessary to use the following descriptive terms. For completeness, all soil textures are shown that are based upon soil particles less than 2 millimeters in diameter.*

* Source: *Soil Survey Manual*. U. S. Department of Agriculture Handbook No. 18, 1951, pp. 210-211.

SANDS. Soil material that contains 85 per cent or more of sand, less than 10 per cent clay, and less than 15 per cent of silt plus clay.

Coarse sand: 25 per cent or more of very coarse and coarse sand and less than 50 per cent of any other grade of sand.

Sand: 25 per cent or more of very coarse, coarse, and medium sand, and less than 50 per cent fine or very fine sand.

Fine sand: 50 per cent or more of fine sand or less than 25 per cent of very coarse, coarse, and medium sand, and less than 50 per cent of very fine sand.

Very fine sand: 50 per cent or more of very fine sand.

LOAMY SANDS. Soil material that contains at the upper limit 85 to 90 per cent sand and between 10 and 15 per cent clay. At the lower limit, a loamy sand may contain from 70 to 85 per cent sand, and the percentage of silt plus twice the percentage of clay shall not exceed 30.

Loamy coarse sand: 25 per cent or more very coarse and coarse sand, and less than 50 per cent of any other one grade of sand.

Loamy sand: 25 per cent or more very coarse, coarse, and medium sand, and less than 50 per cent fine or very fine sand.

Loamy fine sand: 50 per cent or more fine sand or less than 25 per cent very coarse, coarse, and medium sand and less than 50 per cent very fine sand.

Loamy very fine sand: 50 per cent or more of very fine sand.

SANDY LOAMS. Soil material (1) that contains more than 52 per cent sand but less than 20 per cent clay and in which the percentage of silt plus twice the percentage of clay exceeds 30, or (2) that contains between 43 and 52 per cent sand but less than 7 per cent clay and less than 50 per cent silt.

Coarse sandy loam: 25 per cent or more very coarse and coarse sand and less than 50 per cent of any other one grade of sand.

Sandy loam: 30 per cent or more of very coarse, coarse, and medium sand, but less than 25 per cent very coarse sand and less than 30 per cent very fine or fine sand.

Fine sandy loam: 30 per cent or more fine sand and less than 30 per cent very fine sand or between 15 and 30 per cent very coarse, coarse, and medium sand.

Very fine sandy loam: 30 per cent or more of very fine sand or more than 40 per cent fine and very fine sand, at least half of which is very fine sand and less than 15 per cent very coarse, coarse, and medium sand.

LOAM. Soil material that contains 7 to 27 per cent clay, 28 to 50 per cent silt, and less than 52 per cent sand.

SILT LOAM. Soil material that contains 50 per cent or more silt and 12 to 27 per cent clay or 50 to 80 per cent silt and less than 12 per cent clay.

SILT. Soil material that contains 80 per cent or more silt and less than 12 per cent clay.

SANDY CLAY LOAM. Soil material that contains 20 to 35 per cent clay, less than 28 per cent silt, and 45 per cent or more sand.

CLAY LOAM. Soil material that contains 27 to 40 per cent clay and 20 to 45 per cent sand.

SILTY CLAY LOAM. Soil material that contains 27 to 40 per cent clay and less than 20 per cent sand.

SANDY CLAY. Soil material that contains 35 to 55 per cent clay and 45 to 65 per cent sand.

SILTY CLAY. Soil material that contains 40 to 60 per cent clay and 40 to 60 per cent silt.

CLAY. Soil material that contains 40 per cent or more clay, less than 45 per cent sand, and less than 40 per cent silt.

Coarse Fragments

Mineral fragments in the soil larger than 2 millimeters in diameter are not strictly a part of the soil but must be recognized because they greatly influence the use of the land. In the classifying and mapping of soils, the names of the large fragments are attached to and precede the textural name of the soil. For example, if a sandy loam contains a large number of stones, the textural name becomes *stony* sandy loam.

The commonly accepted classification of the coarse fragments in soils is set forth in Table 2.2.

Organic Soils

The preceding textural names are used for designating only the mineral particles. When the surface soil is mostly organic matter, the term *muck* or *peat* is used. *Muck* is the name used when the organic surface, to approximately a foot in depth, is so well decomposed that the plant remains are not recognizable. With less decomposition the soil is called *peat*.

Particle Density *

One assumption necessary in making a mechanical analysis is that all soil particles have the same density. While the assumption is fairly accurate for this purpose, the differences in particle density are important in the determination of other soil constants, such as pore space.

* *Particle density* is sometimes called *specific gravity*.

TABLE 2.2.   The Shape, Kind, Size, and Name of Coarse Fragments in Soils *

Shape of Fragment	Kind of Fragment	Size and Name of Fragment		
		Up to 3" in diameter	3"–10" in diameter	More than 10" in diameter
Rounded	Any kind	gravelly	cobbly	stony
Angular	Chert	cherty	coarse cherty	stony
	Other than chert	angular gravelly	angular cobbly	stony
		Up to 6" in length	6"–15" in length	More than 15" in length
Thin, flat	Sandstone, limestone, or schist	channery	flaggy	stony
	Slate	slaty	flaggy	stony
	Shale	shaly	flaggy	stony

* Source: *Soil Survey Manual,* U. S. Department of Agriculture Handbook, No. 18, 1951, p. 214.

Particle density is usually expressed as grams per cubic centimeter. Thus, if a solid soil particle were the shape of a cube, one centimeter on each edge, and it weighed 2.65 grams, it would have a particle density of 2.65.

The particle density of mineral soils over the world varies from approximately 2.60 to 2.80, with an average of approximately 2.65. Soils with a large amount of organic matter will have average particle densities of approximately 2.5 or below.

Accurate determinations of particle density may be made with a specific gravity bottle (pycnometer). An approximate method of determining the average particle density of a handful of pebbles is to:

1. Weigh the pebbles.

2. Drop them into a graduated cylinder which is partly full of water and observe the increase in volume. For example, if 300 grams of pebbles displaced 113 cubic centimeters of water, the particle density is obtained

by dividing the 300 by 113, or approximately 2.65. This example merely illustrates a principle and is not suggested as an accurate method.

Bulk Density *

Bulk density is the density or weight of a given bulk (unit volume) of soil. The grams per cubic centimeter of soil, including the pores, is the bulk density.

It may be easier to visualize bulk density if a method for its determination is described. Obtain an iron cylinder with no ends which is slightly smaller than a pint ice-cream container. One edge should be sharpened for ease of driving in the soil. Drive the cylinder into the soil so that the top is even with the soil surface. Dig out the buried cylinder, using care to slice off the bottom evenly without disturbing the soil core. Transfer the entire contents into a pint ice-cream container and place in an oven to dry. (Drying this large a soil volume will take a week or more.) Weigh the soil daily after it has been in the oven for a week. When two successive daily weighings are the same, it can be assumed that the soil has reached oven dryness. The bulk density can be calculated by dividing the oven-dry weight in grams by the volume of the soil in cubic centimeters. Thus, if the oven-dry weight of the soil core is 630 grams and the volume of the same soil core is 450 cubic centimeters, the bulk density is obtained by dividing 630 by 450 = 1.4.

Pore Space

The pore spaces in a soil consist of that portion of a given volume of soil not occupied by solids, either mineral matter or organic matter. Under field conditions, the pore spaces are occupied at all times by water and air.

The relative amounts of air and water in the pore spaces fluctuate almost hourly. During a rain, water drives air from the pores, but as soon as deep percolation and evaporation carry away some of the water, air replaces the water which is lost.

The percentage of any given volume of soil which is occupied by pore space may be calculated from the formula:

$$\% \text{ pore space} = 100 - \frac{\text{Bulk density}}{\text{Particle density}} \times 100$$

It is easier to understand why this formula is correct by using the following line of reasoning:

* *Bulk density* was formerly called *volume weight* and *apparent specific gravity*.

$$\text{The \% solid space} = \frac{\text{Bulk density}}{\text{Particle density}} \times 100$$

and the % pore space plus % of solid space = 100%

so the % pore space = 100 − % solid space

and therefore $\text{\% pore space} = 100 - \dfrac{\text{Bulk density}}{\text{Particle density}} \times 100$

Soil Structure

The relative proportion of primary (individual) particles in a soil mass is known as *texture;* how these particles are grouped together into aggregates is *structure.* Natural aggregates are called *peds* and are fairly water-stable; while the word *clod* is restricted to an artificially formed aggregate that is usually not water-stable. Plowing a clay soil when it is too wet will make the soil cloddy.

FIG. 2.3. An example of desirable soil structure. Type—spheroidal; Class—medium; Grade—moderate.
Courtesy Ezee Flow Division, Avco Distributing Corp.

Two other terms are often confused with a ped. One is a *fragment,* which consists of a broken ped, and the other is a *concretion,* which is formed within the soil by the precipitation of salts dissolved in percolating waters.

FIG. 2.4. An example of undesirable soil structure. Type—blocklike; Class—coarse; Grade—strong.
Courtesy Ezee Flow Division, Avco Distributing Corp.

Soil structural terms are divided into three categories: [*]

1. Type (shape and arrangement of peds)
2. Class (size of peds)
3. Grade (degree of distinctness of peds)

Each of these three categories of soil structure will be discussed separately.

Type of Soil Structure (Shape and Arrangement of Peds)
There are four principal types of soil structure:

1. *Platy.* Peds exhibit a matted, flattened, or compressed appearance.
2. *Prismlike.* Peds exhibit a long vertical axis and are bounded by flattened sides.
3. *Blocklike.* Peds resemble imperfect cubes like baby blocks, but are usually smaller.
4. *Spheroidal.* Peds are imperfect spheres like marbles, but are usually smaller.

Class of Soil Structure (Size of Peds)
The five general classes of soil structure are:

1. Very fine or very thin
2. Fine or thin
3. Medium
4. Coarse or thick
5. Very coarse or very thick

[*] Source: *Soil Survey Handbook*, U. S. Department Handbook No. 18, 1951, pp. 225-230.

Actual size designations of the peds vary with each *type* of soil structure.

Grade of Soil Structure (Degree of Distinctness of the Peds)

The four terms in common use to designate the grade of soil structure are:

1. Structureless. No noticeable peds. This may mean the condition exhibited by loose sand or the cementlike condition of some clay soils or cemented soils.
2. Weak. Indistinct formation of peds.
3. Moderate. Moderately well-formed peds.
4. Strong. Very well-formed peds.

Summary

To be in the proper physical condition to support luxuriant plant growth, the soil must be sufficiently open to permit water and air to circulate freely but not so open as to lower the necessary retention of water for plant growth.

In order to study the physical parts of a soil, it is necessary to make a mechanical analysis, using only the mineral particles which are less than two millimeters in diameter. These mineral particles are classified by size ranges into seven groups known as **soil separates**. From the relative percentages of each soil separate, a special equilateral triangle is consulted in assigning the proper textural name to a particular soil. Mineral particles larger than two millimeters in diameter, known as coarse fragments, are classified by shape, kind, and size. Organic soils do not enter the textural classification scheme but are called "peat" if relatively undecomposed and "muck" if well decomposed.

For the mineral soil, particle density averages approximately 2.65 and bulk density, which includes pore space, 1.4.

Soil structure is classified by type (shape and arrangement of peds), class (size of peds), and grade (degree of distinctness of peds).

Questions

1. Why is the physical condition of a soil important in plant growth?
2. How should the soil be prepared for making a particle size-distribution analysis?
3. What assumptions or conditions are necessary in making a mechanical analysis of soil?
4. Name the soil separates and their diameter ranges.
5. Name five soil textures in the order of increasing fineness.
6. How does a loamy sand differ from a sandy loam?

7. How does the percentage of sand, silt, and clay differ in a silty clay loam and a silty clay?

8. What is the proper designation for a limestone fragment up to six inches in length?

9. Differentiate between bulk density and particle density.

10. What is meant by type, class, and grade of soil structure?

References

Baver, L. D., *Soil Physics*, John Wiley and Sons, New York, 3rd ed., 1955.

Shaw, Byron T., ed., *Soil Physical Conditions and Plant Growth*, Vol. II, Academic Press, Inc., New York, 1952.

Soils and Men, The 1938 Yearbook of Agriculture. United States Department of Agriculture.

Soil Survey Manual. Agriculture Handbook No. 18. United States Department of Agriculture, 1951.

3

Parent Materials of Soils

Soils have developed from minerals and rocks that were weathered by climatic forces until sufficient nutrients became available to support plants. Productive soils develop only from minerals and rocks plentifully supplied with all essential elements. Soils rich in available phosphorus are found only on parent materials that are well supplied with this element. The same is true for soils containing large amounts of available calcium, magnesium, potassium, and other mineral nutrients.

But the converse of this statement is not always true. Intense weathering and leaching may produce soils low in available phosphorus, calcium, magnesium, potassium, and other minerals, even though these nutrients are plentiful in the minerals and rocks comprising the parent materials. The Maury silt loam in central Tennessee is an example of a soil that responds to applications of phosphorus and calcium, even though the soil was developed on parent materials very rich in these elements. Warm temperatures cause year-round weathering, and a high rainfall leaches downward some weathered phosphorus and calcium.

Of the elements essential for plants, only nitrogen did not come from minerals and rocks. Nitrogen in the soil has its origin in bacterial and lightning fixation of atmospheric nitrogen.

Classification of Parent Materials

Parent materials from which soils are derived may be classified as *residual, transported,* or *cumulose.* Residual materials are those that have remained in place long enough for a soil to develop from them. Transported materials are mineral and rock fragments that have been moved in place by one or more of these agencies: water, wind, ice, and gravity. Cumulose materials are peats and mucks that have developed in place from plant residues and have been preserved by a high water table.

29

An outline may help to visualize the relationships among the parent materials.

I.   Residual material
     A. Igneous—granite, basalt, and andesite.
     B. Sedimentary—limestone, sandstone, and shale.
     C. Metamorphic—marble, quartzite, and gneiss.

II.   Transported material
     A. Water
         1. Alluvial—running water
         2. Lacustrine—lakes
         3. Marine—ocean
     B. Wind
         1. Eolian
         2. Loess
     C. Ice
         1. Moraine
         2. Till Plain
         3. Outwash Plain
     D. Gravity—colluvial

III.   Cumulose material (Organic)—peat and muck

Residual Materials (Minerals and Rocks)

A mineral is a substance that occurs in nature, has distinct physical properties, and is of a chemical composition which can be written in formula.

Rocks are mixtures of minerals; for that reason, their physical and chemical composition varies with the characteristics of the minerals comprising them. But a single mineral is seldom the parent material from which a soil develops; a soil is formed mainly from rocks.

Rocks are classified into *igneous, sedimentary,* and *metamorphic.* Igneous rocks have formed from molten material that has solidified. Sedimentary rocks have formed from sediments accumulated at the surface of the earth. These sediments may have been derived from either minerals, rocks, or organisms, or from precipitates from sea water. Metamorphic rocks have come from either igneous or sedimentary rocks that have later been transformed beneath the surface of the earth by heat, pressure, and chemically active liquids.

It is estimated that 3 per cent of the soils in the United States are residual and have developed in place from the underlying igneous,

FIG. 3.1.   This soil has developed from limestone, a sedimentary bedrock.
Courtesy W. T. Carter, Texas Agricultural Experiment Station.

sedimentary, or metamorphic bedrock. The principal examples are soils
from:

   1. Igneous rocks in the Piedmont Region and in the Rocky Mountains.

   2. Sedimentary rocks, such as limestone in central Tennessee, central Kentucky, along the Grand Canyon in Arizona, and in southern Mis-

FIG. 3.2.   A large metamorphic
rock is in the foreground;
note its layer-like structure.
*Courtesy T. C. Richardson, The
Farmer-Stockman.*

souri; and sandstone and shale in the Appalachian Mountains and in Oklahoma, northwest Arkansas, and north central Texas.

There are only a few areas where the soils have developed from metamorphic rocks such as marble, quartzite, and gneiss.

Materials Transported by Water

Materials that have been transported by water are classified as *alluvial, lacustrine,* or *marine.*

Alluvial materials are sediments that have been deposited by flowing water, such as small streams or large rivers. If the material that lies along the river is subject to periodic flooding, the deposit is known as a *flood plain.* Older deposits that were laid down by the river but are not now subject to flooding are called *terraces.*

Lacustrine materials were deposited in fresh-water lakes during glacial times. Depressions that were filled with water from melting glaciers gradually became filled with sediment. When the glacier retreated, the level of the lake receded, exposing sediments that had been deposited in the bottom of the lake. These are called *lacustrine* materials. The principal lacustrine deposits in the United States are found bordering the Great Lakes, in northeastern North Dakota and northwestern Minnesota, northwestern Nevada, and northwestern Utah.

Marine materials were formed by the deposition of sediments carried into the ocean by rivers. As the land surface was uplifted or the ocean receded, the sediments became weathered into soil. The principal marine sediments in the United States occur adjacent to the Gulf Coast and the Atlantic Coast.

FIG. 3.3.   Sand dunes in California.
Courtesy U. S. Geological Survey.

Materials Transported by Wind

Sand dunes and some deposition from present-day dust storms are called *eolian* deposits. Soil materials that were deposited following the last glacial period are known as *loess*, which is the German word for "loose."

Loessial soil materials are mostly silt loam in texture and occur mainly in the Mississippi Valley. There are large areas of loess in Kansas, Nebraska, Iowa, Missouri, Illinois, Indiana, Kentucky, Tennessee, and Mississippi. Extensive deposits also occur in Washington and Idaho.

FIG. 3.4.   Loess deposit in Iowa.
Courtesy U. S. Geological Survey.

Materials Transported by Ice

From perhaps 1,000,000 years ago to as recently as 10,000 years ago, continental ice occupied intermittently the land which is now the northern border of the United States. Some geologists claim that we are now simply in another interglacial period. Parts of Alaska, Greenland, and Iceland and the mountains of northern Europe are now occupied by a mass of ice similar to that which once covered parts of northern United States.

As snow continued to accumulate, pressure from its weight changed the snow to ice. After centuries of such build-up, the ice, under tremendous pressure, moved outward. In moving across rocks, sand, silt, and clay, the glacial ice picked them up, making a mass of dirty and stony ice. Apparently there was a greater movement outward during the winter build-up of snow; during the summer, the ice front melted. Water flowing from the melting ice carried sediment, while the larger rocks were dropped in place.

When the ice front melted more slowly than it advanced, deposits of sediment were built up, resulting in a series of stony hills at the ice margin. These are known as *moraines*. But when the ice front melted faster than it advanced, a smoother deposition resulted, known as *till plains*. Water gushing forth from a rapidly melting ice front carried fairly coarse sand particles and deposited them in a level plain. These are *outwash plains*.

FIG. 3.5. An example of a soil that has developed from glacial till plain materials. Such soils are usually stony in the entire profile. *Courtesy U. S. Geological Survey.*

Materials Transported by Gravity

Soil debris at the foot of a slope that moved there in response to gravity is called *colluvial* material. Colluvial material exists to some extent at the base of all slopes, but it is especially noticeable in mountainous topography where rock slides, slips, and avalanches are common.

Cumulose Materials (Peat and Muck)

Plant remains that for centuries have been preserved in shallow lakes are the peat and muck which we recognize today. *Peat* is the term used when the plants are recognizable; when plants decay beyond recognition, the deposit is called a *muck*.

Physical Weathering (Disintegration)

Minerals exposed at the surface of the earth in rocks, sands, silts, and clays are constantly being broken down by chemical and physical weathering.

Physical weathering processes include:

1. Freezing and thawing. The expanding force of freezing water is sufficient to split any mineral or rock.

2. Heating and cooling. This gives rise to differential expansion and contraction of minerals in rocks, tending to tear them apart. Temperature changes also bring about exfoliation, a loosening of an entire "cap" on a mineral or rock.

3. Wetting and drying. Wetting and drying disrupt clods of soil by causing them to swell and contract. Abrasion within the lump of soil makes the particles finer.

4. Erosion. Water carrying sediments in suspension or rolling them along the bottom of streams exerts a strong scouring action that grinds particles finer. Wind erosion acts in a similar manner.

5. Action of plants, animals, and man. Plants grow between rocks, splitting them apart. Animals are constantly scratching rocks, and this action on soft rocks aids in their disintegration. Man helps in physical weathering by plowing and cultivating, an action that results in breaking minerals and rocks into finer fragments.

Chemical Weathering (Decomposition) and Chemical Transformation

Physical disintegration is accompanied by chemical decomposition in weathering processes. Chemical weathering includes:

1. Oxidation. Oxygen readily combines with nearly all minerals to aid in chemical decomposition. An example of oxidation is:

$$4FeO \quad + \quad O_2 \quad \rightarrow \quad 2Fe_2O_3$$

ferrous oxide   plus   oxygen   ferric oxide (hematite)

2. Reduction. Under conditions of excess water, such as may be encountered during a flood, oxygen is less plentiful and, as a consequence, reduction takes place. Reduction may be illustrated in this manner:

$$2 Fe_2O_3 \quad - \quad O_2 \quad \rightarrow \quad 4FeO$$

ferric oxide (hematite)   minus   oxygen   ferrous oxide

3. Solution. Soluble minerals, such as halite (rock salt), dissolve readily in this manner:

$$NaCl \quad \rightarrow \quad Na^+ \quad + \quad Cl^-$$

halite   sodium ion   plus   chlorine ion

4. Hydrolysis. This process consists of a reaction with water and the formation of an hydroxide. An example of hydrolysis of a mineral is shown for orthoclase:

$$K\,Al\,Si_3O_8 \quad + \quad HOH \quad \rightarrow \quad H\,Al\,Si_3O_8 \quad + \quad KOH$$

orthoclase   plus   water   acid   potassium
                                    silicate   hydroxide
                                    clay

5. Hydration. A common example of hydration is the formation of limonite from hematite:

$$2Fe_2O_3 \quad + \quad 3H_2O \quad \rightarrow \quad 2Fe_2O_3 \cdot 3H_2O$$

hematite   plus   water   limonite
(red)   (yellow)

6. Carbonation. The atmosphere contains 0.03 per cent carbon dioxide but decomposing plants liberate it in large amounts. Carbon dioxide aids in chemical weathering because it makes minerals more soluble, for example:

$$Ca\,CO_3 \quad + \quad CO_2 \quad + \quad H_2O \quad \rightarrow \quad Ca\,H_2(CO_3)_2$$

calcite   plus   carbon   plus   water   calcium
(slightly   dioxide   bicarbonate
soluble)   (readily
                                                 soluble)

Summary

Soils have developed from minerals and rocks. All elements in the soil that are essential for plant growth, except nitrogen, originally came from the parent minerals and rocks.

Parent materials of soils are classified as **residual, transported,** and **cumulose.**

Residual materials are grouped into **igneous, sedimentary,** and **metamorphic** rocks. The accepted classification of transported soil materials is based upon the agencies of transport: **water, wind, ice,** and **gravity.** Cumulose materials have formed in place by the preservation of organic remains in shallow lakes.

Rocks and minerals are weathered into parent materials of soil by physical disintegration and chemical decomposition. Physical processes are: freezing and thawing, heating and cooling, wetting and drying, erosion, and the action of plants, animals, and man. Chemical weathering processes include: oxidation, reduction, solution, hydrolysis, hydration, and carbonation.

Questions

1. Why is it true that rich soils come only from minerals and rocks that contain an abundance of elements essential for plant growth? Why is not the converse also always true?
2. Residual and cumulose parent materials have both formed in place. In what way are the processes different?
3. What is a mineral?
4. Give an example of an igneous rock.
5. Compare marine and lacustrine sediments as to origin.
6. Contrast the texture of eolian and loess deposits.
7. Where are loessial soil materials found?
8. How does a moraine differ from a till plain?
9. Which physical weathering processes are most important in your community?
10. Give an example of oxidation.

References

Flint, R. F., *Glacial Geology and the Pleistocene Epoch.* John Wiley and Sons, Inc. New York. 1947.

Gilluly, James, Aaron C. Waters, and A. O. Woodford, *Principles of Geology.* W. H. Freeman and Co., San Francisco, California. 1953.

Longwell, C. R., et al., *Outlines of Geology,* 2nd ed. John Wiley and Sons, Inc. New York. 1941.

Lyon, T. L., H. O. Buckman, and N. C. Brady, *The Nature and Properties of Soils.* The Macmillan Co., New York. 1950.

Soils and Men, The Yearbook of Agriculture for 1938. U. S. Department of Agriculture.

Soil Survey Manual. U. S. Department of Agriculture Handbook No. 18. U. S. Department of Agriculture, 1951.

4

Soil Formation and Classification

At any specific location on the surface of the earth, five factors are acting simultaneously to produce the soil which we now observe. These five factors are:

1. Climate
2. Parent material
3. Relief
4. Biosphere
5. Time

Based upon the relative influences among these factors, soils are classified into *zonal, intrazonal,* or *azonal* soil groups. Zonal soils (sometimes called *normal* soils) have developed on well-drained parent materials, and their well-developed profiles are in equilibrium with the environment. Intrazonal soils have a distinct profile but are dominated in their characteristics by parent material or relief. Azonal soils have almost no profile because their parent materials have not been sufficiently weathered.

Climate and Soil Formation

Climate influences soil formation largely through precipitation and temperature. The average annual precipitation in the United States is presented as a hyetograph in Figure 4.1. Average annual temperature is portrayed by isotherms in Figure 4.2.

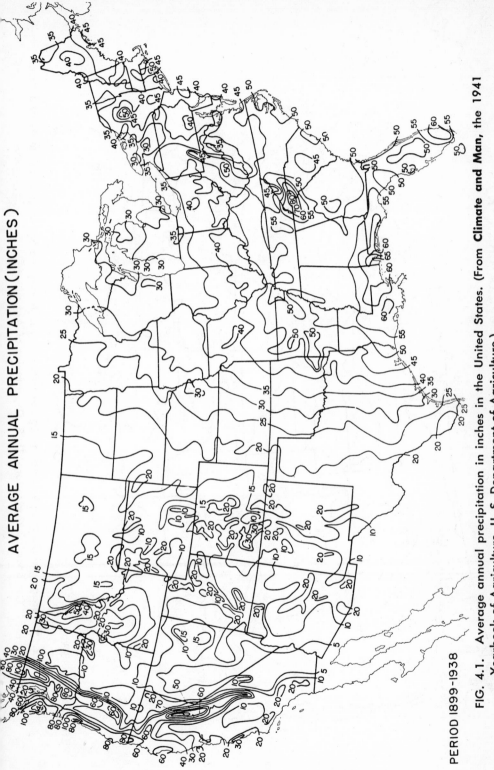

AVERAGE ANNUAL PRECIPITATION (INCHES)

PERIOD 1899-1938

FIG. 4.1. Average annual precipitation in inches in the United States. (From **Climate and Man,** the 1941 Yearbook of Agriculture. U. S. Department of Agriculture.)

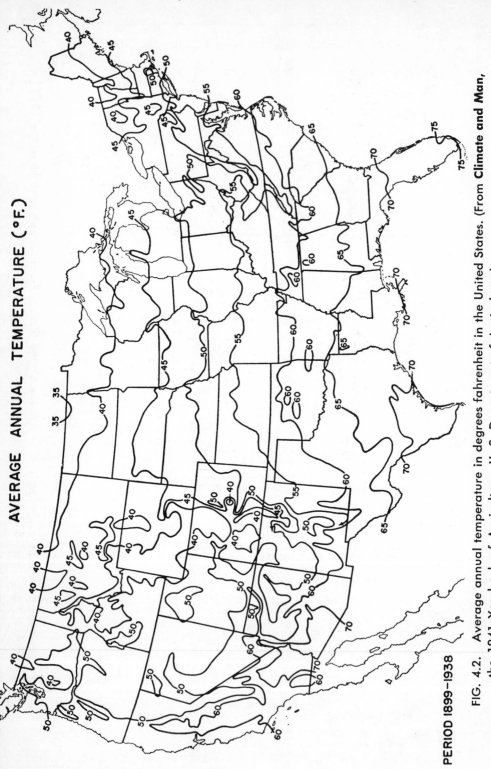

AVERAGE ANNUAL TEMPERATURE (°F.)

PERIOD 1899–1938

FIG. 4.2. Average annual temperature in degrees fahrenheit in the United States. (From **Climate and Man,** the 1941 Yearbook of Agriculture, U. S. Department of Agriculture.)

40

East of a line drawn from Chicago to New Orleans, the precipitation averages mostly 40 to 50 inches a year. West of this line, the precipitation decreases fairly regularly to approximately 10 inches, where again annual precipitation increases to more than 80 inches on some of the western slopes in Washington and Oregon.

Average annual temperatures in the West are primarily a result of differences in elevation; in the East, temperatures are influenced mostly by latitude. The 40-degree isotherm is dominant across the United States-Canadian border. From New York to Chicago to Denver, the 50-degree isotherm is present. High elevations in the West are also represented by this line. Sixty degrees average annual temperature is reported for parts of North Carolina, Tennessee, Arkansas, Oklahoma, northwestern Texas, southern New Mexico, southern Arizona, and California. Central Florida and southern Texas lie within the 70-degree isotherm.

Over the face of the earth, climate is the dominant factor in soil formation. Any soil profile is both the direct as well as the indirect result of the action of centuries of climatic forces. Some direct effects of climate on soil formation include:

1. A shallow accumulation of lime in areas of low rainfall.

2. Acid soils in humid areas due to intense leaching.

3. Thin soils on steep hillsides because of the amount and intensity of rain, which result in erosion.

4. Deposition of soil material downstream.

FIG. 4.3. In areas of low rainfall, lime accumulates in the profile. Here lime has accumulated in Miles clay loam at a depth of two feet, in an area receiving approximately 20 inches of average annual precipitation. Lime layers are deeper in sandy soils.
Courtesy W. T. Carter, Texas Agricultural Experiment Station.

5. More intense erosion in warm regions where the soil does not freeze.

Climate influences soil formation indirectly largely through its action on vegetation. Forests are the dominant vegetation in humid climates. The soil profile that develops in a forest has many more horizons than one that develops under grass. Semiarid climates encourage only prairie grasses, and a deep, dark, uniform surface soil results. Arid climates supply only enough moisture for sparse, short, plains grasses, which inadequately protect the soil against wind and water erosion.

Parent Material and Soil Formation

Rocks on the surface of the earth are weathered until all essential elements become available to support lichens and other lower forms of plant life. As continuing generations of lichens grow, die, and decay, they leave increasing amounts of organic matter. Organic acids further hasten decay of the rock. With an increasing build-up of organic matter and of fine rock fragments, more rainwater is available for use by larger numbers of plants and animals.

In time, mobile materials near the surface will be leached downward and some of them deposited a few inches below the surface. The zone of deposition constitutes the beginnings of a B horizon. A few hundred more years, and the leached surface soil (A horizon) and the concentrated subsurface (B horizon) are well developed and are contrasting in nearly all characteristics. Surface erosion removes the top of the A horizon as fast as the A and B horizons slowly settle into the parent rock from whence they came. The soil is then in equilibrium with its environment.

The kind of soil that develops depends in part upon the kind of rock present. Granite is slow to weather, and soils developing from it are usually not very productive. From limestone as the parent rock there develops a dark-colored soil of greater productivity. Sandy soils of low fertility develop from sandstone, and shale results in silt loam soils of low productive potential.

But most parent materials of soils in the United States are not from the rocks directly beneath them. Approximately 97 per cent of the parent materials are deposits that were moved in place by water, wind, ice, or gravity or a combination of these transporting agencies. The kind of soil which develops from these unconsolidated deposits depends to a large extent on the texture, structure, nutrient content, and topographic position of the parent materials.

Relief and Soil Formation

Relief influences soil formation primarily through its associated water relations. With the same kind of climate and parent material, soils that have developed on steep hillsides have thin A and B horizons. This is because, first, the surface erodes quite rapidly and, second, less water moves down through the profile.

Soil materials on gently sloping hillsides have more water passing through them. The profile generally is deep, the vegetation more luxuriant, and the organic matter level higher than in soils on steep topography.

Materials lying in land-locked depressions receive runoff waters from above. Such conditions favor a greater production of vegetation but a slower decomposition of the dead remains; the result is the existence of soils with large amounts of organic accumulations. If the area is wet at the surface for nearly the whole year, a peat or muck soil develops.

Biosphere and Soil Formation

Plant and animal life greatly influence the soil-forming processes. This influence is especially noticeable in the tension zone where trees and grasses meet. Minnesota, Illinois, Missouri, Oklahoma, and Texas are some of the states in which these differences can be observed.

Soils developed under forest vegetation have more horizons, a more highly leached A horizon, and less humified organic matter than do soils which have developed under grass vegetation. Grassland soils near the tension zone are rich in humified organic matter for a foot or more and contain a weakly developed B horizon.

When they exist in large numbers, burrowing animals such as moles, gophers, and prairie dogs and earthworms and ants are highly important in soil formation. Animals in the soil tend to interfere with the weathering processes which lead to distinct horizon differentiation. Soils with many burrowing animals will have fewer horizons because of constant mixing within the profile.

Time and Soil Formation

The length of time required for a soil to develop horizons depends upon many interrelated factors, such as climate, nature of the parent material, burrowing animals, and relief. Horizons tend to develop faster under cool, humid, forested conditions. Acid sandy loams lying on gently rolling topography appear to be most conducive to rapid soil-profile development.

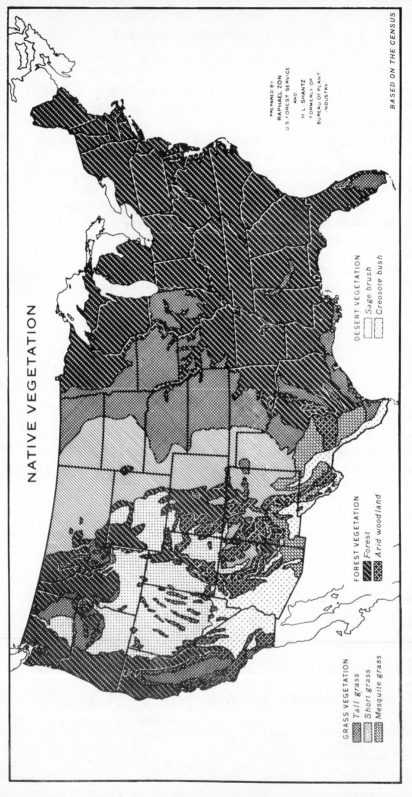

NATIVE VEGETATION

PREPARED BY
RAPHAEL ZON
U.S FOREST SERVICE
AND
H. L. SHANTZ
FORMERLY OF
BUREAU OF PLANT
INDUSTRY

BASED ON THE CENSUS

GRASS VEGETATION
Tall grass
Short grass
Mesquite grass

FOREST VEGETATION
Forest
Arid woodland

DESERT VEGETATION
Sage brush
Creosote bush

FIG. 4.4. The native vegetation exerts a tremendous influence on soil formation. This influence is particu-larly noticeable in the tension zone between forests and grasslands (see Figs. 4.5 and 4.6).
Courtesy Bureau of Agricultural Economics, U. S. D. A.

44

FIG. 4.5. Under a forest vegetation, the A horizon is more highly leached and contains a well-developed B horizon. (Minnesota) (Compare with Fig. 4.6.)
Courtesy U. S. D. A.

Under ideal conditions, a recognizable soil profile may develop within 200 years; under less favorable circumstances, the time may be extended to several thousand years.

Factors which retard soil-profile development are:

1. Low rainfall
2. Low relative humidity
3. High lime content of parent material
4. Excessive sandiness, with very little silt and clay
5. A high percentage of clay
6. Resistant parent material, such as granite
7. Very steep slopes
8. High water tables
9. Constant accumulations of soil material by deposition
10. Severe wind or water erosion of soil material
11. Large numbers of burrowing animals
12. All of man's activities, such as plowing, liming, and fertilizing

FIG. 4.6. Under a grass vegetation the A horizon is dark and deep, and the B horizon is seldom present. (Minnesota) (Compare with Fig. 4.5.)
Courtesy U. S. D. A.

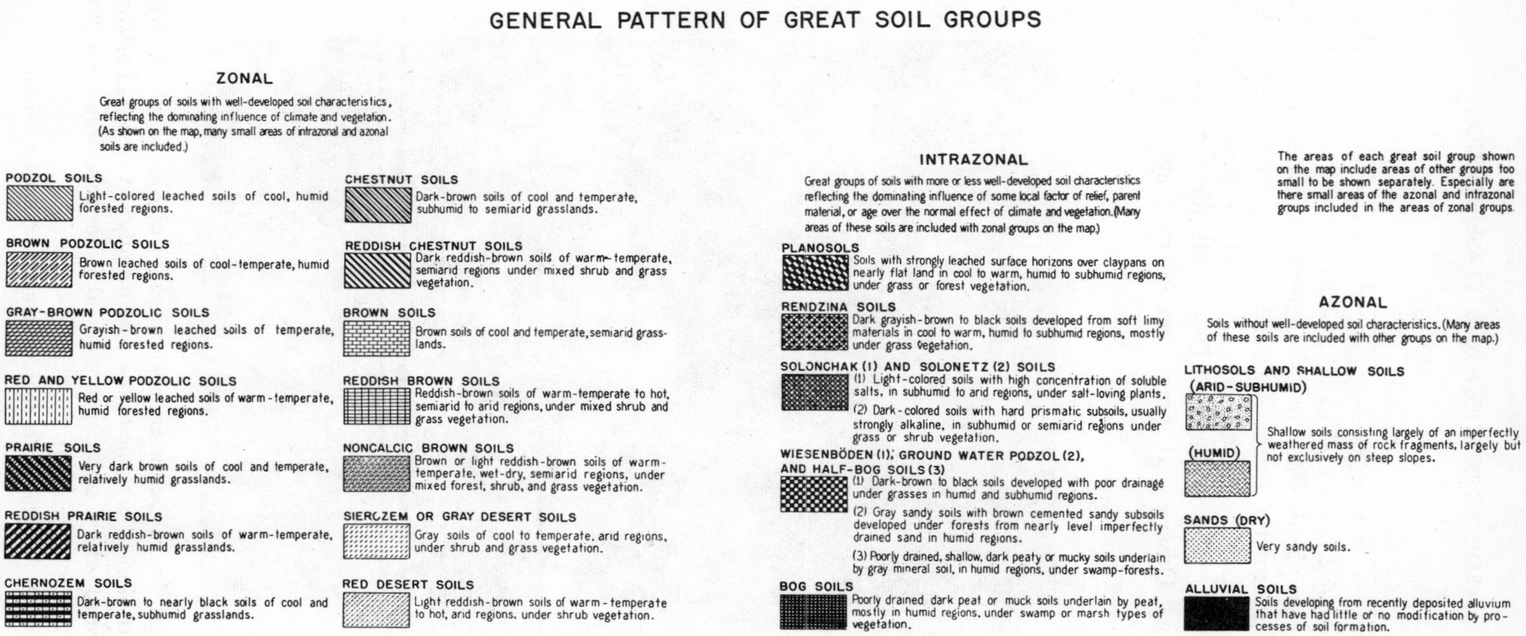

GENERAL PATTERN OF GREAT SOIL GROUPS

ZONAL

Great groups of soils with well-developed soil characteristics, reflecting the dominating influence of climate and vegetation. (As shown on the map, many small areas of intrazonal and azonal soils are included.)

PODZOL SOILS
Light-colored leached soils of cool, humid forested regions.

BROWN PODZOLIC SOILS
Brown leached soils of cool-temperate, humid forested regions.

GRAY-BROWN PODZOLIC SOILS
Grayish-brown leached soils of temperate, humid forested regions.

RED AND YELLOW PODZOLIC SOILS
Red or yellow leached soils of warm-temperate, humid forested regions.

PRAIRIE SOILS
Very dark brown soils of cool and temperate, relatively humid grasslands.

REDDISH PRAIRIE SOILS
Dark reddish-brown soils of warm-temperate, relatively humid grasslands.

CHERNOZEM SOILS
Dark-brown to nearly black soils of cool and temperate, subhumid grasslands.

CHESTNUT SOILS
Dark-brown soils of cool and temperate, subhumid to semiarid grasslands.

REDDISH CHESTNUT SOILS
Dark reddish-brown soils of warm-temperate, semiarid regions under mixed shrub and grass vegetation.

BROWN SOILS
Brown soils of cool and temperate, semiarid grasslands.

REDDISH BROWN SOILS
Reddish-brown soils of warm-temperate to hot, semiarid to arid regions, under mixed shrub and grass vegetation.

NONCALCIC BROWN SOILS
Brown or light reddish-brown soils of warm-temperate, wet-dry, semiarid regions, under mixed forest, shrub, and grass vegetation.

SIEROZEM OR GRAY DESERT SOILS
Gray soils of cool to temperate, arid regions, under shrub and grass vegetation.

RED DESERT SOILS
Light reddish-brown soils of warm-temperate to hot, arid regions, under shrub vegetation.

INTRAZONAL

Great groups of soils with more or less well-developed soil characteristics reflecting the dominating influence of some local factor of relief, parent material, or age over the normal effect of climate and vegetation. (Many areas of these soils are included with zonal groups on the map.)

PLANOSOLS
Soils with strongly leached surface horizons over claypans on nearly flat land in cool to warm, humid to subhumid regions, under grass or forest vegetation.

RENDZINA SOILS
Dark grayish-brown to black soils developed from soft limy materials in cool to warm, humid to subhumid regions, mostly under grass vegetation.

SOLONCHAK (1) AND SOLONETZ (2) SOILS
(1) Light-colored soils with high concentration of soluble salts, in subhumid to arid regions, under salt-loving plants.
(2) Dark-colored soils with hard prismatic subsoils, usually strongly alkaline, in subhumid or semiarid regions under grass or shrub vegetation.

WIESENBÖDEN (1), GROUND WATER PODZOL (2), AND HALF-BOG SOILS (3)
(1) Dark-brown to black soils developed with poor drainage under grasses in humid and subhumid regions.
(2) Gray sandy soils with brown cemented sandy subsoils developed under forests from nearly level imperfectly drained sand in humid regions.
(3) Poorly drained, shallow, dark peaty or mucky soils underlain by grey mineral soil, in humid regions, under swamp-forests.

BOG SOILS
Poorly drained dark peat or muck soils underlain by peat, mostly in humid regions, under swamp or marsh types of vegetation.

AZONAL

The areas of each great soil group shown on the map include areas of other groups too small to be shown separately. Especially are there small areas of the azonal and intrazonal groups included in the areas of zonal groups.

Soils without well-developed soil characteristics. (Many areas of these soils are included with other groups on the map.)

LITHOSOLS AND SHALLOW SOILS
(ARID - SUBHUMID)

Shallow soils consisting largely of an imperfectly weathered mass of rock fragments, largely but not exclusively on steep slopes.
(HUMID)

SANDS (DRY)
Very sandy soils.

ALLUVIAL SOILS
Soils developing from recently deposited alluvium that have had little or no modification by processes of soil formation.

FIG. 4.7. General pattern of Great Soil Groups. (After map, "Soil Associations of the United States," published in **Soils and Men,** Yearbook of Agriculture for 1938.)
Courtesy Division of Soil Survey, Bureau of Plant Industry, U. S. D. A.

Zonal Soils

The zonal soils have well-developed soil characteristics that reflect the influence of climate and living matter. These soils are found on the gently sloping uplands with good drainage and have developed from any parent materials not of extreme texture, such as coarse sands or very fine clays, or of extremely unbalanced chemical composition. Of the zonal soils, the Podzol, Chernozem, and Desert soils illustrate the main "Great Soil Groups." Other zonal groups are intermediate in their characteristics.

FIG. 4.8.   A Podzol soil is characterized by a thick layer of surface soil that is high in organic matter, a strongly leached A_2 horizon which is almost white, and a pronounced B horizon. Trees are the native vegetation. (Vermont)

Courtesy A. R. Midgley, Vermont Agricultural Experiment Station.

The Podzol Soils have developed in a cool, moist climate under evergreen or mixed evergreen and hardwood forests. These kinds of soils occur in the northern Lake States, northern New England, and on some of the high mountains in all parts of the United States. They are also found in northern Europe and Asia under similar conditions. In the evergreen forest, the ground is well-shaded and the trees are shallow-rooted. The needles are highly resinous and therefore decompose slowly. The needles of pines and most other conifers return less calcium and magnesium to the surface to counteract the leaching influence of the rainfall than do grasses. Under the forest, the soil becomes acid, and the slow decomposition of the organic matter is accomplished more by fungi and less by bacteria than in grassland areas.

The relatively soluble products of this decomposition are rapidly leached downward in the soil. There is a small accumulation of humus as compared with the abundant amount in the soils of the grasslands. The surface mineral layers of forest soils become gray and are strongly leached of both organic matter and plant nutrients, while some of the clay, iron, and other relatively insoluble but mobile materials accumulate in the B horizon.

This process is called *podzolization,* and with modifications it is important in the development of all zonal soils of the humid regions.

The Chernozem Soils have developed in temperate, subhumid, or semiarid regions under tall-grass vegetation. The grasses absorb large amounts of calcium and magnesium and return them to the surface fast enough to prevent the soil from becoming acid by leaching. Large quantities of humus accumulate, but it is well mixed with mineral matter, and the soils are nearly black in color for from one to three feet in depth. Since there is little movement of insoluble material, there is little difference in clay content between the different layers of the soil profile. By contrast, in podzolized soils the A horizons have less clay than the B horizons.

In the Chernozem area, the soil particles are grouped into granular or crumb-like aggregates and provide an excellent structure for good plant growth. There is sufficient leaching to remove the most soluble salts, such as sodium, but not enough to completely remove the calcium and magnesium carbonates. These carbonates accumulate in the lower part of the B horizon or in the upper C horizon. Beneath this horizon is frequently a layer of accumulation of the slightly more soluble calcium sulfate (gypsum). All of the zonal soils of the semiarid and arid regions have such a layer of carbonate accumulation. One of the most significant differences between the Chernozem soils of eastern North Dakota, South Dakota, and Nebraska and the Prairie soils of Iowa and Illinois is that the Prairie soils have no horizon of carbonate accumulation.

FIG. 4.9. The organic matter in a Chernozem soil is well mixed to depths of two or three feet and the soil is underlain by accumulations of lime. The native vegetation is a tall-grass prairie. (South Dakota) *Courtesy U. S. D. A.*

The *Desert Soils* have developed in arid regions under a scanty shortgrass and shrub vegetation. The soils are light in color and are relatively unleached. Because of the sparse vegetation and the extremely variable rainfall, both water and wind erosion are severe. Wide areas are swept by the wind, which carries away the finer particles, leaving a layer of protective stones called the *desert pavement.*

When the soil is barren of vegetation, a surface crust develops which is relatively impermeable to water; only the water from gentle rains sinks into the soil. Elsewhere in the desert are large areas of shifting or partially stabilized sand dunes. These conditions result in a great variation in the physical and chemical characteristics of desert soils. Soils which have developed on smooth alluvial fans and along broad stream valleys are often suitable for farming if irrigation water can be supplied.

Intrazonal Soils

Intrazonal Soils have well-developed soil characteristics that reflect the dominating influence of local relief or parent material more than the normal effects of climate and vegetation. Usually such soils are found intermingled in small areas with those of two or more zonal groups. The principal intrazonal soils are *Bog Soils, Planosol Soils,* and *Rendzina Soils.*

Bog Soils occur in the very poorly drained areas of humid regions in which the remains of plants decompose so slowly that thick deposits of peat or muck accumulate. With slightly better drainage, the Half-Bog

FIG. 4.10. Soils in desert regions develop a wind-swept appearance and a **desert pavement** of pebbles on the surface. Lime accumulates at or near the surface. The native vegetation is sparse short-grasses and low shrubs.
Courtesy C. C. Nikiforoff, U. S. D. A.

soils developed under a forest vegetation, and the meadow soils (Wiesenboden) under a grass vegetation.

Planosol Soils of medium to fine texture in humid and sub-humid regions have developed on such flat relief that under natural conditions there has been little or no erosion. In such instances the light-colored, acid, leached material accumulates in the A horizon and a claypan or siltpan develops as a part of the B horizon. These are called Planosols. On the other hand, in normal soils, as the surface soil is gradually removed by erosion, the profile slowly sinks into the parent material; in this way new, fresh minerals are incorporated into the soil beneath and no claypan is formed. Any accelerated erosion is now very serious because it exposes at the surface the claypan or siltpan that is too dense for best plant growth.

Rendzina Soils are black and have developed from soft limestone. Under these conditions the soil cannot readily become acid, and grasses form the dominant vegetation, even in humid regions. Large areas occur in central Alabama and central Texas.

FIG. 4.11. A Rendzina soil that has developed from soft limestone in an area of 30 inches of average annual precipitation. This is sufficient water to support a forest, but the limey parent material has favored tall grasses instead of trees. (Texas) *Courtesy Texas Agricultural Experiment Station.*

Azonal Soils

The *Azonal Soils* are without well-developed soil characteristics, owing to their extreme youth or to conditions of parent material or slope that prevent normal soil formation. Such soils are found on steep, rocky slopes, on fresh alluvial deposits, and on coarse sands. Azonal soils may be found in any climatic region.

Lithosols: Of greatest extent are the Lithosols, which are very shallow soils consisting largely of an imperfectly weathered mass of rock fragments. These are found especially on steep slopes where little or no true parent material for soil has accumulated. The characteristics of Lithosols are essentially those of the nearly barren rock.

Alluvial Soils: The alluvial soils are of great agricultural importance. They represent recently river-deposited material that has been modified little by processes of soil formation. Such soils are confined to recent deltas or flood plains along streams. As soon as these soils acquire well-developed soil-profile characteristics, they are grouped with the appropriate zonal Great Soil Group. Thus, a great many different soils may be developed from similar alluvium, depending upon other factors of soil formation, especially vegetation and climate.

Dry Sands: Soils developed from well-drained deposits of nearly pure sand are also included with the Azonal group as Dry Sands. Dry sands do not readily develop into mature soils with distinct horizons because they contain so little clay, humus, or soluble salts to move downward and concentrate in the B horizon.

Summary

Five factors act simultaneously to produce soil. These are climate, parent material, relief, biosphere, and time. Based upon the relative influence of these five factors, Zonal, Intrazonal, and Azonal soils develop. Zonal soils are in equilibrium with their environment, Intrazonal soils are dominated by parent material or relief, and Azonal soils have not had time to develop a profile.

Largely through precipitation and temperature, climate acts both directly and indirectly to influence soil formation. Parent materials influence soil formation by being resistent to weathering or easily weathered; by being rich in plant nutrients or poor in plant nutrients, they can affect the formation of soil. Soils on steep slopes are thin because of erosion. Plants influence soil formation by their low- or high-lime organic residues. Animals stir the soil and thus retard soil-profile formation. Soil materials that have been recently deposited have not had time to develop horizons.

Podzol soils have formed in humid, cool climates under acid-forming vegetation. Chernozem soils are the result of semiarid precipitation and tall-grass vegetation. Desert soils have developed in arid regions under short grasses, bushes, and other sparse vegetation.

Questions

1. Name the five factors of soil formation.
2. Describe three kinds of Zonal soils.
3. What is a hyetograph?
4. What is the dominant factor in soil formation? Explain.
5. How does the kind of bedrock influence soil formation?
6. Explain how burrowing animals retard soil-profile formation.
7. Name ten other factors that retard soil formation.
8. What is a Podzol?
9. Why do Chernozem soils have fewer horizons than Podzol soils?
10. What is a Rendzina?

References

Climate and Man, The 1941 Yearbook of Agriculture. U. S. Department of Agriculture.

Kellogg, C. E., *The Soils That Support Us.* The Macmillan Company, New York. 1941.

Marbut, C. F., *Atlas of American Agriculture.* Part III: "Soils of the United States." U. S. Department of Agriculture. 1935.

Soils and Men, The 1938 Yearbook of Agriculture. U. S. Department of Agriculture.

5

Soil Survey

For almost 60 years many observing farmers over the nation have seen soil surveyors at work. In making soil maps, the soil surveyor walks briskly across the fields with an auger or spade in his hand and a map case over his shoulder. Every few minutes he stops to bore or dig a hole in the soil. Sometimes he merely looks at the surface soil; at other times he rubs the soil between his thumb and forefinger, reflects a moment, and then puts something on a map. He takes a small instrument from his belt and sights through it, looking directly up or down the slope. Occasionally he bores or digs a deep hole, studying the subsoil intently. He glances around, evidently observing farm crops, relief, and erosion; then he sketches for a few moments and moves on. He crosses farm boundaries but doesn't appear to be taking any special notice of them. He is alert and preoccupied, as if he were counting steps and making mental notes between stops. When he is questioned about his work, he explains exactly what he is doing and how this information can help the public.

The surveyor is carrying a base map which is an aerial photograph large enough to show every road, stream, woodland, field, and house. He is studying the color, texture, structure, and moisture condition of the soil—and in so doing he is identifying the soil type. His frequent borings enable him to determine the depth of the various horizons and to estimate the amount of soil that has been lost through erosion. The small instrument through which he sights is an Abney hand level which is used to determine the per cent of slope. He sketches on the aerial photograph what he finds out about the soil type, slope, and degree of erosion.

Work in soil survey started in 1899 with the mapping of four areas: one in the Pecos River Valley of New Mexico, one in the Salt Lake area of Utah, and the other two in the Connecticut River Valley of Massachusetts and Connecticut. The smallest unit of land mapped during the early surveys was 40 acres; now it is approximately one acre. With continuous refinements, soil survey work on an area or county basis has been carried on each year since its beginning.

In 1935 the Soil Conservation Service began a program of soil mapping with the farm or ranch as the mapping unit instead of a county. These maps were made only where the farmer requested such services, and the maps were used primarily for individual farm planning.

In 1952, all agencies of the Federal Government concerned with soil survey work were consolidated to establish the National Co-operative Soil Survey. This new agency makes soil maps in response to requests by co-operators in the Soil Conservation Districts; it also maps the soil areas lying between these farms and ranches and eventually publishes county soil survey maps and reports.

Modern soil surveys are designed to:

1. Determine soil characteristics that are related to their classification.

2. Classify the soils.

3. Map the soil units according to the national scheme of classification.

4. Make predictions as to the potentialities of the soils according to their suitability for agriculture, forestry, range management, and engineering.

The Use of Soil Surveys

Soil surveys are needed to provide our nation with an inventory of the soil resources in order that public policies may be more wisely made and administered. Farmers who have a modern soil map can obtain accurate predictions as to the yield they may expect of a certain crop on that soil or whether or not a new variety would be more desirable. The soil surveys are used in planning management practices, including cropping systems for long-range productivity of the land. Soil surveys are basic to opening new lands to irrigation agriculture and in solving salt, alkali, and drainage problems.

One of the earliest results of the surveys, arising from the studies in the Connecticut Valley, was the introduction of Sumatra tobacco on certain soils. Some soil types produced good tobacco crops while others did not. Similar experiences with other crops are reported by farmers and research scientists.

Other more recent uses of soil survey data are to improve tax assessment, to aid in estimating forest site predictions, and to help in the design and location of roads and airports. Soil surveys have also been used as a basis for land classification and rural zoning.

Survey methods have changed greatly. The first soil scientists equipped their buggy wheels with odometers to measure distances. Few maps of any kind were then available on which to plot the soil types. The soil surveyor started with a blank sheet of paper and made his own base maps on which he put the soil boundaries. Today, aerial photographs on a scale of approximately four inches per mile are used as a base map for showing the soil types.

Actual inspection and interpretation are carried out on the land. To find out exactly what the soil is, scientists dig down to the parent material. Broken rock or other parent material may vary from a few inches to many feet in depth. But most agricultural soils in the United States support plant roots to depths of from three to five feet. Toward the arctic regions, the soils get shallower; toward the equator they get deeper, other things being equal. Laboratory analyses aid greatly in determining the final classification and in indicating the fertility and water relations of the soil.

The soil survey reports give a variety of data such as:

1. How stony the soil is
2. How much sand or clay is in the various parts of the profile
3. Whether or not the soil is acid or alkaline
4. Such below-the-surface information as the height of the water table, the presence of a hardpan, and other usually unseen factors that have an effect on soil productivity and farm management decisions.

Erosion tendencies are carefully noted, and ways to control erosion are explained in the report. Crop yield predictions are made for each soil.

With this basic information, the best possible use and management of the soil can be planned. Experience of farmers and results of research at state experiment stations are used. Estimates are made on how well the soil type will produce and what is needed for its long-range management.

The published report contains a detailed map of the county. From this map a farmer can locate his land and note the type of soils in his fields. Also, the farmer will find complete descriptions of the soils, together with crop management predictions, the relationships of soil and climate, and other pertinent data.

Soil surveys are an important element in the program for worldwide sustained food production. Soil-survey experts from several countries have in recent years come to the United States to learn about our soil-survey principles and practices. Also, the United States has loaned soil surveyors to several nations in order to help solve their agricultural problems.

The primary use of soil surveys is to aid in finding an effective cultural balance between people and the land. In our changing world, soil surveys serve as a basis for the constant and necessary adjustments between man and his land.

The National Co-operative Soil Survey

Making a soil survey is like taking inventory of cattle, tractors, and buildings; neither is essential for day-to-day existence, but both are necessary for long-time efficiency of management.

Since 1899 an agency of the Federal government, in co-operation with the land-grant colleges, has made and published soil surveys of problem areas or counties. Beginning in 1935, another agency of our government began a program of soil mapping on farms as a basis for farm planning. These maps were never published. In November of 1952, by mutual agreement, these two agencies were consolidated, placed in the Soil Conservation Service, and designated The National Co-operative Soil Survey.

The original soil-survey agency and the National Co-operative Soil Survey (since 1952) have made and published more than 1,650 county soil surveys. Most of the maps were made and published on a scale of one inch to the mile. Approximately 650 million acres were mapped by this kind of survey. Farm-by-farm mapping since 1935 has covered approximately 500 million acres.

The National Co-operative Soil Survey continues to make farm maps in co-operation with Soil Conservation Districts; it also maps the soils between the farms. As a result, the objectives of both former agencies are now incorporated in the consolidated program.

Field mapping of soils is now conducted on a scale of approximately four inches to the mile. Aerial photographs are used as a base. Published maps, formerly one inch to the mile, are now approximately three inches to the mile, and they are on a photographic base.

Although soil surveys are made by the best of modern technicians, they cannot be made to satisfy *all* future demands. With an ever-advancing technology, uses of the soil will be made which we cannot now predict. As a consequence of constant change, a soil map once thought useful for all future needs must now be remade approximately every 20 years.

Soil Series, Types, and Phases

In the process of mapping the soils of a county, a tentative legend is made which describes all of the soils in neighboring counties where the survey has been completed. As new soils are encountered during the progress of the survey, these new soils are described and mapped.

After completing the soil survey of a county, a soil correlator inspects the legends and the field mapping to determine if some kinds of soil called by a certain name are not the same soils mapped in another county or state under a different name. Such a system is a guarantee that soil names shall refer to the same kind of soil wherever they are mapped.

Each soil is named after a river, town, mountain, lake, or some other geographic feature near the area where the soil was originally mapped. There is a Mohave soil in the Mohave desert; a Dalhart soil near the town of Dalhart on the High Plains of Texas; a Fargo soil near Fargo, North Dakota; Miami soils near Miami, Ohio; and Norfolk soils near Norfolk, Virginia.

These geographic names apply to *soil series*. A soil series is a group of soils having a similar:

1. Kind, thickness, and arrangement of horizons in the profile
2. Color of horizons
3. Structure of horizons
4. Acidity or alkalinity
5. Consistence
6. Organic-matter content
7. Mineralogical composition
8. Texture

Two particular kinds of soils may have all of these features almost identical but the surface horizon of one may be a loam and the surface horizon of the other may be a silt loam. In this instance, both soils would have the same series name but they would be classified and mapped as different *types*.

A type name consists of the series name plus the name of the texture of the surface horizon. Thus, two soils may be classified in the Miami series, but the types may be *Miami loam* and *Miami silt loam*.

A Miami silt loam may vary widely from the original description as to:

1. Slope
2. Degree of erosion
3. Depth to bedrock
4. Stoniness

When such variations exist, they are called *phases*. There may be a Miami silt loam, *steep phase*, or *eroded phase*, or *shallow phase*, or *stony phase*. The modern way to designate phases is to incorporate the phase name into the type name, such as Miami *stony* silt loam.

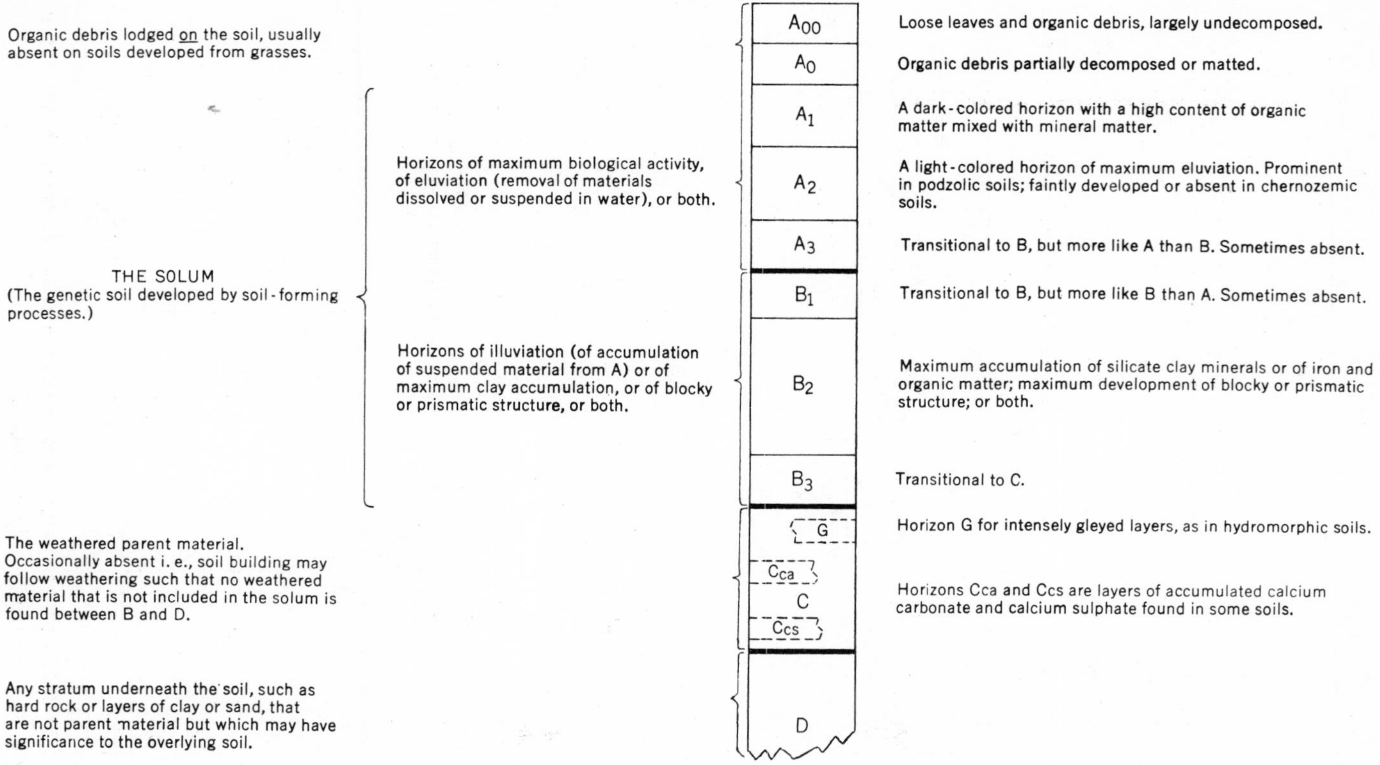

FIG. 5.1. A hypothetical soil profile.
Courtesy U. S. D. A.

A_{00}	Loose leaves and organic debris, largely undecomposed.
A_0	Organic debris partially decomposed or matted.
A_1	A dark-colored horizon with a high content of organic matter mixed with mineral matter.
A_2	A light-colored horizon of maximum eluviation. Prominent in podzolic soils; faintly developed or absent in chernozemic soils.
A_3	Transitional to B, but more like A than B. Sometimes absent.
B_1	Transitional to B, but more like B than A. Sometimes absent.
B_2	Maximum accumulation of silicate clay minerals or of iron and organic matter; maximum development of blocky or prismatic structure; or both.
B_3	Transitional to C.
G	Horizon G for intensely gleyed layers, as in hydromorphic soils.
C, C_{ca}, C_{cs}	Horizons C_{ca} and C_{cs} are layers of accumulated calcium carbonate and calcium sulphate found in some soils.
D	

Organic debris lodged on the soil, usually absent on soils developed from grasses.

Horizons of maximum biological activity, of eluviation (removal of materials dissolved or suspended in water), or both.

THE SOLUM
(The genetic soil developed by soil-forming processes.)

Horizons of illuviation (of accumulation of suspended material from A) or of maximum clay accumulation, or of blocky or prismatic structure, or both.

The weathered parent material. Occasionally absent i. e., soil building may follow weathering such that no weathered material that is not included in the solum is found between B and D.

Any stratum underneath the soil, such as hard rock or layers of clay or sand, that are not parent material but which may have significance to the overlying soil.

The Soil Profile

A vertical section through a soil is a *soil profile*. The profile consists of various layers (horizons) which differ from one another in either color, texture, structure, or consistence.

Soil profiles vary in endless ways, and only by a detailed description of the horizons in a profile can any classification of soils be consistently made.

Soil Profile Description

To insure uniformity in describing soils, standard forms have been

Soil type		Date	Stop No.	Soil type
Classification	Area			
Location				
N. veg. (or crop)	Climate			
Parent material				
Physiography				
Relief	Drainage		Salt or alkali	
Elevation	Gr. water		Stoniness	
Slope	Moisture			
Aspect	Root distrib.			
Erosion				
Permeability				
Additional notes				File No.

Hori- zon	Depth	Thick- ness	Bound- ary	Color — Check. D (ry) or M (oist)	Tex- ture	Structure	Consistence	Reac- tion	Spec. Feat.
				D / M					
				D / M					
				D / M					
				D / M					
				D / M					
				D / M					
				D / M					
				D / M					
				D / M					
				D / M					
				D / M					

FIG. 5.2. Standard form for recording the field description of a soil type. **Above:** front; **below:** reverse.

prepared by the National Co-operative Soil Survey. These forms are reproduced as Figure 5.2, and an explanation of terms is given.

Soil Type: Name the soil type, such as Cecil sandy loam, Miami silt loam, Charlton loam, Fruita very fine sandy loam, or Drummer clay loam.

Classification: Name the Great Soil Group, if known, such as:

Red-Yellow Podzolic
Gray-Brown Podzolic
Brown-Podzolic
Gray-Desert
Prairie (Humic-Glei)

Native Vegetation (or Crop): Indicate forest type, such as White oak–Hickory, Loblolly pine–Shortleaf pine–Oak, or Spruce-Fir; grass type, such as Buffalograss, Little Bluestem–Side-Oats Grama, or Muttongrass; or crop, such as apple orchard, cotton, or corn.

Climate: Indicate whether the climate is classified as humid semitropical, cold continental, or warm marine.

Parent Material: Such as acid clay till, sandy alluvium, unconsolidated limestone, or residuum from basalt.

Physiography: Designate whether first bottom (flood plain), moraine, outwash plain, coastal plain, loess, or talus slope.

Relief: Indicate if slope is convex, concave, simple, or complex; and the appropriate slope class, based on relative per cent of slope.

Elevation: Give the approximate elevation in feet above sea level.

Slope: Indicate the approximate gradient of slope.

Aspect: State the general direction of the slope, whether north, east, south, or west.

Erosion: Use appropriate number for the relative degree of erosion.

Permeability: Indicate the proper name, such as Very Slow, Moderate, or Very Rapid.

Drainage: Use standard names, such as Poorly Drained, Moderately Well Drained, or Well Drained.

Ground Water: Give depth to ground water.

Moisture: Show whether wet, moist, moderately dry, or dry.

Root Distribution: Indicate relative numbers of roots in each horizon.

Salt or Alkali: Describe general saltiness, when such conditions exist.

Stoniness: Use terms to describe relative numbers of stones or rocks, such as *stony phase*, or *rock outcrop*.

The Soil Survey Report

Published soil maps include a report which is written to aid in understanding and using the information on the maps. The modern report includes the items listed on the following page.

1. A description of soil characteristics and their significance to the classification and use of soils.

2. Actual and predicted responses of various soils to different levels of management.

3. Information on the climate, geology, and physiography of the county.

4. Sections on forestry practices or grazing management, depending on the relative importance of each in the county.

5. Suggestions for erosion control, cropping systems, and fertilization practices as they are influenced by soil characteristics.

6. Relationships of soils to irrigation practices, drainage characteristics, and salinity control.

7. Predictions on the engineering properties of the soil types as described and mapped.

8. Special problems of soil management in relation to the soil types shown on the soil map, such as reclamation of alkali soils, watershed management, and the management of hard-to-manage soils.

Land-Capability Classification

As a part of modern soil survey reports, the soils are classified for safe land use into capability classes. (Figure 5.3). The primary purpose of the capability classification is to help farmers to understand the limitations of their land, so that practices can be modified to permit use of the land without its abuse. This is soil conservation.

In the land-capability classification, bodies of land are grouped for easy reference in judging the soil-conservation significance of selected farm management practices. The groupings in the figure are made at four levels of generalization:

1. Major Land-Use Suitability—land suited or not suited for cultivation, based mainly on the hazard of erosion.

2. Land-Capability Class—eight land-capability classes distinguished according to the degree of limitation imposed by the physical land features. The slope of the land may be so steep, for example, that serious erosion would result if the soil were in continuous cultivation.

3. Land-Capability Subclass—subclasses which are separated on the basis of the kind and degree of limitation imposed on the use of the land. For example, use of the land may be limited by an excess of water and may therefore require drainage.

4. Land-Capability Unit—land-capability units which represent land-management groups, such as moderately sloping land with highly acid soils overlying acid sandstone or shale.

MAJOR LAND-USE SUITABILITY (Broad grouping of limitations)	LAND-CAPABILITY CLASS (Degree of limitations)	LAND-CAPABILITY SUBCLASS (Kind of limitations) (Grouping of land-capability units. Examples of possible subclasses in class III:)	LAND-CAPABILITY UNIT (Distinctive physical characteristics) (Land-management groups based on permanent physical factors. Example:)
Suited for cultivation	I — Few limitations. Wide latitude for each use. Very good land from every standpoint.		
	II — Moderate limitations or risks of damage. Good land from all-around standpoint.		
	III — Severe limitations or risks of damage. Regular cultivation possible if limitations are observed.	Limited by hazard of water erosion; moderately sloping land.	13-C-2 Moderately sloping, slightly acid soils on limestone.
			9-C-2 Moderately sloping, highly acid soils on sandstone or shale.
		Limited by excess water; needs drainage for cultivation.	
		Limited by low moisture capacity; sandy land.	
		Limited by tight, very slowly permeable subsoils; claypan land.	
	IV — Very severe limitations. Suited for occasional cultivation or for some kind of limited cultivation.		
Not suited for cultivation; suited for permanent vegetation	V — Not suited for cultivation because of wetness, stones, overflows, etc. Few land limitations affect grazing or forestry use.	Groupings of range, pasture, or forest sites.	Land-management groups based on permanent physical factors, such as range sites or forest sites.
	VI — Too steep, stony, arid, wet, etc., for cultivation. Moderate limitations for grazing or forestry.		
	VII — Very steep, rough, arid, wet, etc. Severe limitations for grazing or forestry.		
	VIII — Extremely rough, arid, swampy, etc. Not suited for cultivation, grazing, or forestry. Suited for wildlife, watersheds, or recreation.		

FIG. 5.3. Outline of the land-capability classification. (From **A Water Policy for the American People**, Vol. I, Report of the President's Water Resources Policy Commission, 1950.)

LAND CAPABILITY CLASSES			
SUITABLE FOR CULTIVATION		NO CULTIVATION-PASTURE, HAY, WOODLAND AND WILDLIFE	
I	REQUIRES GOOD SOIL MANAGEMENT PRACTICES ONLY	V	NO RESTRICTIONS IN USE
II	MODERATE CONSERVATION PRACTICES NECESSARY	VI	MODERATE RESTRICTIONS IN USE
III	INTENSIVE CONSERVATION PRACTICES NECESSARY	VII	SEVERE RESTRICTIONS IN USE
IV	PERENNIAL VEGETATION – INFREQUENT CULTIVATION	VIII	BEST SUITED FOR WILDLIFE AND RECREATION

FIG. 5.4. Land-capability classes.
Courtesy Soil Conservation Service.

Productivity Ratings

As the soil survey of a county is being made, the technician in charge obtains information on the crop adaptations and crop yield potentials of the major soils under various levels of management. The soil surveyors are constantly alert in assembling data on the present and predicted future yields of the major crops. This information may be obtained from farmers, county agricultural agents, farm planners, experimental fields, and the United States Census of Agriculture.

In tabular form in the Soil Survey Report, each soil type is listed and the estimated yields are given for each of the major crops. The yields are predicted for each of two management levels; namely, (1) yields under average management, and (2) yields under intensive management practices. Where forestry, pasturing, or range grazing are important uses of the land, estimates are made regarding the respective yield predictions for each kind of use.

Forest Site Classification

In any climatic zone, soil moisture seems to be the principal factor in determining what species of trees are naturally present and how fast they will grow. The significant factors of the forest site are:

1. Soil moisture: whether the soil is excessively drained, well drained, moderately well drained, somewhat poorly drained, or poorly drained.
2. Effective depth to which tree roots extend.
3. Relative lime content of the soil.
4. Degree of stoniness.
5. Steepness of slope: whether more than approximately 30 per cent or less than 30 per cent.
6. Aspect: this relates to the direction which the slope faces, whether north, east, south, or west.
7. Slope position: whether upper, middle, or lower, and whether the slope is convex or concave.
8. Relative degree of erosion: this relates primarily to an evaluation of the forest site for planting trees.

Most of the information necessary for forest site evaluation can be obtained directly from the published county soil survey map and report.

Soil Maps as an Aid to Engineering

The basic facts about the physical, chemical, and biological properties of soils needed to predict their behavior under farm use must be given different interpretations when the data are used for predicting their physical behavior in subgrades or foundations. Detailed soil maps are helpful in planning locations of highways and airports and in predicting answers to problems in construction and maintenance. Soil maps and reports are also useful in locating materials such as sand, gravel, clay, or stone, for use in construction. Without a scheme of classification such as that developed through soil surveys, extensive and costly testing of soils for each highway or airport project is necessary. Information gained on one project cannot readily be applied to another on a contrasting soil.

Nutritional Predictions

In various places throughout the United States, certain soils contain such small amounts of essential elements that the forage is deficient, and livestock deficiency symptoms for this element are exhibited. In other places there is an excess of an element in the soil which concentrates in the forage and becomes toxic to animals.

Phosphorus is deficient in certain soils in the Northwest, the South, the Lake States, and along the Atlantic Coast. Calcium is deficient in many soils in humid regions. Cobalt deficiency occurs in the Northwest, the Lake States, the South, and the Northeast.

Toxic amounts of selenium exist in the forage grown on certain soils in Montana, North Dakota, South Dakota, Wyoming, Utah, Colorado, Arizona, Kansas, and Nebraska. Molybdenum toxicity exists in cattle grazing the forage on some soils in California, Nevada, Utah, Colorado, and Florida.

Many correlations have been made between deficient and toxic elements in relation to the soil types as shown on the soil map. Where this information is known, it is valuable in the prediction of land use and farm management practices.

Land Classification for Irrigation

Areas which are considered for their irrigation possibilities must first have a modern soil survey. Upon completion of the soil survey, the soils are classified as to their suitability for irrigation into one of six classes in this manner:

Class 1—Lands which are highly suitable for irrigation farming, being capable of producing sustained yields of a wide range of climatically adapted crops at reasonable costs. They are smooth-lying with gentle slopes. The soils are deep and of medium to fairly fine texture, with granular structure which allows for easy penetration of roots, air, and water; yet they must have free drainage and good water-holding capacity. Land development, such as leveling and establishing a drainage sytem, is relatively simple to accomplish and can be attained at reasonable cost.

Class 2—Lands measurably below Class 1 in productive capacity, adapted to a somewhat narrower range of crops. These are more costly to prepare for irrigation or to farm. These soils have one or more deficiencies in soil texture, saltiness, topography, or drainage.

Class 3—Lands which are inferior to Class 2 because of greater deficiencies in soils and unsuitable topography or drainage. Although approaching marginal utility for general crop production, they are still considered suitable for irrigation, especially if intermingled with better lands.

Class 4—Lands having an excessive deficiency or restricted utility but which special engineering and economic studies show to be suited to irrigation under certain restricted conditions.

Class 5—Lands temporarily held as nonarable pending completion of economic or engineering studies to determine their suitability for irrigation.

Class 6—Lands not meeting the minimum requirements of Class 5, and small areas of suitable land lying within larger bodies of nonarable land.

Land Classification for Drainage

A modern soil map presents information pertinent to the making of accurate predictions on the feasibility of establishing drainage projects. All drainage systems need suitable outlets, and this information can be predicted from a soil map before costly engineering surveys are made. Information on soils suitable for various kinds of drainage systems can be obtained from the soil map and report. Coarse-textured soils, for example, can be tile-drained successfully. Fine-textured soils usually must be drained by open ditches, although tile drainage is used in some areas.

Other Uses of Soil Surveys

In certain places, soil surveys are used as a basis for rural zoning, watershed planning, range-site classification, land appraisal, the settlement of new lands, and tax assessment. Modern soil maps and reports are essential for the wise extension and application of research results, demonstrations, and farmer experiences from one region to another. To achieve efficient use of agricultural science, a world-wide scheme of soil classification is now being made by the United States Department of Agriculture in cooperation with other countries.

Summary

Soil surveys have been made since 1899, and constant refinements have kept the program both fundamental and useful. The National Co-operative Soil Survey now carries on the work in co-operation with the land-grant colleges of the United States. The primary purpose of soil surveys is to make predictions regarding national land policies and predicted responses of the soil for use in agriculture, forestry, pasture, range management, and engineering.

Soils are classified into series, types, and phases, the soil type being the unit of mapping. The soil profile and its characteristics are the basis for dividing soils into series and types. A uniform system is presented for describing a soil profile. For special conservation purposes, soils may also be classified into land-capability units.

The soil survey report contains productivity ratings for farm crops, pastures, range management, and forests and for engineering purposes. The soil map and report are likewise useful in predicting nutritional problems with plants and animals, suitability of the soil for irrigation or drainage, resettlement policies, land appraisal, and rural zoning.

Questions

1. Briefly describe the development of soil survey.
2. State five important uses of soil surveys.
3. Differentiate between soil series, soil types, and soil phases.
4. Name the eight criteria on which a soil series is based.
5. Draw and describe a hypothetical soil profile.
6. In a soil profile description, what is meant by "aspect"?
7. What is meant by "capability classification"?
8. What are productivity ratings?
9. What seems to be the most important factor in determining forest species distribution and tree growth?
10. How can soil maps and reports aid in the engineering uses of soils?

References

Climate and Man, the United States Department of Agriculture Yearbook for 1941. Washington, D.C.

Soils and Men, the United States Department of Agriculture Yearbook for 1938.

Soil Survey Manual, U. S. Department of Agriculture Handbook No. 18, 1951.

6

Chemical and
Colloidal Properties

Approximately 100 years ago, chemists began a scientific study of the soil. For more than 50 years the soil chemist analyzed soils and the crops growing on them for the purpose of finding out why some soils were more productive than others. The early concept consisted of the soil as a "bank" into which nutrients were stored for use by plants. As the plant grew, it drew "checks" from the "bank." Thus, if the total amount of calcium carbonate in the soil was 1,000 pounds per acre and if alfalfa removed 100 pounds each year, the lime would therefore be enough to last 10 years.

As research techniques improved, concepts changed. The present concept is that soils consist of solids, liquids, and gases. The chemically active fraction of the solids is confined primarily to clay and humus particles which are between 0.5 micron to 1.0 millimicron in diameter, known as the *colloidal range*. Almost all colloidal clay is now known to be crystalline, while humus is amorphous.

Plants feed by releasing ions and absorbing other ions. As a result, ions in the liquids and gases are in a continuously changing equilibrium with ions on the surfaces of the clay crystals and humus particles.

Colloidal Clay (Clay Crystals)

Nearly all clay in natural soils is colloidal, and almost all colloidal clay is crystalline. For that reason the term *clay crystals* will be used when referring to clay and its activity.

While sands and silts are mostly finely ground and unaltered primary minerals (mostly quartz), clays are composed of secondary minerals which have been built in nature from the products of chemical transformation of primary minerals. Clay minerals are mostly silica and alumina in definite spatial arrangements which constitute clay crystals.

Clay crystals are of many kinds, but all of them resemble the pages of this book, or could be likened to the cells of a car battery; that is, they are thinner in one dimension than in the other two dimensions, and the clusters of molecules are arranged in sheets. The clay minerals have a close semblance to the mica minerals, such as muscovite and biotite.

If clay crystals are examined under an electron microscope or an x-ray, their crystalline structure can be seen. All clay crystals are composed of one of two types, known as two-layer and three-layer crystals. The two-layer type consists of one layer of silicon and oxygen atoms and the other layer of aluminum and oxygen atoms, all in definite spatial arrangement. Three-layer clay crystals have two outside layers made of silicon and oxygen and the middle layer of aluminum and oxygen.

An example of a two-layer type of clay crystal is *kaolinite,* a diagrammatic sketch of which may be seen in Figure 6.1. This figure portrays the unit arrangement as one layer of Al_2O_3 and one of SiO_2. Whereas the entire crystal consists of many of such units, only two units are shown here. In addition to its two-layer characteristic, another feature of kaolinite is the nonexpanding space between the sheets. The rigid crystal structure is responsible for the low cationic exchange capacity, because there is not sufficient space between the sheets for this activity. The rigid structure also helps to explain the fact that kaolinite is not very plastic when wet.

Montmorillonite is the best-known example of a three-layer type of clay crystal, as seen in Figure 6.2. In this mineral, the unit consists of a layer of SiO_2, one of Al_2O_3, and another of SiO_2. The complete crystal consists of many such layers, but in this diagram only two are shown. There is an expanding lattice which allows for an exchange of cations between each two adjoining sheets. This mineral's cationic exchange capacity is therefore greater per given weight of soil than that of kaolinite. The plasticity of montmorillonite is also higher.

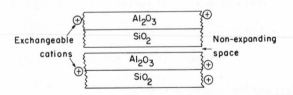

FIG. 6.1.   Diagram of a kaolinite clay crystal.
(After John G. Cady.)

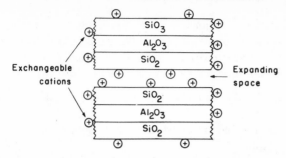

FIG. 6.2.   Diagram of a montmorillonite clay crystal.
(After John G. Cady.)

The chemical formulas for kaolinite and montmorillonite are

Kaolinite $= (OH)_8\ Al_4\ Si_4\ O_{10}$
Montmorillonite $= (OH)_4\ Al_4\ Si_8\ O_{20} \cdot nH_2O$

Organic Soil Colloids (Humus)

Organic soil colloids are a temporary end-product of the decomposition of plants and animals—temporary because the organic soil colloids are themselves slowly decomposing. *Humus* is a term used to designate organic matter which is colloidal in size. In chemical composition, humus contains approximately 30 per cent each of lignin, protein, and polyuronides (complex sugars plus uronic acid).

Humus is amorphous, dark brown to black, nearly insoluble in water but soluble in dilute alkali solutions. It contains approximately 5 per cent nitrogen and 60 per cent carbon. Humus has a cationic exchange capacity many times greater than that of colloidal clay.

Cationic Exchange

Place a filter paper in a funnel, add several grams of soil, then pour a solution of ammonium acetate through the soil. Catch the filtrate and test it for calcium, magnesium, potassium, sodium, and hydrogen. Filtrates from most soils will contain at least traces of all of these cations. Where did the cations come from when only ammonium was added?

The NH_4^+ replaced calcium, magnesium, potassium, sodium, and hydrogen on the surfaces of the clay crystals and humus particles. These cations were released to the soil solution and were moved down into the filtrate. This mechanism is known as *cationic exchange.*

Cationic exchange takes place when any cation is added to the soil, such as Ca^{++} when lime is used, K^+ from potassium fertilizers, and NH_4^+ from anhydrous ammonia, ammonium phosphate, or ammonium sulfate.

The exchange of cations takes place almost entirely on the surfaces of clay crystals and humus particles. This is because these surfaces have a net negative charge and therefore attract positive ions (cations).

The exchange of cations in the soil takes place between:

1. Cations in the soil solution and those on the surfaces of clay crystals and humus.

2. Cations released by plant roots and those on the surfaces of clay crystals and humus.

3. Cations on the surface of either two clay crystals, two humus particles, or a clay crystal and a humus particle.

Research in Florida, as well as that in many other states, has repeatedly shown that the capacity of a soil to exchange cations is the best single index of soil fertility.

Representative exchange capacities of soils throughout the nation are shown in Table 6.1. The variation in exchange capacity is from 1 for a fine sand to more than 100 for a mucky, fine sand. In between these values, the cationic exchange capacity increases with increasing amounts of clay and humus in the soil.

TABLE 6.1. The Cationic Exchange Capacity of Representative Surface Soils in the United States *

Soil	State	Cationic Exchange Capacity (Milliequivalents per 100 gm. of soil)
Charlotte fine sand	Florida	1.0
Ruston fine sandy loam	Texas	1.88
Gloucester loam	New Jersey	11.9
Grundy silt loam	Illinois	26.3
Gleason clay loam	California	31.6
Susquehanna clay	Alabama	34.3
Davie mucky fine sand	Florida	100.8

* Data from several sources.

Soil Texture and Exchange Capacity

In general, the more clay there is in a soil, the higher the cationic exchange capacity. This fact is clearly demonstrated in Table 6.2. For sandy soils, the exchange capacity is between 0 and 5 milliequivalents per 100 grams of oven-dry soil. The value of greatest frequency (mode) for fine sandy loams is 5-10 milliequivalents; for loams and silt loams, it is from 0 to 15; for clay loams, 15-20; and for clay soils, over 30.

TABLE 6.2. The Relationship Between Soil Texture and Cationic Exchange Capacity *

Soil Texture	Cationic Exchange Capacity (Number of soils in each group, In milliequivalents per 100 grams of soil)						
	0—5	5—10	10—15	15—20	20—25	25—30	over 30
Sands	8	0	0	0	0	0	0
Fine sandy loams	27	35	13	4	2	0	0
Loams and silt loams	2	2	2	1	1	1	2
Clay loams	0	0	3	14	7	7	2
Clays	0	1	0	3	4	6	40

* G. S. Fraps and J. F. Fudge, Texas Agr. Exp. Sta. Bul. 520, 1935.

Organic Matter and Exchange Capacity

Several studies have demonstrated that the cationic exchange capacity of soils is due as much, if not more, to soil organic matter as to the percentage of clay. In fact, there was a fairly definite increase in the exchange capacity of sandy Florida soils of two milliequivalents for each one per cent increase in organic matter.[*]

Research in New York on Honeoye silt loam compared the exchange capacity of each horizon of the profile with that of the extracted soil organic matter. Data are given in Table 6.3. The percentage of the total exchange capacity due to organic matter varied from 51 for the A_{22} horizon to 22 for the B_3 horizon. The most important fact given in this table is that less than 4 per cent organic matter in the A_{22} horizon is responsible for more than 50 per cent of the total cationic exchange capacity.

Adsorption and Exchange of Anions

Under certain conditions, soils have the ability to hold a *small* amount of anions in the exchangeable form. Nutrient anions, such as NO_3^-, SO_4^{--}, and $H_2PO_4^-$, are sometimes held in an exchangeable form for use by plants. Nitrates are capable of slight anionic exchange under acid conditions; but almost no exchange is exhibited when the soil is nearly neutral. This means that anionic exchange with nitrates is negligible because they do not form readily under acid conditions. Sulfates are also present in greater amounts in the exchangeable form when the soil is acid.

* Michael Peech and T. W. Young, "Chemical Studies on Soils from Florida Citrus Groves," Florida Agr. Exp. Sta. Bul. 448, 1948.

TABLE 6.3. A Comparison of the Cationic Exchange Capacity of Each Horizon of Honeoye Silt Loam Due to Soil Organic Matter *

Horizon	Depth (Inches)	Organic Matter %	Cationic Exchange Capacity (m. e./100 gm)	Exchange Capacity Due to Organic Matter (m. e./100 gm)	Percentage of Total Exchange Capacity Due to Organic Matter
A_1	0–2.5	7.30	27.1	13.5	50
A_{22}	5–12	3.88	13.8	7.0	51
B_{21}	12–16	1.48	15.7	4.5	29
B_{22}	16–20	1.88	17.3	6.0	35
B_3	20–25	1.61	14.3	3.1	22
C_2	29	1.39	9.6	2.2	23

* F. E. Broadbent, "Basic Problems in Organic Matter Transformations." Soil Microbiology Conference. Purdue University, June 21-24, 1954.

Phosphates are held in the soil in fairly large amounts, and the more acid the soil, the more the phosphates are retained. But most of the adsorption is not exchangeable. In acid soils, iron and aluminum readily form relatively insoluble compounds with phosphates.

In general, the relative order of anionic exchange is

$$H_2PO_4 - > SO_4- -> NO_3-$$

Organic matter increases the amount of anionic exchange.

Soil pH

Freshly distilled water contains the same number of H^+ and OH^- ions; it is therefore neutral. When the soil solution contains the same number of H^+ and OH^- ions, it also is neutral. Add $Ca(OH)_2$ to the soil and there will be more OH^- than H^+; then the soil will be alkaline. Conversely, when HCl is added, the soil will contain more H^+ than OH^-, and the soil will become acid.

The most convenient method of expressing the relationship between H^+ and OH^- is pH. By pH is meant the logarithm of the reciprocal of the hydrogen-ion concentration in grams per liter, usually written:

$$pH = \log \frac{1}{[H^+]}$$

At neutrality, the hydrogen-ion concentration has been determined to be:

0.000 000 1 or 1×10^{-7} grams of hydrogen per liter of solution.

Substituting this concentration into the formula, we get

$$pH = \log \frac{1}{0.000\ 000\ 1}$$
$$= \log 10,000,000$$
$$= 7$$

At a pH of 6, there would be 0.000 001 grams of active hydrogen, or 10 times the concentration of H^+. At each smaller pH unit, the H^+ increases by 10 in concentration. It therefore follows that a pH of 6 is 10 times more acid than a pH of 7; a pH of 5 is 10 times more acid than a pH of 6, and so on. The entire pH range is given diagrammatically in Figure 6.3.

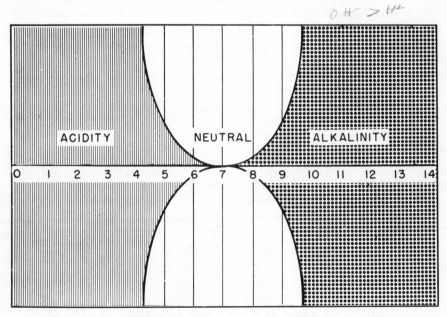

FIG. 6.3.   The entire pH scale.

Soils vary considerably in pH, but the most common range is between 4 and 8. Acid forest humus layers in the Northeast have been known to test as low as pH 3.5, and some high-sodium soils in the West may test pH 10.

The Fixation of Potassium

Long-time experiments have shown that there is some mechanism in the soil that fixes available potassium in a form which is not available to plants. The factors influencing the amount of potassium fixation are:

1. The kind of clay minerals present. Kaolinite does not appear to fix potassium, while large quantities are fixed by montmorillonite.

2. The relative amount of exchangeable potassium. The greater the percentage of exchangeable potassium in relation to the total exchange capacity, the greater the potassium fixation.

3. Wetting and drying of the soil. Soils that are wetted and dried fix large amounts of exchangeable potassium. One explanation for this mechanism is that potassium ions move inside the clay-crystal lattice when it is wet and expanded, and, upon drying, the ions are trapped inside. Any soil treatment that would keep the soil more uniform in moisture content, such as shading or the use of a mulch, would therefore tend to reduce potassium fixation.

4. The presence of organic matter. Humus particles exist in the soil in all sizes. Some particles are small enough to enter the clay-crystal lattice and to reduce the amount of contraction upon drying. This mechanism tends to lessen the amount of entrapped potassium.

FIG. 6.4. An example of chelation. Both pots contain the same kind of soil that received the same amounts of manure and superphosphate. The only difference in treatment was that in the pot on the left the superphosphate was mixed with the soil and the manure was added later. On the right, the superphosphate was added to the manure, then mixed with the soil. The manure contains chelating compounds that reduced the fixation of phosphorus by the soil. (Vermont)

Courtesy A. R. Midgley, Vermont Agricultural Experiment Station.

Phosphorus Fixation and Chelation

When phosphorus fertilizers are added to a soil, the plant may recover only from 2 to 25 per cent of the phosphorus. Most of the phosphorus is tied up in relatively insoluble compounds of iron, aluminum, and tricalcium phosphates. If sugar, starch, manure, cover crops, or any readily decomposable organic materials are then applied to such soils, a larger percentage of the unavailable phosphorus soon becomes available.

Research scientists have examined the reason for this and have found that decomposing organic materials form citrates, tartrates, acetates, oxalates, malates, malonates, and other organic anions which release fixed phosphorus. These anions form highly stable complex ions with Ca^{++}, Fe^{+++}, and Al^{+++}, and, in fact, have a greater affinity for these cations than does phosphorus. That is to say, in the relatively insoluble iron, aluminum, and tricalcium phosphates, the organic anions such as citrates readily combine with the iron, aluminum, and calcium and thereby release the phosphorus for plant growth.

Inorganic anions also act as chelating agents, but they are much less effective than organic anions. Fluorides, arsenates, borates, sulfates, chlorides, and nitrates to some extent solubilize phosphorus from iron, aluminum, and tricalcium phosphates.

Summary

The chemically active part of the soil is on the surfaces of clay crystals and humus particles. Clays are secondary minerals which exist as a two-layer unit such as kaolinite, or a three-layer unit like montmorillonite. Organic soil material in the colloidal state is called **humus**. Humus is amorphous (noncrystalline), dark brown to black, and contains approximately 5 per cent nitrogen and 60 per cent carbon.

Cations in the soil are freely exchanged among the surfaces of plant roots, clay crystals, and humus, as well as between these and the soil solution. Cationic exchange capacity may vary from 1 milliequivalent for sandy soils to 100 milliequivalents per 100 grams of soil for a muck. The exchange capacity varies directly with the amount of clay or humus in a soil. The exchange capacity for humus, however, may be as much as ten times that of clay.

Under restricted conditions, small amounts of certain anions may also be held in the soil in an exchangeable condition. The relative order of anionic exchange is:

$$H_2PO_4 \longrightarrow > SO_4 \longrightarrow - > NO_3 -$$

pH is the logarithm of the reciprocal of the hydrogen ion concentration in grams per liter. This may be written:

$$pH = \log \frac{1}{[H^+]}$$

Most soils have a pH between 4.0 and 8.0, but the extreme range is from 3.5 to 10.0.

Certain soils are capable of fixing large amounts of potassium. Montmorillonite fixes more potassium than does kaolinite. Wetting and drying tends to fix potassium in all soils. Humus reduces the fixation of potassium.

Citrates, tartrates, acetates, oxalates, malates, malonates, and other products of organic decay are capable of releasing, through the process of chelation, fixed phosphates and of rendering them available for plant growth. Fluorides, arsenates, borates, sulfates, chlorides, and nitrates, to a much lesser extent, are capable of chelation.

Questions

1. What is the present concept of plant nutrition?
2. Why are clay crystals called secondary minerals?
3. Draw and label a kaolinite and a montmorillonite crystal.
4. Describe a humus particle.
5. Illustrate cationic exchange in a sample of soil by the use of a salt solution (NaCl).
6. What two fractions of the soil are responsible for nearly all cationic exchange?
7. List the anions in the order of the amounts of exchange.
8. What is the pH of a soil with an H^+ concentration of 0.00001 grams per liter?
9. What can be done to reduce K fixation?
10. Explain chelation.

References

Bear, Firman E., ed., *Chemistry of the Soil.* Reinhold Publishing Corporation. New York. 1955.

Bertramson, B. R., and J. L. White, *Soil Chemistry Notes.* Student Book Corporation. Washington State College, Pullman, Washington. (Mimeographed) 1948.

Kelley, W. P., *Cation Exchange in Soils.* Reinhold Publishing Corp. New York, 1948.

Lyon, T. L., H. O. Buckman, and N. C. Brady, *The Nature and Properties of Soils.* The Macmillan Co. New York. 1950.

7

Life in the Soil

L ife in the soil consists of plant roots, mammals, earthworms, arthropods, gastropods, microscopic protozoa and nematodes, and such microscopic plants as bacteria, fungi, actinomycetes, and algae. The total population of all soil life is numbered in the billions per gram of soil, and the live weight per acre may be as much as five tons.

Because of the production of enzymes, carbon dioxide, and organic matter, the life in the soil is responsible for making plant nutrients more readily available and in making and stabilizing desirable soil structure for better plant growth.

Soil Microflora and Soil Structure

Bacteria, fungi, and actinomycetes aid in the development of desirable soil structure by their secretions of gummy substances that are not water-soluble. A comparison was made of the relative amount of good soil structure that was produced by each of these three groups of plants, and the results are graphed in Figure 7.1.

From Figure 7.1 it is obvious that bacteria are responsible for the creation of the least relative amount of large soil aggregates. Whereas actinomycetes are 17 times more efficient than bacteria, fungi are the best of all for this purpose.

It is of interest to compare the soil-aggregating influence of cow manure and alfalfa when added to the soil. Figure 7.2 portrays these data for a Declo loam in Ohio. With soil only, the percentage of soil aggregates greater than 50 microns in diameter was approximately 30 throughout the entire incubation period of 100 days. The percentage of large aggregates was 46 with cow manure the first day and rose to a peak of 56 on the 50th day of incubation, then dropped slightly on the 100th day.

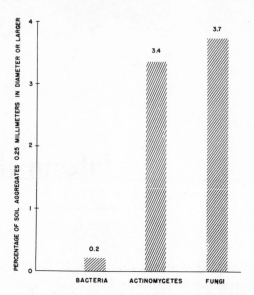

FIG. 7.1. A comparison of the aggregating influence of bacteria, actinomycetes, and fungi when incubated with sterile Gila clay at 26° C for 21 days. (D. S. Hubbell and Glen Staten, **Studies on Soil Structure**, New Mexico Agr. Exp. Sta. Technical Bul. 363, 1951.)

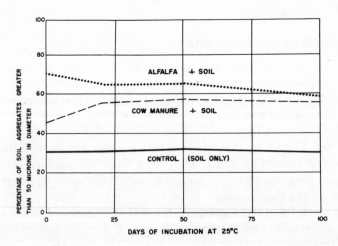

FIG. 7.2. A comparison of the soil-aggregating effect of alfalfa and cow manure with time on Declo loam. (J. J. Doyle, **Organo-Clay Relationships in Soil Aggregate Formation**. Ph.D. Thesis, Ohio State University, 1952.)

Alfalfa gave the best results, with 69 per cent large aggregates in the beginning and declining slowly to 58 per cent on the 100th day of incubation.

Plant Roots

Plant roots serve as a mechanical support, absorb water and plant nutrients, act as a storehouse for plant foods, and transport water and nutrients for the growth of the aerial parts of the plant.

The growth of plant roots is influenced by the kind of plant, the physical conditions of the soil, available nutrients, soil temperature, available water, oxygen supply, and carbon dioxide concentration.

Most grasses have a finely fibrous root system that usually extends several feet deep. Alfalfa has a tap root and may grow 20 feet deep or more, depending on soil conditions. Cotton has a combination of a tap root and strong lateral roots. Some trees, like the walnut, have a tap root, while most trees have lateral roots.

All plant roots are modified by the physical conditions of the soil.

FIG. 7.3. Cotton normally has a combination of a strong tap root and long lateral roots. In this soil, however, a compacted layer prevented the normal development of the tap root.
Courtesy Morris Bloodworth, Texas Agricultural Experiment Station.

FIG. 7.4. Normal development of the fibrous root system of rape plants. (Compare with Fig. 7.5.)

Courtesy Henry de Roo, Connecticut Agricultural Experiment Station.

Almost no roots will penetrate a compacted zone such as a natural fragipan (siltpan), claypan, or ortstein (cemented B horizon of some Podzol soils). Neither will roots freely penetrate plow pans or tillage pans formed by heavy machinery.

FIG. 7.5. Root system of rape plants restricted by a plow pan. (Compare with Fig. 7.4.)

Courtesy Henry de Roo, Connecticut Agricultural Experiment Station.

Available nutrients influence the kinds and amounts of roots produced. Roots will grow into a band of fertilizer and form a mass of fine roots. Roots will also concentrate in a lump of manure which has been buried in the soil.

The roots of most plants will grow at soil temperatures lower than those necessary for top growth. Apple-tree roots start to grow at 35°F and grow vigorously at 45°F. Roots stop growing when soil temperatures are high.

Available water is another factor which determines the nature of plant roots. In the Great Plains, where most of the moisture comes in the winter or spring and where the summers are usually dry, most grasses and forbs have root systems to depths of at least five feet. In humid regions, roots systems of plants are much shallower. Virgin forests in the Adirondack Mountains of New York are rooted to depths of four feet in well-drained soils and to one foot in poorly drained soils.* In deserts, the plants in general have very shallow but extensive roots.

Plant roots cannot grow in soils when the water is held with an equilibrium tension greater than 15 atmospheres or less than one-third atmosphere. It has been demonstrated, however, that plant roots may grow into a soil drier than at a 15-atmosphere equilibrium if a part of the roots of the same plant have adequate moisture. It appears that the root system translocates water where it is plentiful to areas where it is needed for growth.

Root development of some plants is retarded when the oxygen content of the soil is below 10 per cent, and growth may cease when it is less than 5 per cent. As the soil temperature increases, the percentage of oxygen required for root growth also increases. But plants such as rice, buckwheat, and willow trees apparently do not need this much oxygen in the soil atmosphere for satisfactory root growth. The roots of tomatoes, peas, and corn may need even more oxygen than do most plants.

Concentrations of carbon dioxide greater than 10 per cent seem to kill roots; however, 1 per cent carbon dioxide appears to be necessary for normal root growth.

Soil-Inhabiting Mammals

Burrowing mammals such as prairie dogs, gophers, mice, shrews, moles, rabbits, badgers, woodchucks, armadillos, and chipmunks all contribute to an alteration of the soil. In the long run, it appears that the burrowing activity of these mammals makes the soil more productive for

* Roy L. Donahue, "Forest-Site Quality Studies in the Adirondacks." Part I, *Tree Growth as Related to Soil Morphology.* Cornell Univ. Agr. Exp. Sta. Memoir 229. 1940.

FIG. 7.6. (a) Mole. (b) Gopher. (c) Prairie dog. (d) Woodchuck. All alter
the soil by their burrowing habits.

Courtesy U. S. Fish and Wildlife Service.

plant growth. In the short run, however, most of these animals eat vegetation and thereby damage native vegetation and many of the farmers'
crops.

In the forests of the Northeast, an estimate was made of the numbers
of the various species of mammals on a representative acre. The figures
are given in Table 7.1.

TABLE 7.1. Soil-Inhabiting Mammals in a Forest in the Northeast *

Species	Number Per Acre	Unit Live Weight (Grams)	Total Live Weight Per Acre (Grams)
Deer Mouse	35	20	700
Red-backed Mouse	12	21	252
Flying Squirrel	1	60	60
Short-tailed Shrew	40	18	720
Long-tailed Shrew	9	6	54
Hairy-tailed Shrew	3	54	162
Total	100	—	1948 grams or 4.3 pounds

* W. J. Hamilton, Jr., and David B. Cook, "Small Mammals and the Forest."
Journal of Forestry, 38, pp. 468-473. 1940.

FIG. 7.7. Continuous tillage on the left has created an undesirable environment for earthworms. On the right, a rotation of crops has left sufficient residues to feed earthworms. Note the amount of earthworm casts. Both photos were taken the same day. (Texas Blacklands)
Courtesy D. O. Thompson, Texas Agricultural Experiment Station.

Shrews dominate the soil-inhabiting mammals in a northeastern forest, as shown in Table 7.1. The deer mouse is next in abundance, followed by the red-backed mouse and the flying squirrel. The average number of all mammals per acre was 100, and they weighed a total of 4.3 pounds.

Earthworms

Earthworms are very important soil macrofauna, especially in undisturbed pasture and forest soils with a pH above 4.5. Earthworms ingest fresh organic matter and excrete it in a form in which the nutrients are more readily available to growing plants. They stir the soil in the process of making their burrows and thus improve soil aeration and hasten the infiltration of water into the soil.

It is difficult to differentiate among many of the species. Four common species in northeastern United States are:

1. *Lumbricus terrestris*, 5-8 inches long
2. *Lumbricus rubellus*, 4-6 inches long
3. *Allolobophora caliginosa*, 4-7 inches long
4. *Octolasium lacteum*, 2½-4 inches long

Lumbricus terrestris, one of the "nightcrawlers," makes burrows as deep as five feet, and rolls leaves, grass, and other organic materials into the surface openings. Many species do not come to the surface but feed mostly in the first six inches of soil. Several earthworm species leave spherical excreta (casts) at the surface around their burrow. Almost all species feed on manure, dead grasses, legumes, and selected forest tree leaves. The leaves of elm, ash, basswood, sugar maple, and birch are readily eaten, while the leaves of beech and red oak are not so desirable. Pine, spruce, and hemlock needles are rejected as food by earthworms.

The soil most suitable for earthworms is one that is slightly too wet in the spring for the best growth of most crop plants. A moderately well drained to poorly drained fine-textured soil which is continuously supplied with fresh palatable organic matter is the best habitat for earthworms. Silt loam or silty clay loam soils are usually the most desirable. Clay soils are less desirable, while earthworms are seldom found in sandy soils. Continuous tillage tends to reduce the population of earthworms, although they recover quickly when perennial grasses and legumes are in the cropping system. (Figure 7.7)

A study was made in Connecticut, on arable soil, which compared the chemical composition of earthworm casts with that of the surrounding surface soil.* The results are summarized in Table 7.2.

TABLE 7.2.   The Nutrient Content of Earthworm Casts as Compared with That of the Surrounding Soil

Nutrient	Surface Soil (Parts per Million)	Earthworm Casts (Parts per Million)	Increase Due to Earthworms (%)
Calcium (exchangeable)	1990	2790	40
Magnesium (exchangeable)	162	492	204
Nitrogen (nitrate)	4.7	21.9	366
Phosphorus (available)	9	67	644
Potassium (exchangeable)	32	358	1,019
Percentage Base Saturation	74	93	26
pH	6.4	7.0	—

Data in Table 7.2 indicate that available nutrients in earthworm casts are greater by 40 to 1,019 per cent than in the surrounding soil. The least difference was 60 per cent in calcium and the greatest difference was in potassium with a 1,019 per cent increase due to earthworm activity. The base saturation was increased 26 per cent and the pH was 0.6 less acid in the earthworm casts.

* H. A. Lunt and H. G. Jacobson, *Soil Science* 58, p. 367. 1944.

Arthropods and Gastropods

The common soil arthropods include mites, millipedes, centipedes, springtails, and larvae of beetles, flies, ants, and termites. These macrofauna feed mostly on decaying vegetation and help to aerate the soil with their burrows.

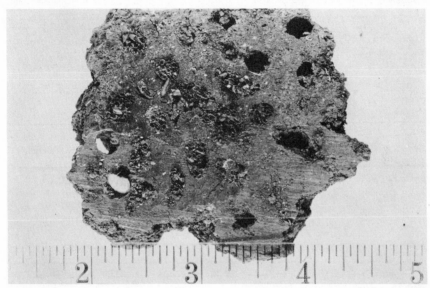

FIG. 7.8. Larvae of grasshoppers have altered the structure of this soil. (Texas)
Courtesy Texas Extension Service.

Slugs and snails are important members of the gastropods that inhabit the soil. Slugs and snails feed mostly on decaying vegetation but will eat and damage living vegetables when other foods are scarce. Counts as high as 600,000 slugs per acre have been reported, and their weight was approximately 400 pounds. Slugs and snails typically are scavengers.

Protozoa and Nematodes

Protozoa are microscopic animals that feed mainly on bacteria; in that way they influence the balance of microbiological populations. The three main groups of protozoa are amoebae, flagellates, and ciliates.

Nematodes are microscopic eel worms and are classified according to their activity into:

1. Omniverous. This is the most common of the soil nematodes. They live mainly on decaying organic matter.

2. Predaceous. This group prey on soil fauna, including other nematodes.

3. Parasitic. These nematodes infest plant roots, usually causing knots on the roots and low crop yields.

Distribution of Soil Microflora

The soil microflora consists of bacteria, actinomycetes, fungi, and algae. Table 7.3 gives recent estimates of the average number of microflora per gram of soil and the live weight per acre to plow depth.

TABLE 7.3   The Average Number of the Soil Microflora and Their Live Weight Per Acre to Plow Depth *

Group	Average Number Per Gram of Soil	Live Weight per Acre to Plow Depth (Pounds)
Bacteria	1 billion	500
Actinomycetes	10 million	750
Fungi	1 million	1000
Algae	100 thousand	150
Total		2400

* Francis E. Clark, *A Perspective of the Soil Microflora*. Soil Microbiology Conference, Purdue University, June, 1954.

Bacteria are estimated to average 1 billion per gram; actinomycetes, 10 million; fungi, 1 million; and algae, 100 thousand per gram of soil (Table 7.3). Inasmuch as the several microflora are not the same size, the live weight per acre to plow depth is not in the same order as the numbers. Fungi exceed in live weight per acre, with 1,000 pounds, followed in order by actinomycetes with 750 pounds, bacteria with 500 pounds, and algae with 150 pounds. This totals 2,400 pounds of live weight of microflora per acre to plow depth.

Physiological Classification of Bacteria

  I.   Autotrophic Bacteria
      A. Ammonia
      B. Nitrite
      C. Sulfur
      D. Iron
      E. Manganese
      F. Hydrogen
      G. Carbon monoxide
      H. Methane

II. Heterotrophic Bacteria
    A. Nitrogen-fixing bacteria
        1. Symbiotic
        2. Nonsymbiotic
            a. Aerobic
            b. Anaerobic
    B. Nonnitrogen-Fixing Bacteria
        1. Aerobic
        2. Anaerobic

Autotrophic Bacteria

The autotrophic bacteria obtain carbon from the carbon dioxide of the atmosphere and their energy from the oxidation of simple carbon compounds or of inorganic substances. Specific groups of autotrophic bacteria are capable of oxidizing ammonia, nitrite, sulfur, iron, manganese, hydrogen, carbon monoxide, or methane.

Probably the most important groups of autotrophic bacteria are those that oxidize ammonia to nitrites and nitrites to nitrates. These groups are known generally as nitrifying organisms. The environmental conditions necessary for the maximum growth of the nitrifying organisms are:

1. The presence of proteins to form ammonia; or the presence of ammonia salts such as ammonium sulfate.

2. Adequate aeration.

3. A moist but not a wet soil.

4. A large amount of calcium.

5. The proper temperature. The production of nitrates is greatest at 37°C (98.6°F), and the process stops at 5°C (41°F) and 55°C (131°F).

The nitrification process is shown diagrammatically as follows:

Ammonification   Nitrification

$$NH_4 \quad \rightarrow \quad NO_2 \quad \rightarrow \quad NO_3$$

ammonium (utilized   nitrite   nitrate
by plants)   (apparently toxic   (utilized by plants)
          to plants)

Heterotrophic Bacteria Classified

Heterotrophic bacteria are those that depend upon organic matter for their source of energy. In this group are most of the soil bacteria. Some groups of bacteria are capable of fixing atmospheric nitrogen, while other groups depend upon fixed nitrogen compounds for their nutrition. Members of this broad group of heterotrophic bacteria are the symbiotic *

---

* The word *symbiotic* has been derived from a Greek word which means "living together."

nitrogen-fixing legume bacteria, the nonsymbiotic nitrogen-fixing bacteria, and the nonnitrogen-fixing bacteria.

Symbiotic (Legume) Bacteria

The symbiotic or legume bacteria are the most important heterotrophic bacteria in a study of soils and plant growth.

It was known in ancient Greece that legumes had a beneficial effect upon the following crop. This fact is mentioned in several places in the Bible. But it was not until 1838 that Boussingault demonstrated the fact that the beneficial effect of legumes was due to their power to fix atmospheric nitrogen. The next major advance in our knowledge about legume bacteria was made by Frank, in 1879, when he proved that artificial inoculation with specific bacteria resulted in nodule formation on the roots of legumes, and that these nodules could fix atmospheric nitrogen.

Symbiotic bacteria attack the root hairs of legume plants, and the injury induces the root cells to grow around the bacteria. These cell extensions are the nodules in which the legume bacteria live. The legume roots supply to the bacteria the essential minerals and organic matter for energy; in return, the bacteria are able to use atmospheric nitrogen to build their body proteins.

FIG. 7.9. Symbiotic bacteria live in the nodules on legume roots. Nodules differ in size and shape from one legume to another. These nodules are on bur clover roots.
Courtesy Nitragin Co.

Since the life span of a single bacterium is only a few hours, the bodies of some bacteria are continuously in the process of decay, releasing fixed ammonium and nitrates for use by the host legume. Likewise, entire nodules are constantly being replaced by new ones. The fixed nitrogen in the old nodules is made available by decomposition to the host legume, as well as to other plants growing in association with the legume. The nitrogen fixed by legume bacteria is therefore made available to the legume, to any associated plants, and to the crop that follows in the cropping system.

FIG. 7.10. Nodules on soybean roots.
Courtesy Nitragin Co.

The symbiotic organisms belong to the genus *Rhizobium*, and there are several species which are named after the host legume. *Rhizobium meliloti* is the species which inoculates alfalfa and sweetclovers, and *Rhizobium trifolii* is compatible for the true clovers such as white clover and red clover. The groups of legumes which can be inoculated by the same species of symbiotic bacteria are:

Group 1. Alfalfa, sweetclovers, and trefoils.

Group 2. White clover, Ladino clover, red clover, alsike clover, and crimson clover.

FIG. 7.11. All legume seed should be inoculated before planting. **Left:** Soybeans not inoculated. **Right:** Soybeans properly inoculated.
Courtesy Nitragin Co.

Group 3. Lespedezas, cowpeas, kudzu, and velvetbean.
Group 4. Garden pea, sweetpea, Canada field pea, and vetches.
Group 5. Soybean.
· Group 6. Garden bean.
Group 7. Lupine.

There are also many specialized groups in addition to the above list.

Nonsymbiotic Nitrogen-Fixing Bacteria

In 1891 Winogradsky first demonstrated that, when soil was exposed to the atmosphere, its content of nitrogen was increased. The organism responsible for the fixation of atmospheric nitrogen without the association of a legume was isolated and recognized as *Clostridium pasteurianum*. These bacteria are anaerobic and belong to the same group as butyric acid bacteria.

Beijerinck in 1901 showed that there were also aerobic bacteria that could fix atmospheric nitrogen without symbiosis with legumes. The first bacteria isolated was *Azotobacter chroococcum.**

Several other soil bacteria are capable of obtaining their nitrogen from the atmosphere. Among these are purple bacteria, a group known as *Granulobacter,* and several others of minor importance. As the techniques of soil bacteriology improve, there will probably be more bacteria discovered that are capable of utilizing nitrogen as a gas from the atmosphere.

As a general rule, Clostridium are more abundant in soils than Azotobacter. Clostridium develop best in poorly drained, acid soils, while Azotobacter are more abundant in well-drained, neutral soils. The amounts of atmospheric nitrogen fixed by these bacteria are variable, depending upon the soil environment. Under ideal conditions, the total nitrogen fixed by both groups varies from 25 to 50 pounds per acre per year.

Nonnitrogen-Fixing Heterotrophic Bacteria

Most of the bacteria in the soil are classified as nonnitrogen-fixing heterotrophic bacteria; these are the organisms which are responsible for the decomposition of organic matter and from which bacteria obtain energy. Some members of the group include the thermophilic bacteria that cause self-heating and burning of hay, myxobacteria, and certain of the genus Bacillus, some of which produce antiobiotics.

Fungi

Soil fungi may be parasitic, saprophytic, or symbiotic. Parasitic fungi produce plant diseases such as cotton root rot, and many kinds of wilts, rusts, blights, and smuts. Saprophytic fungi obtain their energy from the decomposition of organic matter. Symbiotic fungi live on the roots of certain plants and both fungus and plant are mutually benefited.

Fungi are especially useful in the soil because they break down the somewhat resistant cellulose, lignin, and gum, as well as the more readily decomposed sugars, starches, and proteins. A large part of the slowly decomposing soil humus consists of the dead remains of fungal hyphae.

Mycorrhiza is the name given to a group of fungi that are symbiotic on certain forest trees and shrubs. It is presumed that mycorrhiza aid the host plant in the absorption of certain nutrients. Forest nurseries that have been established to raise tree seedlings that are not native to the area usually need an artificial inoculation of a suitable mycorrhiza.

* There are at least five species of the genera Azotobacter capable of fixing atmospheric nitrogen: Azotobacter chroococcum, Azotobacter beijerinckii, Azotobacter vinelandii, Azotobacter agilis, and Azotobacter indicum.

The reasoning behind this practice is that in a new region the compatible mycorrhiza are usually not present in the soil. There are two general types of mycorrhizae, based upon their manner of growth.

Ectotrophic mycorrhiza grow as threadlike filaments into small roots and *between* the root cells, but not *into* the cells. Their function appears to help the tree roots absorb nutrients by increasing its absorbing surfaces. Trees that have the ectotrophic type of mycorrhiza are the pines, spruces, oaks, elms, beech, hickories, chestnut, and birches.

Endotrophic mycorrhiza penetrate the tree root cells. Upon dying, mycorrhizal tissues are absorbed and utilized by the growing trees. Trees whose roots often have endotrophic mycorrhiza growing into them are sweet gum, poplars, maples, laurels, azaleas, and rhododendrons.

Actinomycetes

Actinomycetes are taxonomically and morphologically related to both fungi and bacteria. They are characterized by branched mycelia, similar to fungi, and resemble bacteria when the mycelia break into short fragments.

In recent years, actinomycetes attracted world-wide attention after it was discovered that they produced many antibiotics. At present, approximately 75 antibiotics have been isolated from actinomycetes. The most common antibiotics from actinomycetes are streptomycin, aureomycin, terramycin, and neomycin.

Actinomycetes are found in fairly large quantities in all soils where the environment is satisfactory. They thrive best when there is ample fresh organic matter, when the soil is neutral to slightly acid, and when soil moisture is fairly abundant. They grow better than fungi, however, when the soil is fairly dry.

The primary function of actinomycetes is in decomposing organic matter, especially cellulose and other resistant forms.

Potato scab, an actinomycete, can be readily controlled by keeping the pH of the soil below 5.0.

Algae

Soil algae are microscopic chlorophyll-bearing organisms. The main groups are:
1. Green
2. Blue-green
3. Yellow-green
4. Diatoms

Algae develop best in moist, fertile soils. The green color of the soil surface following the application of commercial fertilizers is due to an increase in the number of algae.

The probable effect of algae on plant growth is to:

1. Add organic matter to the soil. The organic matter is manufactured by the chlorophyll in the algae.

2. Improve soil aeration—especially of rice paddies by excreting oxygen for use by the rice plants.

3. Fix atmospheric nitrogen. Only a few groups of the blue-green algae can do this.

Certain members of the blue-green algae have been demonstrated to fix atmospheric nitrogen. The best pH range for this fixation is between 7.0 and 8.5. In flooded rice fields, this group of algae helps to maintain the nitrogen level of the soil by utilizing atmospheric nitrogen. Also, in desert soils blue-green algae are the dominant microorganisms and may be responsible for the high nitrogen content of many surface soils.

Summary

Life in the soil consists of both macro- and micro-plants and animals. Macro-plants include the roots of higher plants. Micro-plants are the bacteria, fungi, actinomycetes, and algae. Macro-animals comprise mammals, earthworms, arthropods, and gastropods. Protozoa and nematodes are the principal soil-borne micro-animals.

All plant and animal life in the soil helps to make nutrients more available and to aid in the creation and stabilization of desirable soil structure. Fungi and actinomycetes are more effective than bacteria in creating good soil structure. When alfalfa is added to the soil, the structure is better than when manure is added.

Plant root growth is influenced by the genetics of the plant, the physical condition of the soil, the availability of nutrients, soil temperature, and the supply of water, oxygen, and carbon dioxide. Shrews are the most numerous of the mammals in forest soils of the Northeast. Earthworm casts have a higher pH, a higher base saturation, and more available calcium, magnesium, nitrogen, phosphorus, and potassium than does the nearby soil. The greatest increase in availability of any nutrient is in potassium, where the earthworm casts are more than ten times richer than is the surrounding surface soil.

Bacteria are found in largest numbers in the average soil, but the live weight of fungi is the greatest of all microflora, averaging 1,000 pounds per acre.

Bacteria are classified into autotrophic (such as ammonia bacteria) and heterotrophic, like the symbiotic bacteria. Autotrophic bacteria obtain carbon from the carbon dioxide of the atmosphere and their energy from the oxidation of specific inorganic or simple compounds. Heterotrophic bacteria obtain their energy from the decomposition of organic matter.

Symbiotic bacteria form a mutually desirable living arrangement with legumes. The legumes supply housing in their nodules, as well as water and minerals. The bacteria utilize atmospheric nitrogen in synthesizing their body protoplasm. After death and decay, some of this nitrogen is utilized by the legumes.

Azotobacter are important aerobic nonsymbiotic bacteria, and Clostridium are well known as anaerobic nonsymbiotic bacteria.

Fungi may be parasitic (disease-producing), saprophytic (aiding in decay), or symbiotic (helping certain plants to grow better). Actinomycetes are best known because one species causes Irish potato scab. More recently, many new antibiotics have been isolated from several species of actinomycetes. Algae contribute to the amount of soil organic matter and improve soil aeration in rice paddies, and one species of blue-green algae is capable of fixing atmospheric nitrogen.

Questions

1. What are the two main functions of life in the soil?
2. How does soil microflora improve soil structure?
3. What are the critical concentrations of oxygen and carbon dioxide for plant roots?
4. What mammals are most numerous in northeastern forests?
5. What are some food preferences of earthworms?
6. What nutrient is made most available because of earthworm activity?
7. Name two autotrophic bacteria and tell how they obtain their energy.
8. Explain the function of symbiotic bacteria.
9. Differentiate between Azotobacter and Clostridium.
10. What are mycorrhizae?

References

Eaton, Theodore H., Jr., and Robert F. Chandler, Jr., *The Fauna of Forest-Humus Layers in New York.* Cornell University Agr. Exp. Sta. Memoir 247. 1942.

Fred, Edwin B., Ira L. Baldwin, and Elizabeth McCoy, *Root Nodule Bacteria and Leguminous Plants.* University of Wisconsin Press, Madison. 1932.

Gilman, Joseph C., *A Manual of Soil Fungi.* The Iowa State College Press. Ames. 1945.

Lyon, T. L., H. O. Buckman, and N. C. Brady, *The Nature and Properties of Soils.* The Macmillan Co. 1950.

McCalla, T. M, and T. H. Gooding, *Microorganisms and Their Effect on Crops and Soils.* Neb. Agr. Exp. Sta. Cir. 90. 1953.

Plant Diseases, The Yearbook of Agriculture for 1953. U. S. D. A. Washington, D.C.

Russell, E. John, and E. Walter Russell, *Soil Conditions and Plant Growth.* Longmans, Green and Co. New York. 8th ed. 1950.

Waksman, Selman A., *Soil Microbiology.* John Wiley and Sons. New York. 1952.

8

Organic Matter

Organic matter in the soil comes from the remains of plants and animals. This includes grasses, trees, bacteria, fungi, protozoa, earthworms, rodents, and animal manures.

Fresh organic matter helps physically by keeping the soil open and spongy, and aids chemically by releasing carbohydrates for energy and nutrients for the growth of organisms. Upon decomposition, organic matter releases carbon dioxide, which acts as a solvent on soil minerals to make them more available to plants. As organic matter breaks down, the nitrogen, phosphorus, and sulfur, and to some extent all nutrients, are released from the plant and animal tissues to become available for the growth of the next crop.

When organic matter decomposes, the slime which is formed helps to improve and stabilize soil aggregates. Better air and water relations in the soil thereby result.

Functions of Organic Matter

Organic matter serves many purposes in the soil that may be summarized as follows:

1. Coarse organic matter on the surface reduces the impact of the falling raindrop and permits clear water to seep gently into the soil. Surface runoff and erosion are thus reduced, and as a result there is more available water for plant growth.

2. Decomposing organic matter produces slimes which help to form and to stabilize desirable soil structure.

3. Live roots decay and provide channels down through which new plant roots grow more luxuriantly. The same root channels are effective in transmitting water downward, a part of which is stored for future use. by plants.

4. Fresh organic matter supplies food for such soil life as earthworms, ants, and rodents. These animals burrow in the soil and, in so doing, permit plant roots to obtain oxygen and to release carbon dioxide as they grow.

5. Trashy and coarse organic matter on the surface of soils will reduce losses of soil by wind erosion.

6. Surface mulches lower soil temperatures in the summer and keep the soil warmer in winter.

7. Evaporation losses of water are reduced by organic mulches.

8. Upon decomposition, organic matter supplies some of all nutrients needed by growing plants, as well as many hormones and antibiotics. These nutrients are released in harmony with the needs of the plants. When environmental conditions are favorable for rapid plant growth, the same conditions favor a rapid release of nutrients from the organic matter.

9. A soil high in organic matter has more available water for plant growth than has the same soil with less organic matter.

10. Organic matter helps to buffer soils against rapid chemical changes due to the addition of lime and fertilizers.

11. Organic acids released during the decomposition of organic matter help to dissolve minerals and to make them more available to growing plants.

12. Humus (decomposed organic matter) provides a storehouse for the exchangeable and available cations: potassium, calcium, and magnesium. Temporarily, humus holds ammonium in an exchangeable and available form.

13. Fresh organic matter has a special function in making soil phosphorus more readily available in acid soils. Upon decomposition, organic matter releases citrates, oxalates, tartrates, and lactates which combine with iron and aluminum more readily than does phosphorus. The result is the formation of less of the insoluble iron and aluminum phosphates and the availability of more phosphorus.

Chemical Properties

Organic matter from plants is a very complex substance. It contains the following materials, but in varying percentages, depending upon the kind of plant and its state of decomposition:

1. Carbohydrates, including sugars, starches, and cellulose
2. Lignin
3. Tannin
4. Fats, oils, and waxes
5. Resins
6. Proteins
7. Pigments
8. Minerals, such as calcium, phosphorus, sulfur, iron, magnesium, and potassium

TABLE 8.1.   The Lignin and Protein in Representative Surface Soils *

Soil	Lignin %	Protein %
Podzol Soil from Michigan (A₂ horizon)	46	28
Chestnut Soil from New Mexico (0—15 cm.)	40	33
Sierozem Soil from Arizona (0—15 cm.)	35	50
Chernozem Soil from Oklahoma (0—20 cm.)	33	38

* *Soil Science, 40:347-363, 1935.*

By far the largest percentage of soil organic matter is lignin and protein, although humus may contain as much as 30 per cent polyuronides. In representative soils over the nation, lignin and protein percentages will each vary from approximately 25 to 50 per cent. Table 8.1 indicates typical composition values of lignin and protein for soil organic matter in a Podzol, a Chernozem, a Chestnut, and a Sierozem soil. The Podzol is highest in lignin while the Chernozem is the lowest in lignin percentage. The Sierozem soil organic matter contains the most protein, and the Podzol the least protein.

Fresh plant material varies in percentage of lignin and protein from one species to another. Alfalfa, for example, contains more protein and less lignin than a rye plant. However, in common with all plants approaching maturity, the percentage of lignin increases and the percentage of protein decreases. This relationship is shown in Figure 8.1 for rye.

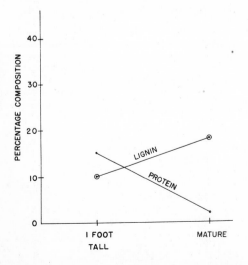

FIG. 8.1.   The change in the lignin and protein percentage of a rye plant with maturity. (**Soil Science,** 24:317, 1927.)

When the rye plant was 1 foot high, the lignin was 10 per cent; at maturity the percentage had increased to 17. Protein decreased from 15 per cent to 1.5 per cent during the same two stages of growth.

Biological Properties

Organic matter supplies energy and nutrients for all forms of life in the soil. The fresher the organic matter, the more energy and nutrients it contains and therefore the more valuable it is in the soil. There are certain hazards to the use of fresh organic matter, however.

Fresh straw plowed under contains so much carbon and so little nitrogen that the yield of the following crop is usually decreased. Table 8.2 gives the nitrogen-to-carbon ratio of several common organic materials which are frequently incorporated in the soil.

Alfalfa has the narrowest ratio of nitrogen to carbon—a ratio of 1:13; while oat straw has the widest ratio—namely, 1:80.

What happens when alfalfa and oat straw are plowed under is seen diagrammatically in Figure 8.2. Available nitrogen is not depressed but is increased immediately when alfalfa is incorporated in the soil. This means that the following crop can be planted as soon as desired after the alfalfa has been plowed under.

By contrast, available nitrogen is depressed when oat straw is plowed under. It would be best to plant the next crop about six weeks after the straw is incorporated, according to Figure 8.2. However, the safe time to wait will vary with moisture, temperature, and the general fertility level of the soil.

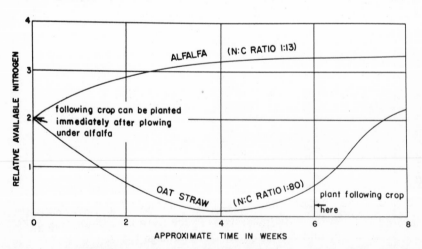

FIG. 8.2.   The relationship between the N:C ratio of plant material and available nitrogen following their incorporation in the soil.

TABLE 8.2.   The Nitrogen, Carbon, and N:C Ratio of Common Organic Materials *

Organic Material	Total Nitrogen %	Total Carbon %	N:C Ratio %
Alfalfa	3.0	39	1:13
Green Sweetclover	2.5	40	1:16
Mature Sweetclover	1.7	39	1:23
Legume-Grass Hay	1.6	40	1:25
Oat Straw	0.5	40	1:80

* Data from various sources.

Maintaining Soil Organic Matter in Humid Regions

Maintaining soil organic matter is difficult almost everywhere, and under continuous tillage it is nearly impossible. Figure 8.3 summarizes long-time studies in Ohio.

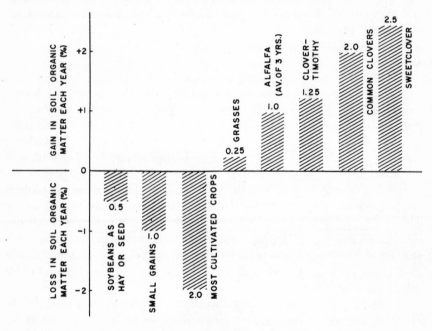

FIG. 8.3.   The annual gain or loss in percentage of soil organic matter under different cropping systems in the Corn Belt. (Robert M. Salter, R. D. Lewis, and J. A. Slipher, **Our Heritage the Soil**, Ohio Agr. Ext. Bul. 175, 1941.)

FIG. 8.4. Sweetclover and cotton are rotated on this field. Sweetclover helps to maintain soil organic matter in both humid and arid regions. (Texas)
Courtesy Texas Extension Service.

In the Corn Belt, under continuous tillage of corn, potatoes, tobacco, sugar beets, or similar cultivated crops, the soil loses organic matter each year at the rate of approximately 2 per cent of the organic matter present. When the soil is supporting wheat, oats, barley, rye, or buckwheat, the annual loss of the soil organic matter is approximately 1 per cent, and for soybeans, 0.5 per cent. Mixed clover-timothy for hay or pasture results in an annual gain of 1.25 per cent; clovers alone for hay or pasture account for an annual gain of 2.0 per cent; sweetclover turned under gained 2.5 per cent a year; and three years of alfalfa increased 3.0 per cent, or an average of 1.0 per cent increase in soil organic matter each year for three years. There is no gain in soil organic matter under alfalfa after the third year. Under continuous grass, the gain in organic matter is 0.25 per cent a year.

When cultivated crops are grown, the cropping system designed to maintain organic matter must include those crops which result in increases of organic matter. The figure shows that cultivated crops such as corn result in a loss of soil organic matter equal to 2 per cent a year. Each year that a clover like red clover is grown, an increase of 2 per cent in organic matter may be expected. One year of corn and one year of red clover will therefore maintain soil organic matter. In like manner, a rotation of alfalfa—alfalfa—alfalfa—corn—wheat will just maintain the organic-matter level of the soil. Grass—grass—soybeans in a rotation will accomplish the same purpose. Another rotation to maintain organic matter is sweetclover (plowed under)—corn—soybeans.

Research in Illinois indicates that approximately 5 tons of straw per acre or its equivalent is necessary to maintain soil organic matter under conditions of continuous tillage.*

FIG. 8.5.   Sudangrass and cotton are rotated on this Texas Blackland farm to maintain organic matter and to reduce cotton root rot.
Courtesy Dale Stockton, Enloe, Texas.

Maintaining Soil Organic Matter in Semiarid Regions

Losses of soil organic under different cropping systems are given in Figure 8.6. Continuous bluegrass and a rotation of corn—oats—wheat are equally effective in reducing losses of soil organic matter. Next in order of desirability are continuous wheat, sweetclover—corn—wheat, corn—oats—wheat, continuous oats, and continuous corn. These losses took place during an 8-year period in South Dakota.

* S. W. Melsted, *Organic Matter Management in Agronomic Practices*. Soil Microbiology Conference, Purdue University, June 23, 1954.

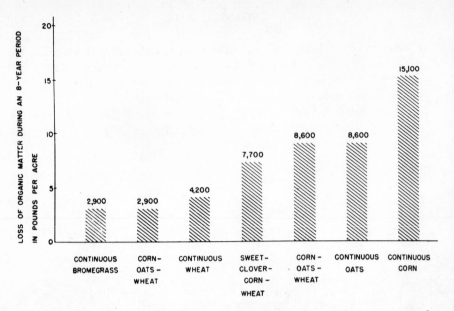

FIG. 8.6. Losses of soil organic matter during an eight-year period under different cropping systems in South Dakota (average annual precipitation, 20 inches). (Leo F. Puhr and W. W. Worzella, **Fertility Maintenance and Management of South Dakota Soils**, South Dakota Agr. Exp. Sta. Cir. 92, 1952.)

Summary

Soil organic matter consists mainly of plant and animal residues in all stages of decomposition. Coarse organic matter serves to supply food for life in the soil, to cushion the impact of the falling raindrop, to increase available water for plant growth, and to provide a protective mulch to equalize soil temperatures and reduce evaporation losses of water from the soil. Decomposing organic matter releases some of all essential elements, provides slimes which stabilize desirable soil structure, and keeps open the channels down through which plant roots may grow. Decomposed organic matter holds more water for use by plants, maintains good structure, and serves as a storehouse for exchangeable and available nutrient cations such as calcium, magnesium, potassium, and ammonium.

Organic matter consists mostly of lignin and protein; young plants have a higher percentage of protein, but this percentage decreases rapidly upon maturity. Lignin percentage is just the converse; that is, lignin is found in young plants only in small amounts. When plants mature, the percentage of lignin rapidly increases.

When a crop with a narrow N:C ratio, such as alfalfa, is plowed under, the following crop can be planted right away. However, if organic matter with a wide N:C ratio, like straw, is plowed under, approximately six weeks must be allowed for decomposition before planting the next crop.

In humid regions, soil organic matter cannot be maintained under any system of continuous tillage. Grasses and legumes are necessary in the rotation to rebuild organic matter lost by accelerated decomposition caused by stirring the soil in the process of raising cultivated crops. Soil organic matter is even more difficult to maintain in semiarid regions.

Questions

1. How can coarse organic matter increase the amount of water available to plants?
2. How can decomposing organic matter improve soil structure?
3. What is the principal food for most animal life in the soil?
4. Explain this statement: Nutrients are released from organic matter in harmony with the needs of growing plants.
5. What are the two principal substances in organic matter? How does the percentage of these substances vary with the stage of maturity?
6. What is the practical significance of the N:C ratio?
7. Give an example of a cropping system adapted to the humid region which will maintain soil organic matter.
8. In the humid region, following one year of potatoes, how many years of grass are required to maintain soil organic matter?
9. Will a rotation of alfalfa—alfalfa—alfalfa—corn—small grain maintain soil organic matter?
10. In semiarid regions, how much loss in organic matter per acre per year may be expected from a cropping system of continuous corn?

References

Bear, Firman E., *Soils and Fertilizers*. John Wiley and Sons. New York. 1953.
Donahue, Roy L., *Our Soils and Their Management*. The Interstate Printers and Publishers. Danville, Illinois. 1955.
Ignatieff, Vladimir, *Efficient Use of Fertilizers*. Food and Agriculture Organization of the United Nations. Leonard Hall, Limited. London. 1952.
Kellogg, Charles E., *Our Garden Soils*. The Macmillan Co. New York. 1952.

9

Soil Water

_____

The average acre of land in the nation each year receives 30 inches of precipitation. If all of this precipitation were absorbed by the soil and later all used by crops, it would be enough for corn but not enough to raise alfalfa. This is assuming that there is no runoff, no percolation, and no evaporation. On the average, however, only about 10 of the 30 inches is available for crop growth. This amount of water will support certain range grasses but not the common farm crops.

The major problem with soil water is understanding how it moves into and through the soil, how it is classified and measured, and what can be done to reduce leaching losses of nutrients by percolation. A knowledge of soil water and how it behaves is the first step in making better use of this very critical natural resource.

Infiltration

Infiltration refers to the movement of water *into* the soil. By contrast, *percolation* is the movement of water *through* a column of soil. *Permeability* permits the movement of water *within* the soil.

It is obvious that a soil should be in such physical condition as to provide channels down through which water may move as rapidly as it is received on the surface as rainfall or irrigation. Water which cannot move into the soil moves off over the surface, often carrying soil with it. The result is a reduced productivity due to the loss of fertile topsoil and less water for plant growth.

The principal factors controlling the rate of movement of water into a soil are:

1. The percentage of sand, silt, and clay in a soil. Coarse sands encourage increased infiltration.

FIG. 9.1. The rate of infiltration of water in this Texas
Blackland soil is classified
as very low to low, with a
rate of 0.1 inch per hour.
*Courtesy Texas Agricultural Ex-
periment Station.*

2. The structure of a soil. Soils with large, water-stable aggregates
have higher infiltration rates.

3. The amount of organic matter in the soil. The more the organic
matter and the coarser it is, the greater the amount of water entering the
soil. Organic surface mulches are especially helpful in increasing infiltration.

4. The depth of the soil to a hardpan, bedrock, or other impervious
layer is a factor in infiltration. Shallow soils do not permit as much water
to enter as do deep soils.

5. The amount of water in the soil. In general, wet soils do not have
as high an infiltration rate as do moist or dry soils.

6. The soil temperature. Warm soils take in water faster than do
cold soils. Frozen soils may or may not be capable of absorbing water,
depending upon the kind of freezing that has taken place.

Infiltration rates may be classified as follows:

1. *Very Low.* Soils with infiltration rates of less than 0.1 inch per
hour are classified as very low. In this group are the soils that are very
high in percentage of clay. (Figure 9.1)

2. *Low.* Infiltration rates of 0.1-0.5 inch per hour are considered low.

FIG. 9.2. Roots in this soil help to make the infiltration rate high, with a value of five inches of water per hour.

Courtesy Texas Agricultural Experiment Station.

This group includes soils high in clay, soils low in organic matter, or shallow soils.

3. *Medium.* Rates of infiltration of 0.5-1.0 inch per hour are classified as medium. Most soils in this group are sandy loams and silt loams.

4. *High.* High rates include soils with greater than 1.0 inch per hour of infiltration. Deep sands, and deep, well-aggregated silt loams are in this group. (Figure 9.2)

Permeability

The characteristics that determine how fast air and water move through the soil describe what is known as *permeability*. The rate of water movement through a soil is determined by the least permeable horizon. Plowpans or natural claypans reduce the permeability of a soil. Past management practices also determine permeability: continuous tillage reduces permeability, while the growth of deep-rooted grasses, legumes, and trees increases permeability.

Water moves in the soil as a liquid or as a vapor, mainly through the large pores. This means that the larger and more numerous the pores, the greater the permeability.

Suggested permeability classes are as follows: *

1. Very slow—less than 0.05 inch per hour.
2. Slow—0.05-0.20 inch per hour.
3. Moderate—0.20-5.0 inches per hour.
4. Rapid—5.0-10.0 inches per hour.
5. Very rapid—more than 10.0 inches per hour.

Soil Water Classified

Water in the soil has been classified in many ways and by many people. One of the most modern and meaningful classifications is based upon the force with which water is held by the soil. In this way, soil water is more directly related to the force which plant roots exert in absorbing water.

When plants permanently wilt for lack of water, it means that the pull of the roots is not great enough to get sufficient water in time to prevent wilting. This amount of water in the soil is held with a force of 15 atmospheres and is called the *wilting percentage*. Plants cannot grow normally beyond the *field capacity*. The moisture at the field capacity is held with a force of one-third atmosphere.

The common soil moisture constants are presented in Figure 9.3 in terms of atmospheres of tension.

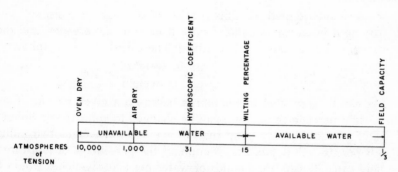

FIG. 9.3. Soil-moisture constants and their equivalent in atmospheres of tension. (Data from various sources.)

Oven-dry weight is the basis for nearly all soil-moisture calculations. The equilibrium tension of the moisture at oven-dryness is 10,000 atmospheres. In its actual determination in soils, oven-dryness is determined by placing the soil in an oven at 105°C until it loses no more water.

* As determined on undisturbed, saturated soil cores under a constant one-half-inch head of water.

Air-dry weight is a somewhat variable term, mainly because the moisture in the air fluctuates. Under average conditions, moisture at air-dryness is held with a force of 1,000 atmospheres. This water is not available to plants.

The *Hygroscopic Coefficient* is determined by placing an air-dry soil in a nearly saturated atmosphere at 25°C until it absorbs no more water. This tension is equal to a force of 31 atmospheres. Water at this tension is not available to plants but may be available to certain bacteria.

Water at the *Wilting Percentage* is held with a force of 15 atmospheres (220.5 pounds per square inch). It is almost a marvel of nature that plant roots can pull water with such a force.

The *Field Capacity* of a soil with good drainage can readily be determined. After a soaking rain or a heavy irrigation, cover the surface of a well-drained soil to reduce evaporation losses and wait two or three days. At this time the surface soil moisture is at the field capacity. In atmospheres of tension, this is one-third.

Between the wilting percentage (15 atmospheres) and the field capacity (one-third atmosphere) the water is available to plants. This is the range of moisture with which we are primarily concerned.

Measuring Soil Moisture

Water in a soil may be measured in a number of ways. These methods include:

1. Gravimetric method. This consists of obtaining a moist soil sample, drying it in an oven at 105°C until it loses no more water, and then determining the percentage of moisture. The calculation is as follows:

$$\% \text{ moisture} = \frac{\text{Loss in weight}}{\text{Oven-dry weight}} \times 100$$

As can be seen, this calculation is based on a given *weight* of soil. The weight percentage of water can be changed to approximate volumes of water per acre by assuming that an average soil weighs two million pounds per six-inch depth. For example, if the percentage of moisture at the field capacity is 5, the pounds of water per acre-six-inches would be 0.05 × 2 million, or 100,000. To convert to acre-inches of water, divide by 22,658 (pounds of water per acre-inch), and the answer is approximately 4.4 inches.

To carry this calculation to its logical conclusion, the acre-inches of water at the wilting percentage must be calculated and then subtracted from the field capacity to obtain the inches of available water per six-inch depth of soil. Assuming the wilting percentage of the same soil to be 3, the moisture will be 0.03 × 2 million, which equals 60,000. This divided by the pounds per acre-inch (22,658) gives approximately 2.6

acre-inches. The acre-inches of available water per six-inch depth is obtained by subtracting 2.6 from 4.4, which gives 1.8. Normally the figures are given on a per-acre-foot basis, and in this case the answer is $2 \times 1.8 = 3.6$ acre-inches of available water per acre-foot.

2. Methods that depend upon measuring the equilibrium tension of soil moisture with the use of a porous clay cup (tensiometer) filled with water. The water in the porous cup is attached to a vacuum gage or a mercury manometer. As the soil dries out, water moves through the porous cup, setting up a negative tension or vacuum. These tension readings are then calibrated to interpret the percentage of moisture. The principal limitation of the use of tensiometers is the fact that they do not measure soil moisture as low as the wilting percentage. The actual range is from 0 to 0.85 atmosphere. The tensiometers are more useful for measuring moisture in sandy soils than in fine-textured soils.

3. Methods that are based on the changes in electrical conductivity with changes in soil moisture. In 1940, G. J. Bouyoucos at Michigan State University introduced a gypsum block inside of which were two electrodes a definite distance apart. The blocks were to be buried in the soil and the conductivity across the electrodes measured with a modified Wheatstone bridge. With proper calibrations, the percentage of moisture from the field capacity to the wilting percentage can be readily determined.   (Figure 9.4)

Improved Bouyoucos blocks have been made of nylon or fiberglass. Blocks made of these substances do not deteriorate in the soil as do gypsum blocks.

FIG. 9.4. A farmer measures soil moisture in his corn field with a Bouyoucos Bridge. The lead wires from a gypsum block buried in the soil are fastened to the Bridge and the electrical resistance is measured. This method measures moisture in the soil from the wilting coefficient to the field capacity.

Courtesy Henry Corrow, New Hampshire Extension Service.

Available Water

Available water is the range of soil moisture between the wilting percentage and the field capacity. Table 9.1 gives representative information on available water for five Florida soils and three soils from the state of Washington. The data are in acre-inches of water in the top three feet of soil—the normal rooting depth of many plants.

The range in available water capacity in the Florida soils varies from 1.0 acre-inch in a fine sand to 6.2 acre-inches in a peat. For Washington

TABLE 9.1 Acre-Inches of Water in the First Three Feet of Representative Soils in Florida and Washington

| | Acre-Inches of Water in First 3 Feet of Soil, by Volume | | |
State and Soil Type	Field Capacity (1/3 atmosphere)	Wilting Percentage (15 atmospheres)	Available Water Capacity (in.)
FLORIDA *			
Lakeland fine sand	1.6	0.6	1.0
Felda fine sandy loam	6.1	3.0	3.1
Manatee fine sandy loam	7.4	3.9	3.5
Manatee sandy clay loam	9.4	5.1	4.3
Everglades Peat	20.2	14.0	6.2
WASHINGTON **			
Sagemoor fine sandy loam	6.0	2.4	3.6
Ephrata fine sandy loam	7.2	2.4	4.8
Ephrata sandy loam	9.3	3.0	6.3

* T. W. Young, "Soil Moisture Relations in the Coastal Citrus Areas of Florida," Florida Agr. Exp. Sta. Bul. 526. 1953.

** Anonymous, "Soil, Water, and Crop Management Investigations in the Columbia Basin Project," Bul. 520. U. S. Dept. of Agr. 1950.

soils, the variation is from 3.6 to 6.3 acre-inches. These data show that the more clay there is in the soil, the greater the capacity for available water.

Whereas Table 9.1 gives data which imply that the greater the clay percentage in a soil, the greater the available water capacity, the relationship is not always linear. Figure 9.5 clearly shows that soils with a very large amount of clay have less available water capacity. A loam or silt loam soil in general has the largest amount of available water capacity. Sandy soils and clay soils are intermediate in this respect.

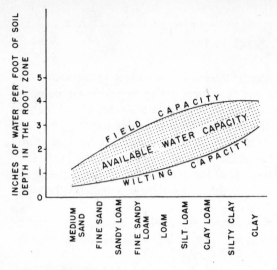

FIG. 9.5. The relationship between soil texture and available water. (Water: The Yearbook of Agriculture, 1955, p. 120.)

Percolation

The movement of water through a column of soil is called *percolation*. Percolation studies are important for at least two reasons. Percolating waters are the only source of recharge of water for springs and wells. Also, percolating waters carry plant nutrients down and often out of reach of plant roots.

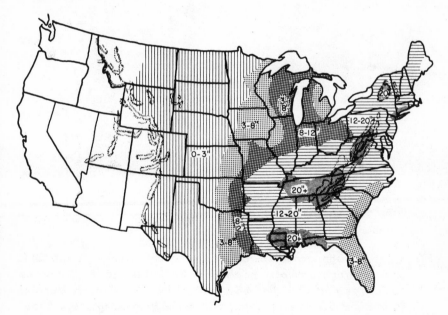

FIG. 9.6. Average annual percolation. (Source: L. B. Nelson and R. E. Uhland, "Factors That Influence Loss of Fall Applied Fertilizers and Their Probable Importance in Different Sections of the United States," **Soil Science Society of America Proceedings**, 19:4, 1955.)

Not all places in the United States have sufficient precipitation to percolate through the surface soil. A glance at Figure 9.6 clearly demonstrates that the Great Plains have annual percolation rates of 0-3 inches per year. Coming eastward, the percolation rate varies mostly with the amount of precipitation, but with some exceptions. The notable exception is Florida, where 3 to 8 inches is the annual percolation rate. Here the annual precipitation is in excess of 50 inches, but the temperature is so high as to evaporate a large part of the rain before it percolates through the soil.

Within these areas of generalized percolation, sandy soils permit greater percolation and clay soils will permit less water to move through them.

Percolation through three Ohio soils is demonstrated graphically in Figure 9.7. These values compare three silt loams which, at the time of these studies, had supported grass for a period of four years: 1947, 1948, 1951, and 1952. The lysimeters consisted of a column of soil 8 feet deep. The precipitation averaged 37 inches annually.

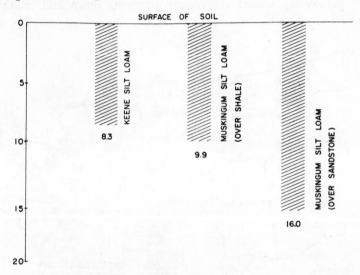

FIG. 9.7. Average annual percolation losses of water in three Ohio soils (average annual precipitation, 37 inches). (F. R. Dreibelbis, "Soil Type and Land Use Effects of Soil Water Through Monolith Lysimeters," **Soil Science Society of America Proceedings**, 18:4, 1954.)

The Keene silt loam permitted 8.3 inches of water to percolate through the eight-foot column each year, or approximately 22 per cent of the precipitation. Muskingum silt loam over shale had an annual percolation rate of 9.9 inches per year, or 27 per cent of the annual precipitation.

The greatest percolation rate was in Muskingum silt loam over sandstone. Here the amount was 16.0 inches per year, which is 43 per cent of the annual precipitation.

Leaching Losses of Nutrients

The relative hazard of losses of plant nutrients by leaching is represented in Figure 9.8. This map was generalized from Figure 9.6, which shows leaching losses of water.

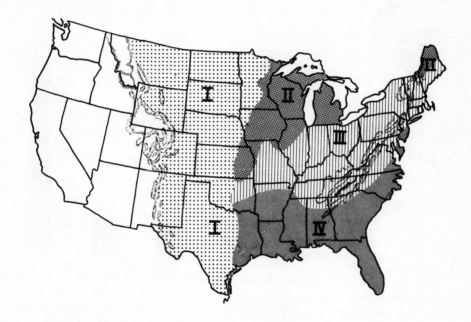

FIG. 9.8. Relative hazard of plant nutrient losses by leaching: I, slight hazard; II, moderate hazard; III, severe hazard; IV, very severe hazard. (L. B. Nelson and R. E. Uhland, "Factors That Influence Loss of Fall Applied Fertilizers and Their Probable Importance in Different Sections of the United States," **Soil Science Society of America Proceedings,** 19:4, 1955.)

Area I—Slight hazard. Includes the Great Plains.

Area II—Moderate hazard. Includes the Lake States, Iowa, Northwestern Illinois, Northwestern Missouri, and Eastern Kansas.

Area III—Severe hazard. Includes the Northeast, the Appalachian Region, and the Corn Belt.

Area IV—Very severe hazard. Covers the South.

Actual leaching losses of plant nutrients in New York are graphically portrayed in Figure 9.9. The relative order of losses is:

$$Ca > Mg > S > K > N > P$$

Only a trace of phosphorus is lost by leaching, while the losses of Ca are the greatest of any nutrient shown.

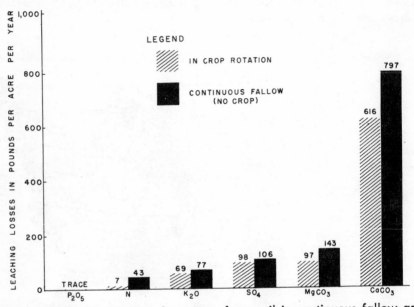

FIG. 9.9. Leaching losses of nutrients from soil in continuous fallow as compared with soil in a crop rotation. (Soil is Volusia silt loam, for a period of 15 years.) (T. L. Lyon and J. A. Bizzell, "Lysimeter Experiments IV," Cornell Univ. Agr. Exp. Sta. Memoir 194, 1936.)

These data compare leaching losses in Volusia silt loam, an acid soil derived from shale. No crop (continuously fallow or bare) is compared with a crop rotation with respect to the loss of plant nutrients by leaching. In every instance, there is less loss by leaching under a crop rotation than under no crop.

Summary

The average acre in the United States does not take in sufficient natural rainfall to grow corn; only range grasses can grow. Better management practices will increase infiltration and the amount of available water with no increase in rainfall. Infiltration rates of soils are influenced by texture, structure, organic matter, soil depth, wetness of the soil, and soil temperature. Infiltration rates less than 0.05 inch per hour are low, while rates above 0.30 inch are high.

Permeability is a term used to express the ease of movement of air and water through a soil. Maximum permeability is limited by the permeability of the least permeable horizon. Tillage pans seriously restrict the movement of water through the soil. Less than 0.05 inch per hour is very slow, and more than 10 inches per hour is considered very rapid permeability.

Soil moisture is normally reported in terms of atmospheres of equilibrium tension. At oven-dryness, the atmospheres of soil moisture tension is 10,000; at air-dryness, 1,000; at the hygroscopic coefficient, 31; at the wilting percentage, 15; and at the field capacity, 1/3. Available water lies between the wilting percentage and the field capacity.

On a percentage basis, soil moisture is calculated in this way:

$$\% \text{ soil moisture} = \frac{\text{Loss in weight in oven}}{\text{Oven-dry weight of soil}} \times 100$$

Gypsum, nylon, or fiberglass is used in making Bouyoucos blocks for measuring soil moisture by the electrical-conductivity method. This method permits the measurement of soil moisture throughout its available range, from the field capacity to the wilting percentage.

Available water capacities are low for sandy soils and for very fine-textured clay soils. Loams and silt loams have the greatest available water capacities of all mineral soils. Peats and mucks have the highest available water capacities of all soils.

Water percolates downward through a deep section of soil only in areas where the precipitation is high. In the Great Plains, percolation seldom exceeds three inches of water a year. In the high-rainfall areas of the Appalachian Mountains and the lower Mississippi and Alabama Gulf Coast, percolation often reaches 20 inches a year.

Leaching losses are proportional to the amounts of water leached through the soil. Plant nutrients are lost in greatest amounts when no crop is growing to absorb the nutrients. Regardless of the use of the land, however, the relative rate of nutrient losses by leaching from the soil are in this order, from high to low:

$$Ca > Mg > S > K > N > P$$

Questions

1. Differentiate between infiltration, percolation, and permeability.
2. Discuss the relationship between infiltration and the degree of water-stable aggregation of soils.
3. Is there possible harm when a cultivated soil has an infiltration rate of 0.25 inch per hour in an area where rainfall is frequently 0.4 inch per hour? Explain.

4. How can a soil be managed to increase permeability?

5. In the surface foot of soil, if there is 0.3 inch of water in the soil at the wilting percentage and 2.1 inches at the field capacity, what is the available water capacity of the soil?

6. In Question 5, if corn roots were all in the first foot of soil and the corn used 0.2 inch of water per day, how many days would the available water last?

7. How is the soil moisture percentage calculated?

8. Why is it possible for two fine sandy loam soils to have different available water capacities?

9. Why are there almost no percolation losses in the Great Plains?

10. Under what conditions would you expect the least leaching losses of nutrients from a soil?

References

A *Water Policy for the American People*. Volume I. Report of the President's Water Resources Policy Commission. Washington, D.C. 1950.

Shaw, Byron T., ed., *Soil Physical Conditions and Plant Growth*. Academic Press. New York. 1952.

Water: The Yearbook of Agriculture for 1955. U. S. Department of Agriculture.

10

Plant Nutrition

Plants contain small amounts of 90 or more elements, only 16 of which are currently known to be essential. It is of interest to note that iron, carbon, sulfur, copper, and zinc have been known since ancient times. Magnesium and boron were discovered as late as 1808. Nitrogen was proved essential to plants in the eighteenth century; during the nineteenth century, seven of the elements were demonstrated to be essential, and eight were so proved in the twentieth century.

Elements Essential for Plants and Animals

There are at present 16 elements which are known to be essential for the growth and reproduction of higher plants. These elements are: carbon, hydrogen, oxygen, phosphorus, potassium, nitrogen, sulfur, calcium, iron, magnesium, boron, manganese, copper, zinc, molybdenum, and chlorine.

Since farm livestock are mostly forage-eating animals, it is of vital concern to know whether the elements essential for plants are also essential for animals. Elements known to be essential for animals are: carbon, hydrogen, oxygen, phosphorus, potassium, nitrogen, sulfur, calcium, iron, magnesium, manganese, copper, zinc, sodium, iodine, chlorine, and cobalt.

Forms in Which Nutrients Are Taken in by Plants

Plants take in nutrients from the soil mostly in the form of ions. The

16 essential elements move into the plant primarily in the following forms:

C	CO_3^{--}, CO_2 (mostly through leaves)
H	H^+, HOH
O	OH^-, CO_3^{--}, SO_4^{--}, HOH, CO_2 (mostly through leaves)
P	$H_2PO_4^-$
K	K^+
N	NH_4^+ NO_3^-
S	SO_4^{--}
Ca	Ca^{++}
Fe	Fe^{++}, Fe^{+++}
Mg	Mg^{++}
B	BO_3^{--}
Mn	Mn^{++}
Cu	Cu^{++}
Zn	Zn^{++}
Mo	MoO_4^{--}
Cl	Cl^-

The Mechanism of Nutrient Uptake

Plants obtain nutrients from these four devices:

1. Through the leaves.
2. From the soil solution.
3. From exchangeable ions on the surface of clay and humus particles.
4. From readily decomposable minerals.

All crop plants feed mostly by root uptake of nutrients from the soil. The principal exception is the intake of carbon as carbon dioxide, which enters the plant almost entirely through the stomates of the leaves. Water also is absorbed through the stomates, but the relative amount is small as compared with that which enters the roots. Many nutrients are capable of being absorbed by the leaves of plants, but that will be discussed in the following section.

Most of the nutrients enter the plant root as ions, either anions or cations. It is quite generally agreed now among plant physiologists that a plant root excretes a cation in exchange for another cation which it absorbs; and an anion is released by the root for each anion which it uses.

The diagram in Figure 10.1 is shown to illustrate cationic exchange between a root and a clay and humus particle, and between the root and the soil solution. The source of additional cations from a limestone fragment is also given in the diagram.

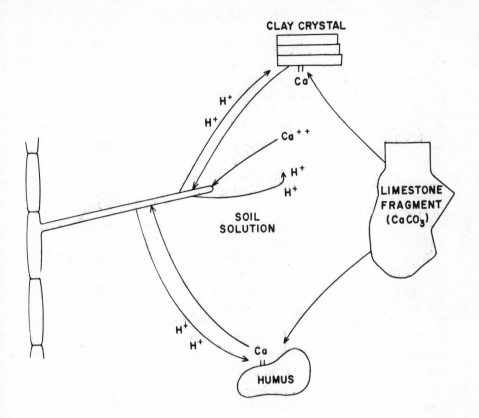

FIG. 10.1. A diagrammatic scheme for showing how a root hair takes in nutrients from the soil solution and from exchangeable ions on a clay crystal and on humus. These nutrients originally came from readily decomposable minerals.

A root hair is an extension of one of the epidermal cells of the plant root and is responsible for nearly all intake of water and nutrients.

As the limestone fragment slowly decomposes, it releases calcium ions (Ca^{++}) to the soil solution and to clay and humus particles. The root hair releases two hydrogen ions for each calcium ion it absorbs from either the soil solution, a clay particle, or a humus particle.

The nutrient cations such as Ca^{++}, K^+, Mg^{++}, and NH_4^+ are held on clay crystals and on humus in an exchangeable and available form for use by plants. Not so with anions. Nitrates, sulfates, phosphates, borates, and molybdates are nutrient anions and therefore are not held by clay and humus by the same mechanism.

Available anions exist either in the soil solution or in some chemical compound in equilibrium with the soil solution. Phosphorus, sulfur, boron, and molybdenum are a part of the crystal structure of such minerals as apatite, tourmaline, and pyrite. But the nutrient elements in these minerals are so slowly soluble as to supply too few anions for normal plant nutrition, even though the minerals are finely ground.

It is soil organic matter that serves as the principal storehouse for the anions. Through the decomposition of organic matter by bacteria, fungi, and actinomycetes and subsequent oxidation, the anions are made available to growing plants.

Almost all nitrogen is held in the soil in the organic matter. Organic phosphorus may account for from 10 to 50 per cent of the total soil phosphorus. Up to 80 per cent of soil sulfur was reported to be held in the organic form. Boron and molybdenum reserves seem to be stored both in organic matter and in clay.

There is good evidence to support the theory that anions are taken into the plant only from the soil solution. But the amounts of anions in the soil solution at any one time are not enough to supply the plant for the entire growing season. The only logical answer is that, as the anions in the soil solution are taken up by the plant, other anions are released to the soil solution by organic decomposition or from slowly soluble compounds. It is also generally agreed that, as plant roots take in nutrient anions, the roots release OH^- or HCO_3^- ions in exchange.

Foliar Nutrition of Plants *

It has been known for many years that plants are able to absorb essential elements through their leaves. The absorption takes place through the stomates of the leaves and also through the leaf cuticle. Movement of elements is usually faster through the stomates, but the total absorption may be as great through the cuticle.

The following elements have been successfully used to supply nutrients for plant growth by applying them as foliar sprays to the leaves:

Primary Nutrients	Secondary Nutrients	Micronutrients
Nitrogen	Magnesium	Iron
Phosphorus	Calcium	Zinc
Potassium	Sulfur	Boron
		Copper
		Molybdenum

Nitrogen fertilizer compounds have been used for several years as foliar sprays. Sodium nitrate, ammonium sulfate, potassium nitrate, and urea have all been used experimentally, but only urea gives satisfactory results. The other fertilizers cause the burning of leaves, due partly to the high osmotic concentration of the spray solution.

* Damon Boynton, "Nutrition by Foliar Application," *Annual Review of Plant Physiology*, Vol. 5, 1954, pp. 31-54.

Urea has been successfully sprayed on apple trees, tomatoes, celery, lima beans, potatoes, cantaloupes, cucumbers, and sugar cane. Amounts up to 15 pounds of urea per acre at one spraying have been used with beneficial results on apple trees. Higher concentrations burn the leaves. The usual concentration for apple trees is five pounds of urea per 100 gallons of water. This is commonly mixed and applied with the regular spray materials at weekly intervals early in the growing season.

The application of urea fertilizer to leaves of plants has given approximately equal response to that of fertilizer applied to the soil. The uptake of urea is faster when it is sprayed on the leaves, but it is cheaper to apply it to the soil.

Phosphorus is capable of being utilized by the plant when it is sprayed on the leaves. Although the practice is not common, there are many good reasons for predicting that there may be an increase in the foliar application of phosphorus.

One reason is that in most soils only a small percentage of phosphorus fertilizers is recovered by the plant; whereas, when phosphorus is sprayed on the leaves, nearly all of it is absorbed. In one experiment, approximately three pounds of P_2O_5 sprayed on tomato leaves gave a greater early growth than did 135 pounds of P_2O_5 applied to the soil. The yield of tomatoes, however, was 12 per cent greater when the 135 pounds of P_2O_5 was applied to the soil than when 3 pounds of P_2O_5 was sprayed on the leaves.

Potassium applications as foliar sprays have been made, using potassium sulfate fertilizer. Some leaf injury resulted, and the conclusion was reached that soil applications are far more satisfactory.

Magnesium is now commonly applied to plant foliage as solutions of magnesium sulfate (Epsom salts). One reason for the popularity of the practice is that soil applications of magnesium commonly take three years to correct magnesium deficiency symptoms of such perennials as apple trees, whereas foliar sprays are effective within a few days after application.

A foliar application of a two per cent solution of $MgSO_4$ to tomatoes, oranges, and apples has relieved magnesium deficiency and has increased crop yields.

Calcium is seldom applied as a foliar spray because it can be efficiently applied to the soil. If $CaCO_3$ is too slow in reaction, then CaO or $Ca(OH)_2$ can be applied to the soil. But there is no good reason why calcium cannot be applied as a foliar spray.

Sulfur sprayed on leaves is readily absorbed by the plants. This fact was demonstrated, however, in connection with the study of the influence of certain sulfur sprays when used as a fungicide. Although there have been no reports of a sulfur deficiency being relieved by sulfur sprays, the practice may become established because it is physiologically sound.

Iron has been sprayed on foliage since about 1916 to relieve chlorosis. The first of such research work was carried out with chlorotic pineapples growing on highly alkaline soils in Hawaii. Periodic sprays of five per cent ferrous sulfate are now common practice on Hawaiian pineapple plantations. The biggest obstacle to this practice is the fact that, even though the iron moves readily into the leaves, it is translocated very slowly. As a result, after spraying with ferrous sulfate, chlorotic spots may still be in evidence in places which did not receive some of the iron spray.

On alkaline soils where iron chlorosis is common, applications of iron compounds to the soil have not been very successful because the iron is soon rendered insoluble.

Zinc is often sprayed on the leaves of apple and pear trees to relieve "leaf rosetting," a symptom of zinc deficiency. Approximately 25 pounds of zinc sulfate in 100 gallons of water (roughly a three per cent solution) applied to apple trees just before the buds open has corrected zinc deficiency. Zinc sulfide, zinc oxide, and zinc carbonate have all been successfully used as sprays. Driving galvanized (zinc-coated) nails in trees also relieves zinc deficiency.

Boron, as boric acid or borax (sodium tetraborate), used as a foliar spray has proved to be a successful method of application. Internal cork of apples has been controlled by spraying the foliage with eight pounds of borax in 100 gallons of water. As little as two pounds of borax per 100 gallons of water has checked "cracked stem" of celery. Boron is also satisfactorily applied to the soil, either alone or in mixed fertilizers.

Copper deficiency has been controlled by spraying the leaves with a mixture of 8 pounds of $CuSO_4$ plus 8 pounds of $Ca(OH)_2$ in 100 gallons of water. Without the calcium hydroxide, the copper sulfate injures the foliage.

Molybdenum, as sodium molybdate, 1 ounce in 100 gallons of water, has eliminated deficiency symptoms in citrus trees. Somewhat like iron, however, molybdenum does not seem to be readily translocated within the plant. Spraying only the lower half of a citrus tree that showed molybdenum deficiency did not cure the deficiency symptoms on the upper half of the tree.

Soil Physical Conditions and Plant Nutrition

Adequate amounts of nutrients for desirable plant growth may be "available" according to any chemical test but actually deficient because of soil physical conditions.

Tillage pans, cloddy surface soils, surface crusts, or lack of soil aggregation may reduce nutrient availability for one of these reasons:

1. By physically restricting root elongation, especially deep root penetration. This reduces the volume of soil in contact with plant roots,

and the total nutrients absorbed by the roots will therefore be limited.

2. By restricting the exchange of oxygen and carbon dioxide in the soil, the ability of plant roots to translocate nutrients to the leaves is reduced.* (Figure 10.2)

3. By retarding the growth of nitrifying bacteria, the soil nitrogen may remain as unavailable protein instead of breaking down to release available ammonium and nitrate ions.

4. By reducing water infiltration, water may become the first limiting factor in plant growth even though all nutrients are present in adequate amounts.

FIG. 10.2. Surface crusts restrict plant growth by reducing the supply of oxygen for the roots.

Courtesy Ben Osborn, Soil Conservation Service.

Nitrogen

There are nearly 12 pounds of nitrogen above every square foot of the surface of the earth, yet nitrogen is one of our most critical elements for plant growth. The reason is that plants cannot utilize nitrogen as a gas; it must first be combined into some stable form.

* Recent research has shown that low oxygen concentration in the soil results in an increase in nutrient absorption by the roots but a decrease in translocation of nutrients to the leaves.

Plants absorb nitrogen either as the ammonium or the nitrate ion. The ammonium ions can be held in an exchangeable and available form on the surfaces of clay crystals and humus, but bacteria soon transform the ammonium to nitrates, which are readily leachable. There is no *good* storehouse for available forms of nitrogen. The only storehouse of any kind for nitrogen is soil organic matter.

Soil organic matter is approximately five per cent nitrogen. It therefore follows that:

$$\%N \times 20 = \% \text{ Organic Matter}$$

Nitrogen is a constituent of all living cells, and each molecule of chlorophyll contains four atoms of nitrogen. Nitrogen makes plants darker green and more succulent; it also makes larger cells with thinner cell walls. In addition, nitrogen increases the proportion of water and decreases the percentage of calcium in plant tissues.

Recent research in Arkansas has demonstrated that many crops when fertilized with nitrogen have an increased ability to absorb not only more nitrogen but also more phosphorus, potassium, and calcium. Nitrogen fertilization increases the cation-exchange capacity of plant roots and thus makes them more efficient in absorbing other nutrient ions.

Phosphorus

Phosphorus nutrition is doubly critical; the total supply of phosphorus in most soils is usually low, and its relative availability is also low. Plants absorb phosphorus from the soil solution mostly in the form of $H_2PO_4^-$ ions.

FIG. 10.3.   The use of radioactive phosphorus in research makes it possible to study phosphorus nutrition in great detail.
Courtesy U. S. D. A.

The total phosphorus in an average arable soil is approximately 0.1 per cent, only an infinitesimal part of which at any one time is available to the plant. Under ideal conditions, as plants take in $H_2PO_4^-$ ions from the soil solution, other ions replace them from slowly soluble compounds in the soil. There is no efficient mechanism on clay crystals or on humus particles for holding exchangeable and available anions such as $H_2PO_4^-$.

Phosphorus availability is low in strongly acid soils because of the formation of iron and aluminum phosphates, from which phosphorus is very slowly available. In alkaline soils, tricalcium phosphate $[Ca_3(PO_4)_2]$ forms readily to reduce the availability of soil phosphorus.

The nucleus of each plant cell contains phosphorus; for that reason, cell division and growth are not possible without adequate phosphorus. Phosphorus is concentrated in cells near the most actively growing part of both roots and shoots, where cells are dividing rapidly.

Potassium

The amount of *total* potassium in all soils is sufficient to last forever; yet the money spent for potassium fertilizers is constantly on the increase. An explanation of this apparent contradiction lies in the fact that most of the potassium is a part of the molecule of very slowly soluble minerals such as orthoclase ($K Al Si_3O_8$). Soils may contain two per cent *total* potassium only one-fiftieth of which at any one time is in a readily available (exchangeable) form. However, during the growing season, approximately half of the potassium absorbed by the plant may come from the exchangeable form and the other half from relatively insoluble minerals which decompose and thereby release their potassium.

Until a few years ago it was thought that all potassium in the plant stayed in a mobile form. Radioactive potassium techniques have demonstrated that as much as one-third of plant potassium is fixed as a part of plant proteins. Potassium also helps to maintain cell permeability, aids in the translocation of carbohydrates, keeps iron more mobile in the plant, and increases the resistance of plants to certain diseases.

Calcium

Calcium in the soil may average one per cent for the United States. Variations are great, however, for calcium minerals are fairly soluble, resulting in low-calcium soils in humid regions.

Most of the reserve calcium in the soil is in the form of calcium carbonate (limestone) or, in the West, a mixture of calcium carbonate and calcium sulfate. When compared with most potassium minerals, calcium-bearing minerals are usually much more soluble. As a consequence, there is nearly always more exchangeable calcium on the clay crystals and on the humus particles than there is potassium.

Calcium tends to make cells more selective in their absorption, since it is a constituent of the middle lamella of each cell wall. Rapidly growing root tips are especially high in calcium, indicating that calcium is needed in large quantities for cell division.

Magnesium

Chlorophyll contains one atom of magnesium in each molecule; therefore, there could be no green plants without magnesium. There is almost as much magnesium as calcium in average soils, yet there are soils in the Northeast that are extremely deficient in magnesium.

Reserve magnesium occurs mostly in dolomitic limestone, a rock which consists of a mixture of calcium and magnesium carbonate. Dolomitic limestone is not so readily decomposed as is calcic limestone; for that reason, the amount of exchangeable magnesium is usually less than that of exchangeable calcium.

It has been demonstrated that magnesium aids in the uptake of phosphorus. This fact is of particular importance to the livestock industry, because the phosphorus content most desirable for the growth of forage is inadequate for satisfactory animal nutrition.

Sulfur

Sulfur is found in small amounts in the soil, averaging perhaps 0.15 per cent in a typical soil. A large part of the sulfur which plants use comes from sulfates, which are a by-product in superphosphate fertilizer, and through biological release from decomposing organic matter.

Many plant proteins contain sulfur, as does an oil produced by members of the cabbage family.

Micronutrients

Iron, manganese, zinc, copper, boron, chlorine and molybdenum are listed as micronutrients because they are used by plants in such small amounts. The exact function is not known. These elements may limit plant growth either because there may not be a sufficient amount of them in the soil, or, as is more often the case, because some condition in the soil reduces their availability.

All of the micronutrients except molybdenum are more soluble in an acid soil; molybdenum solubility increases with liming.

Iron is not a constituent of chlorophyll, but it is essential for its formation. Manganese is related to oxidation-reduction balances in the plant, especially in connection with iron and nitrogen metabolism. Zinc is needed by plants in some of their enzyme systems. Copper activates a group of oxidizing enzymes and is a constituent of certain proteins. The function of boron in the plant is still obscure, although a lack of boron tends to increase the loss of phosphorus from plant roots. Molybdenum seems to take part in nitrogen metabolism in the plant and in nitrogen fixation by bacteria. The exact function of chlorine is not known.

Summary

Plants are now known to need only 16 of the 90 or more elements which they contain. Animals require 14 of the same 16 elements and, in addition, sodium, cobalt, and iodine. Nearly all plant nutrients are taken in by the plant in ionic forms. A plant root releases cations when it absorbs cations, and exchanges anions for other anions in the soil solution.

Nearly all nutrients can also be absorbed by the leaves of plants, through either the stomates or the cuticle.

The physical condition of the soil must be satisfactory so as not to hinder plant nutrition. Tillage pans restrict root penetration, reduce oxygen exchange, retard nitrifying bacteria, and reduce available water.

Organic matter is the only good storehouse for soil nitrogen. Phosphorus is in short supply because the total amount in soils is low, and because it becomes quickly unavailable in acid and alkaline soils. There is plenty of total potassium in all soils, but it does not become available fast enough for normal crop growth. Calcium reserves are easily lost by leaching; as a consequence, soils in humid regions are acid. Magnesium is the only mineral on the chlorophyll molecule. Sulfur nutrition is related to organic-matter decomposition and to the addition of by-product sulfates in superphosphate fertilizer. All micronutrients except molybdenum are more readily available in acid soils.

Questions

1. Name the elements essential for plants and for animals.
2. What elements have in this century been proved essential for plant growth?
3. In what forms are all nutrients absorbed by plant roots?
4. Describe the mechanism of a plant root absorbing potassium.
5. Describe the mechanism of phosphorus absorption.
6. How do leaves absorb nutrients?
7. Can all nutrients be absorbed by the leaves of plants?
8. With what nutrients does a foliar application seem practical?
9. In what ways may a poor soil physical condition reduce plant growth?
10. Explain the reason for a scarcity of nitrogen amid plenty.

References

Arnon, Daniel I., and Leonard Machlis, eds., *Annual Review of Plant Physiology*. Annual Reviews, Inc. Stanford, California. Volumes 1-5, 1950 to 1955.

Russell, Sir E. John, and E. Walter Russell, *Soil Conditions and Plant Growth*. Longmans, Green, and Co. New York. 8th ed. 1950.

Truog, Emil, ed., *Mineral Nutrition of Plants*. The University of Wisconsin Press. 1951.

PART II

Applied Soil Science

11

Lime and Liming Practices

Lime is added to acid soils primarily for three purposes:

1. To supply calcium and sometimes magnesium as a plant nutrient.

2. To reduce the toxicity of aluminum, manganese, and iron.

3. To increase the pH of acid soils and thereby make other plant nutrients more available.

From its beginning the practice of liming land has increased nearly every year. In 1955 the tonnage of lime used on agricultural crops in the United States was almost 25 million.

Areas of major lime use are indicated in Figure 11.1.

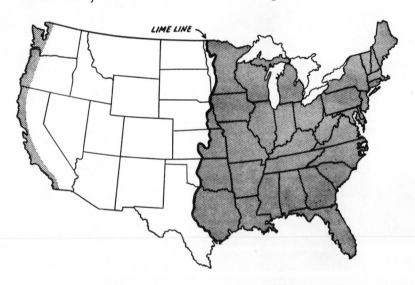

FIG. 11.1. The shaded area east of the Lime Line and the high rainfall areas on the Pacific Coast require a regular liming program for the maximum production of most farm crops. (**About Agriculture Limestone,** The National Agricultural Limestone Institute, 1953.)

FIG. 11.2. Soils are acid partly because acid nitrogen fertilizers are used on them. The center plot received 200 pounds per acre of ammonium sulfate per year for 21 years. (Alabama) (Compare with Fig. 11.3.)

Courtesy Howard T. Rogers, Alabama Agricultural Experiment Station.

Why Soils Are Acid

Soils are acid for many reasons. The main reasons may be summarized as follows:

1. Some soils have developed from parent materials which are acid.
2. Rain leaches lime downward, carrying some of it out of reach of plant roots.
3. Plant roots secrete hydrogen ions, which help to make soils more acid.

FIG. 11.3. The center plot received 200 pounds per acre per year of ammonium sulfate for 21 years, the same as in Fig. 11.2, but, in addition, it received 230 pounds of limestone per acre per year for the same period. (Alabama) (Compare with Fig. 11.2.)

Courtesy Howard T. Rogers, Alabama Agricultural Experiment Station.

4. Most nitrogen carriers are acid and therefore make the soil more acid. (Figure 11.2)

5. Sulfur is an ingredient of some fungicides and its use creates acid conditions.

What Lime Does in the Soil

Strongly acid soils are not productive soils. To increase the productivity of acid soils, lime is the first step, for these reasons:

1. Lime makes phosphorus more available. This is so mainly because in acid soils iron and aluminum phosphates are relatively insoluble. Liming reduces the solubility of iron and aluminum, and therefore less phosphorus is held in these insoluble and unavailable forms.

2. Lime makes potassium more efficient in plant nutrition. All plants absorb more potassium than they need when it is plentiful. Lime reduces the excessive uptake of potassium. Nutritionally and economically, this is a sound practice. When lime is abundant, plants take up more calcium and less potassium. Since calcium is usually deficient in animal rations and potassium has an excess in these, it is desirable to increase the percentage of calcium in the plant. Economically the practice of liming is desirable because the plant absorbs more cheap calcium and less of the expensive potassium.

3. Lime increases the availability of nitrogen by hastening the decomposition of organic matter.

4. Lime furnishes calcium and magnesium (if the lime is dolomitic) for plant nutrition. These are two of the 16 elements essential for plant growth.

5. Beneficial soil bacteria are encouraged by adequate supplies of lime in the soil.

6. Harmful aluminum, manganese, and iron are rendered insoluble and harmless when a soil is well supplied with lime.

7. Over a period of years, a good liming program improves the phys-

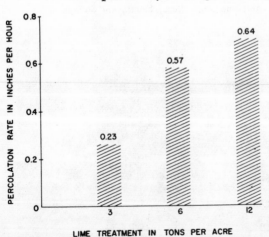

FIG. 11.4. The relationship between the amount of lime applied and the rate of percolation. (C. A. Van Doren and A. A. Klingebiel, "Effect of Management on Soil Permeability," **Soil Science Society of America Proceedings,** 16, 1952.)

ical condition of the soil by decreasing its bulk density, increasing its infiltration capacity, and increasing its rate of percolation of water. Figure 11.4 presents information showing that the more the lime applied, the greater is the rate of percolation.

8. There is less soil erosion following an adequate liming program. This result is due primarily to the increased vigor and density of plants following the application of lime.

Crop Response to Lime

The use of lime on acid soils in a regular cropping system increases the yields of most crops. Alfalfa, corn, oats, wheat, cotton, other legumes, flax, and soybeans all respond to a liming program.

Figure 11.5 gives, for South Carolina, the relationship between crop yields on limed soils and those on soils not limed. Legumes respond the most to lime, but the yields of cotton, wheat, oats, and corn were all increased on the plots which received lime.

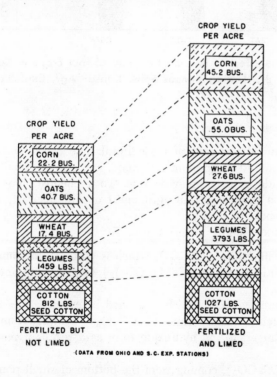

CROP YIELD PER ACRE

CORN 45.2 BUS.

OATS 55.0 BUS.

WHEAT 27.6 BUS.

LEGUMES 3793 LBS.

COTTON 1027 LBS. SEED COTTON

CROP YIELD PER ACRE

CORN 22.2 BUS.

OATS 40.7 BUS.

WHEAT 17.4 BUS.

LEGUMES 1459 LBS.

COTTON 812 LBS. SEED COTTON

FERTILIZED BUT NOT LIMED

FERTILIZED AND LIMED

(DATA FROM OHIO AND S.C. EXP. STATIONS)

FIG. 11.5. The effect of one application of lime per rotation on crop yield per acre (three-year rotation: cotton—corn—small grains and legumes). (H. A. Woodle and E. C. Turner, **Lime for South Carolina Soils,** Clemson Agr. Exp. Sta. Cir. 378, 1952.)

Similar data are shown for Kansas in Figure 11.6, which compares the yields of limed and not limed wheat, oats, corn, and alfalfa. Of these crops, alfalfa shows the greatest percentage increase in yield as a result of liming.

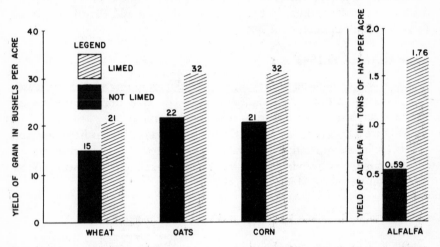

FIG. 11.6. The effect of lime on the yield of four crops in Kansas. (Roscoe Ellis, Jr., **Liming Kansas Soils,** Kansas Agr. Exp. Sta. Cir. 313, 1954.)

Liming Materials

More than 90 per cent of agricultural lime is calcium carbonate; some is calcium and magnesium carbonate, and a much smaller quantity is calcium oxide or calcium hydroxide. To a chemist, lime is calcium oxide, but to a farmer and an agronomist or soil scientist, lime means calcium carbonate equivalent.

The common liming materials are:

1. Calcic limestone ($CaCO_3$), which is ground limestone.

2. Dolomitic limestone ($CaMg(CO_3)_2$), from ground limestone high in magnesium.

3. Quicklime (CaO), which is burned limestone.

4. Hydrated (slaked) lime ($Ca(OH)_2$), coming from quicklime which has changed to the hydroxide form as a result of reactions with water.

5. Marl ($CaCO_3$), coming from the bottom of small ponds in areas where the soils are high in lime. The lime has accumulated by precipitation from drainage waters high in lime. Some marls contain many shell remains from marine animals.

6. Chalk ($CaCO_3$), resulting from soft limestone.

7. Blast-furnace slag ($CaSiO_3$ and Ca_2SiO_4), a by-product of the iron industry. Some slags contain phosphorus and a mixture of CaO and $Ca(OH)_2$. This product is called *basic slag* and is used primarily for its phosphorus content.

FIG. 11.7.   Ground limestone being spread at the rate of three tons per acre on a Kansas farm.
Courtesy U. S. D. A.

8. Miscellaneous sources, such as ground oystershell, and by-product lime resulting from papermills, sugar beet plants, tanneries, and water-softening plants.

Gypsum ($CaSO_4$) is sometimes added to the soil to supply calcium, but it has no influence on soil pH. It is not considered as a liming material.

All of the liming materials mentioned have value for supplying calcium or calcium and magnesium, raising the pH, and making aluminum, manganese, and iron less toxic. The choice of which one to buy is determined by the cost in relation to its purity, the ease of handling, and the speed with which the lime reacts.

Chemical Guarantees of Lime

There are several methods of expressing the chemical guarantee of lime. The most common ones are:

1. Calcium carbonate equivalent, sometimes known as the *neutralizing power*. If chemically pure calcium carbonate were present in a lime, the calcium carbonate equivalent would be 100. If all of the lime were in the calcium carbonate form but it was 95 per cent pure, the calcium carbonate equivalent would be 95. Other forms of lime can be converted to the calcium carbonate equivalent by the use of atomic and molecular weights. One example will be shown. Assume that it is desired to calculate the calcium carbonate equivalent of chemically pure calcium oxide, CaO.

$$\% \text{ CaCO}_3 \text{ equivalent} = \frac{\text{Molecular wt. of CaCO}_3}{\text{Molecular wt. of CaO}} \times 100 =$$

$$\frac{100}{56} \times 100 = 178.6$$

The calcium carbonate equivalent of any quantity of CaO can be obtained by multiplying the pounds of pure CaO by 178.6 per cent.

2. The calcium oxide equivalent. This form of chemical guarantee is obtained also by the use of molecular weights. For example, if pure calcium carbonate were converted to its calcium oxide equivalent, the calculations are:

$$\% \text{ CaO equivalent} = \frac{\text{Molecular wt. of CaO}}{\text{Molecular wt. of CaCO}_3} \times 100 =$$

$$\frac{56}{100} \times 100 = 56.0$$

To obtain the CaO equivalent of magnesium carbonate, the calculations are:

$$\% \text{ CaO equivalent} = \frac{\text{Molecular wt. of CaO}}{\text{Molecular wt. of MgCO}_3} \times 100 =$$

$$\frac{56}{84} \times 100 = 66.7$$

3. Conventional oxides. This form of lime guarantee consists of converting the calcium to calcium oxide, the magnesium to magnesium oxide, and adding the two together.

4. Elemental percentage of calcium and magnesium. This method of expressing lime guarantees is determined in a similar way. If pure

$CaCO_3$ were to be reported as elemental calcium, the calculations would be:

$$\% \text{ calcium} = \frac{\text{Atomic weight of calcium}}{\text{Molecular weight of calcium carbonate}} \times 100 =$$

$$\frac{40}{100} \times 100 = 40$$

Physical Guarantees of Lime

The chemical activity of liming material is determined by the solubility of the chemical compounds in the lime. For example, calcium oxide is more soluble than calcium carbonate, while calcic limestone is more soluble than dolomitic limestone. Calcium silicate is the least soluble of the liming materials.

It is obvious that the finer the lime particles, the faster they react in the soil to become available to plants.

There are no national laws governing the physical guarantee of lime, this regulation being left to the states. Thirty-nine states have lime laws, which are difficult to summarize. In general, the physical guarantees of lime in the respective states may be roughly averaged in this way:

85% must pass through a 15-mesh sieve, and
30% must pass through a 100-mesh sieve.

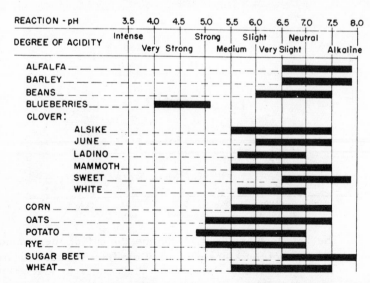

FIG. 11.8. The relative tolerance of selected field crops to soil acidity. (J. A. Porter, P. J. Rood, and E. D. Longnecker, **Lime and Its Uses,** Mich. Extension Bul. 314, 1952.)

Lime Requirement of Crops

To arrive at a satisfactory solution to the problem of how much lime to apply, the requirement of the crop is a good starting place. Since soil acidity and lime level have a fairly good correlation in humid regions, the pH of the soil is used as an index of the lime needs of various crops.

The relative tolerance of selected field crops to soil acidity can be studied from Figure 11.8. This figure indicates that alfalfa, sugar beets, sweetclover, and barley require the highest pH, while blueberries require the lowest.

Effect of Lime on Soil pH

After the pH requirement of the crop is known, it is then necessary to test the pH of the soil. The soil texture and humus content must also be estimated to arrive at the relative buffer capacity.

The relationships between texture and the buffer capacity (resistance to a change in pH) are shown in Figure 11.9. The more clay and humus there is in a soil, the more limestone is needed to change the pH.

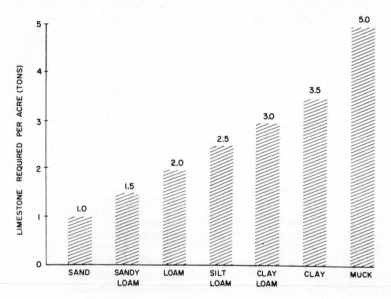

FIG. 11.9.   The limestone required to change the pH of the common soil textures and of muck one pH unit. (Data from various sources.)

Sandy soils require approximately one ton of limestone to effect a change of soil pH one unit—say, from 5.5 to 6.5. Loams require approximately two tons, clay loams three tons, and muck soils five tons. If soils are fairly high in organic matter, as they are in the Northern States, it will take more lime to accomplish the same change in pH. Conversely, in southern soils, which are lower in organic matter, less lime will be needed to accomplish the same pH change.

There is also a variation in lime needs to change the pH, depending upon the type of clay present as well as the range of the pH change desired. As the pH change is closer to 7.0, the amount of lime required to effect the same pH change is greater. For example, it takes perhaps 20 per cent more lime to change the soil pH from 5.5 to 6.5 than it does to change it from 4.5 to 5.5.

Soil pH and Nutrient Availability

The general relationship between soil pH and plant nutrient availability is shown in Figure 11.10. From this chart it is obvious that the primary nutrients—nitrogen, phosphorus, and potassium—as well as the secondary nutrients—sulfur, calcium, and magnesium—are as available or more available at a pH of 6.5 than at any other pH. Molybdenum, manganese, and boron availability is also similar to that of the primary and secondary nutrients.

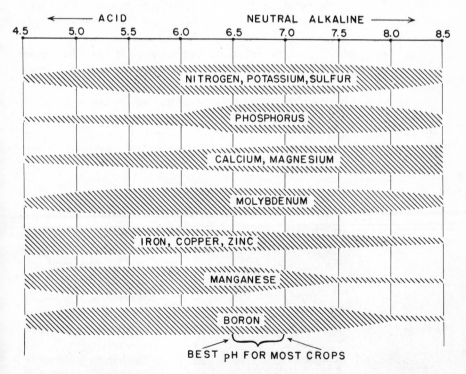

FIG. 11.10. The relationship between soil pH and the relative availability of plant nutrients. The wider the bar, the greater the availability. (Redrawn from Truog, University of Wisconsin.)

The minor elements—iron, manganese, boron, copper, chlorine, and zinc—are less available at a pH of 6.5 than at more acid reactions. In general, however, minor elements are sufficiently available so that plant growth is not limited at a pH of 6.5.

A pH of from 6.5 to 7.0 is therefore considered to be the pH range in which most nutrients are desirably available to plants. It can also be concluded that at this pH range commercial fertilizers are most readily available.

Methods of Applying Lime

The most efficient way to use lime is to apply small amounts every year or two. But this liming program increases the cost of application. The usual liming practice consists of a compromise between what is most effective and what is the cheapest per ton of lime applied. Lime can be applied to advantage at any stage in the cropping system, but normally it is best applied 6 to 12 months in advance of a legume seeding.

The rate of lime application should always be determined by means of soil testing. Applying two tons per acre on a field that needs four tons is short-sighted economy, since there may be little or no return on a considerable cash outlay for legume seed, fertilizer, and lime. Similarly, liming a field that needs no lime will give no benefit at all.

It is desirable that newly spread lime be well mixed with the whole plow layer. On strongly acid soils, where from three to six or more tons per acre of lime are required, it is recommended that one-half of the dose be applied before plowing, and the other half be applied and disked in after plowing.

When not more than two tons per acre are needed, the entire amount can be applied and disked in after plowing and before seeding the legume or legume-grass mixture.

FIG. 11.11. The most accurate method of spreading lime is with the use of a tractor-drawn hopper spreader.
Courtesy New Hampshire Agricultural Experiment Station.

FIG. 11.12. The fastest and cheapest way to spread lime is with a lime-spreading truck. *Courtesy New Hampshire Agricultural Experiment Station.*

The mechanics of getting lime on the field has changed in recent years. In early American days, farmers spread lime on the land with a shovel from the back of a wagon. Then crude spreaders were devised. Later, commercial hopper-type spreaders were available, pulled by a tractor. Now the most common method of spreading lime is to have it spread by a truck with a specially-built V-shaped bed and a spreading mechanism in the rear. (Figures 11.11 and 11.12)

Where equipment for spreading is not readily available, it is satisfactory to put lime in the gutters behind the dairy cows or to spread lime on the loaded manure spreader. Spreading the manure automatically spreads the lime with it.

Overliming

When excessively large amounts of lime are applied to sandy soils low in humus, injury to plant growth sometimes occurs. Injury to plant growth may be due to any one or a combination of these causes:

1. Boron deficiency.
2. Iron, manganese, copper, or zinc deficiency.
3. Phosphorus availability may be reduced to a critically low level.

Overliming injury may be reduced by the application of large amounts of manure, green-manure crops, compost, phosphorus fertilizers, boron, or a mixture of minor elements. Overliming injury is not so common as was once thought.

The Lime Balance Sheet

Lime is lost from the soil by:

1. Leaching.
2. Removal by harvested crops and other products sold, such as milk.
3. Erosion.
4. Neutralization by acid-forming fertilizers.

Some of the rainfall percolates downward in the soil, carrying lime with it. On the average, approximately 100 pounds per acre per year of calcium carbonate is lost in this way. Harvested crops sold and products sold, such as milk, remove another 100 pounds of lime. Erosion may take another 100 pounds per acre per year. Finally, acid fertilizers neutralize approximately 100 pounds of lime an acre each year.

This loss totals 400 pounds on every humid crop-acre each year. Simply to add enough lime to maintain the lime level in the soil would require the application of one ton of lime every five years. An adequate liming program involves the use of sufficient lime to raise the pH of the soil to the desired level for the crop to be grown and the application of one ton each five years for maintenance.

Summary

Lime is added to the soil to supply calcium (and magnesium); to reduce the toxicity of aluminum, manganese, and iron; and to increase soil pH. Lime is applied to soils in humid regions because the high rainfall has leached out large amounts of native lime. Nearly all farm crops respond to lime applications when the soil pH is below 6.5.

The common liming materials are ground limestone, ground dolomitic (high magnesium) limestone, burned lime, and hydrated lime. In some areas, marl and oystershell are important sources of liming materials.

Chemical guarantees include the calcium carbonate equivalent, the calcium oxide equivalent, conventional oxides, and elemental guarantees.

A common physical guarantee for lime is:

85% through a 15-mesh sieve

and

30% through a 100-mesh sieve

Alfalfa, sweetclover, barley and sugar beets all have a high lime requirement.

To change the pH of the soil one unit, such as from pH 5.5 to 6.5, requires on the average 1 ton for sands, 1.5 tons for a sandy loam, 2.0

tons for a loam, 2.5 tons for a silt loam, 3.0 tons for a clay loam, 3.5 tons for a clay, and 5.0 tons for a muck.

Large amounts of lime should be applied in two applications: half before plowing and the other half disked in after plowing. Small applications can be disked into the surface of the soil. Overliming injury has been highly overemphasized. Maintenance rations of lime average approximately one ton every five years.

Questions

1. Why are acid soils limed?
2. Name four causes of acid soils.
3. Give five benefits to be derived from lime when it is properly applied.
4. What kinds of crops respond best to liming?
5. What is the most common liming material?
6. Name three other materials used for agricultural lime.
7. Calculate the calcium carbonate equivalent of 50 pounds of pure calcium oxide.
8. What is a satisfactory physical guarantee for lime?
9. Approximately how much limestone will it take to raise the pH from 5.5 to 6.5 in a sandy loam?
10. What constitutes a maintenance ration of limestone?

References

Liming Soils for Better Farming. U. S. D. A. Farmers Bull. No. 2032. 1951.

Midgley, A. R., and D. E. Dunklee, *The Cause and Nature of Overliming Injury.* Vermont Agr. Exp. Sta. Bull. 460. 1940.

Porter, J. A., P. J. Rood, and E. D. Longnecker, *Lime and Its Use.* Mich. Extension Service Bull. 314. 1952.

Woodle, H. A., and E. C. Turner, *Lime for South Carolina Soils.* South Carolina Extension Service Cir. 378. 1952.

12

Fertilizers
and Their Characteristics

Not many years ago the fertilizer business was a scavenger industry—dependent upon such packinghouse by-products as dried blood, tankage, and bone meal and upon animal manures. Certain plant materials like cottonseed meal also contributed to the supply of commercial fertilizers. Now the fertilizer industry is a complex chemical business, the largest of the heavy chemical industries of the world. But not without good reason.

In 1850 the first chemical fertilizer in the United States was made with a mixture of guano (bird manure) and potash salts at Baltimore, Maryland. One hundred years later, the commercial fertilizer-manufacturing plants in our nation were valued at a billion dollars and were selling each year 900 million dollars' worth of fertilizer.

The scientific use of commercial fertilizers by the farmers has made it possible to feed a hungry world, reduce the cost of production, and reduce the amount of labor required to produce a bushel of corn or a peck of potatoes. More than that, the proper use of fertilizers makes it possible, on the average, for the farmer to get three dollars back in increased production for each dollar invested in fertilizer. Commercial fertilizers have thus increased the efficiency of the farmer and at the same time have reduced the cost of food to the consumer.

The Fertilizer Industry

The tons of fertilizer produced by industry in 1880 was approximately one million. In 1887 Congress passed the Hatch Act, which established agricultural experiment stations in each of the 48 states. This Act encouraged research on the use of fertilizers. Then the Smith-Lever Extension Act of 1914 gave impetus to an expanded use of commercial fertilizers by providing Extension Agronomists and County Agricultural Agents who worked directly with farmers in educational programs to improve agriculture. As a result of research, farm demonstrations, news releases, and bulletins on fertilizer use, fertilizer consumption rose to nearly 25 million tons in 1955. Thus, in 75 years fertilizer use in the United States increased 25 times.

SOME IMPORTANT DATES IN THE FERTILIZER INDUSTRY °
EARLY BEGINNINGS

1824—Two barrels of Peruvian guano arrived in Baltimore.

1825—Ground bone first used as fertilizer in the United States.

1830—Nitrate first imported from Chile into United States (Norfolk, Virginia).

1832—First commercial importation of guano (bird manure) from Peru.

1835—First suggestion to treat bones with acid (by Escher).

1840—Justus von Liebig treated bones with sulfuric acid (Germany).

1840—Sir John Lawes began experiments at Rothamsted (England).

1840—By-product ammonia salts first produced (England).

1845—Value of potash first demonstrated by von Liebig (Germany).

1849—First superphosphate made in United States for private use.

FIG. 12.1. The original kettles in which was made the first mixed fertilizer, in Baltimore, Maryland, 1850.

Courtesy Davison Chemical Co., Div. of W. R. Grace and Co.

° Source: "A Century of Progress with Fertilizers." The National Fertilizer Association. Washington, D. C. 1950.

The Past One Hundred Years

1850—First mixed fertilizers ("manufactured guanos") produced, at Baltimore. (Figure 12.1)

1851—First record of analysis of fertilizer by state officials.

1856—First state fertilizer control law (Massachusetts).

1865—Sulfur deposits discovered on Louisiana Gulf Coast.

1867—Value of South Carolina phosphates first recognized.

1869-1870—Potash first imported into the United States.

1872—First fertilizer experiments in United States by an agricultural experiment station, began at State College, Pennsylvania.

1879—Fertilizing value of basic slag discovered.

1881—Florida phosphate deposits discovered.

1889—Western phosphate deposits discovered in Utah.

1890-1891—Concentrated superphosphate first produced in the United States (Baltimore, Maryland).

1893—By-product ammonium sulfate produced in the United States.

1893-1894—Tennessee phosphate deposits discovered.

1909—Cyanamid production begun at Niagara Falls (Canada).

1915—First American potash produced commercially (Searles Lake, California).

1917—First production of ammonium phosphates.

1921—First commercial production of synthetic nitrogen in the United States.

1926—First ammoniation of superphosphate with aqua ammonia.

1928—First use of anhydrous ammonia directly in mixed fertilizers.

1929—First shipment of synthetic nitrate of soda (Hopewell, Virginia).

1931—First shipment of potash from Carlsbad (New Mexico).

1932—First commercial use of anhydrous ammonia in irrigation water.

1939—First experiments using anhydrous ammonia on non-irrigated lands (direct application to soil).

1942—First year of general use of ammonium nitrate in fertilizers in the United States.

1943—First commercial use of anhydrous ammonia for direct application in the soil.

1950—Centennial of first manufacture of mixed fertilizers in the United States.

THE FIRST PATENT ISSUED FOR MAKING COMMERCIAL FERTILIZER *

The first patent for manufacturing a compounded fertilizer was recorded in 1849.

* Source: "A Century of Progress with Fertilizers." The National Fertilizer Association, Washington, D. C. 1950

Patent No. 6234
Issued March 27, 1849
To Philip S. Chappell and William H. Chappell of Baltimore

The components in the mixture covered by this patent include "gas" or "ammoniacal liquor," sulfuric acid, crushed bones, and a number of chemical residues from other operations, which residues contain, among other things, carbonate of potash, calcium sulfate and magnesium sulfate, and other salts of mineral plant-food elements. In this early patent, located by J. E. Totman of Baltimore, there are combined the superphosphate process, the use of liquid ammonia, the use of potash, and even the inclusion of secondary and probably minor elements.

Modern fertilizers are mostly mixtures of combined nitrogen, superphosphate, and potassium. The nitrogen sources are mostly anhydrous ammonia, ammonium nitrate, urea, or any combinations of these materials. Superphosphates are either 18-20 per cent or 45-48 per cent P_2O_5. Potash salts are mostly muriate of potash (KCl) with some sulfate of potash (K_2SO_4).

The location of the fertilizer mixing plants is shown in Figure 12.2.

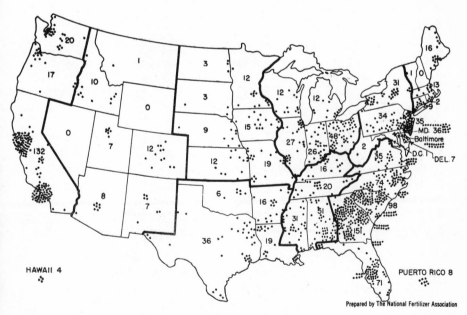

Prepared by The National Fertilizer Association

FIG. 12.2   Location of fertilizer mixing plants, 1952. Three states, New Hampshire, Wyoming, and Nevada, were the only states in the United States without at least one fertilizer mixing plant as of June 30, 1952. Georgia with 151 has the greatest number of mixing facilities, but North Carolina's 74 mixing plants have the highest rated annual capacity—2,647,000 tons.

Solid Nitrogen Materials

1. Nitrate of Soda   4. Urea
2. Cyanamid   5. Ammonium Sulfate
3. Ammonium Nitrate

Production capacity for manufacturing nitrogenous fertilizers has increased faster than that for any other fertilizer material. The increase in plant capacity is shown in Figure 12.3. From 1954 to 1957, the estimated capacity increased from 2.6 to 4.2 million tons of N. This is an increase of more than 60 per cent in the three-year period. It is doubtful whether this rapid rate of increase in production capacity can be maintained for many more years, but no one can accurately predict the future.

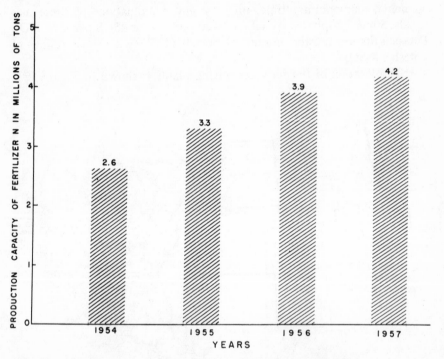

FIG. 12.3. Estimated production capacity for manufacturing nitrogen fertilizer. (Source: U. S. D. A.)

Nitrate of soda ($NaNO_3$) is found as a natural impure product in the interior of Chile and is also made synthetically. Because of its low percentage of N, nitrate of soda is fast disappearing from use. There is also objection to its use on fine-textured soils, where the Na residue disperses the clay particles and causes puddling and crust formation.

Cyanamid ($CaCN_2$) contains 21 per cent N, and the nitrogen is in a non-leachable, synthetic, organic form. Small amounts of cyanamid are sometimes used in mixed fertilizers to give them a better physical condition. Cyanamid is an excellent fertilizer to apply on crop residues or old sod before turning them under, because it hastens organic decomposition. The price per pound of cyanamid is so high that other fertilizers are driving it from the market.

Ammonium Nitrate (NH_4NO_3) is a good, cheap source of solid nitrogen, analyzing 33 per cent N. Half of the N is in the ammonium form and half is in the nitrate form.

Urea ($CO(NH_2)_2$) is now cheaper per pound of N than any other solid nitrogenous fertilizer, and it analyzes 46 per cent N. The nitrogen must be converted to ammonia before plants can use it. It can be used as a plow-down fertilizer in a manner similar to that used with cyanamid. Urea is a synthetic organic fertilizer.

Ammonium Sulfate ($(NH_4)_2SO_4$) comes mostly from recovered coke-oven gases and contains 21 per cent N. Because of its relatively high cost, it is fast losing in sales to ammonium nitrate and urea.

The equivalent basicity and acidity of the common solid nitrogenous fertilizers are shown in Figure 12.4. Also, the acidity of anhydrous ammonia is given for comparison.

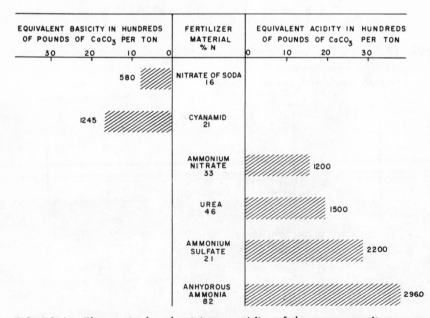

FIG. 12.4.   The equivalent basicity or acidity of the common nitrogenous fertilizers and their percentage of N.

It may be seen in this figure that the only basic nitrogenous fertilizers are nitrate of soda and cyanamid—both high-cost materials. Of the acid-forming fertilizers, anhydrous ammonia is the most acid, having an equivalent acidity of 2960 pounds of $CaCO_3$ per ton of material. In other words, to maintain soil pH, 2960 pounds of $CaCO_3$ must be used for every 2,000 pounds of anhydrous ammonia applied. The equivalent acidity per ton of fertilizer for ammonium nitrate is 1200; for urea, 1500; and for ammonium sulfate, 2200 pounds.

Ammonia

More than 90 per cent of all nitrogenous fertilizers consist of ammonia or a fertilizer made from ammonia. Anhydrous ammonia, liquid ammonia, ammonium nitrate, urea, ammonium sulfate, synthetic sodium nitrate, and ammonium phosphate are made with ammonia as the source of nitrogen. Only cyanamid and Chilean nitrate of soda do not use ammonia in their manufacture.

Ammonia is a colorless gas containing one atom of nitrogen to three atoms of hydrogen (NH_3). Since a nitrogen atom weighs 14 times more than an atom of hydrogen, the per cent N in pure NH_3 is found in this way:

$$\%N = \frac{14}{14 + 3} \times 100 = 82.35$$

FIG. 12.5. Storing and handling anhydrous ammonia requires specialized equipment.
Courtesy Agrciultural Ammonia Institute.

Commercial-grade ammonia is 99.5 per cent pure, and for that reason it contains 82 per cent N.

In recent years the use of ammonia for direct application to crops by injecting it into the soil has increased tremendously. It is supplied for this purpose in pressure tanks and reacts somewhat like butane gas; that is, it is a liquid when under tank pressure but a gas in atmospheric pressure. In this form it is called anhydrous ammonia. ("Anhydrous" means without water.)

Many safety precautions must be observed when handling anhydrous ammonia. Some of these precautions include:

1. Care not to get a flame near a mixture of 16 to 25 per cent ammonia, because these mixtures will burn.

2. Keep away from ammonia when it escapes into the atmosphere. It will cause severe irritations of the eyes, nose, throat, and lungs. The skin can also be easily burned with ammonia. Rubber gloves and goggles will give some protection.

3. Use only pressure tanks in good condition and designed to withstand pressures of at least 250 pounds per square inch. (Figure 12.5)

4. Tanks of ammonia should be painted white and stored in a cool, shady place.

5. Arrange for an inspection of all tanks at least once a year.

Ammoniation

Ammonia solutions are used in the process of adding N to superphosphates. In this way, a greater amount of a less expensive form of nitrogen can be used. This process improves the physical condition of the fertilizer and makes possible the use of more cheap N from nitrogen solutions.

Nitrogen Solutions

Nitrogen solutions are water solutions of ammonium nitrate or urea or both. When the liquid is to be stored under pressure, some anhydrous ammonia is usually introduced.

An example of a nitrogen solution which contains 32 per cent N but which can be stored and used under atmospheric conditions is listed:

Material	Per Cent of Material	Per Cent N in N Solution
Ammonium Nitrate (33% N)	48.5	16.0
Urea (46% N)	34.8	16.0
Water	16.7	—
Total	100.0	32.0

When higher concentrations of N are desired, varying amounts of anhydrous ammonia may be used along with ammonium nitrate. For example, a 37 per cent nitrogen solution can be made which has a pressure of one pound per square inch at 104°F. This product is made with:

Material	Per Cent of Material	Per Cent N in N Solution
Ammonium Nitrate (33% N)	69.8	23.0
Anhydrous Ammonia (82% N)	17.1	14.0
Water	13.1	—
Total	100.0	37.0

Some companies make even higher concentrations of N solutions; to do so, they add more anhydrous ammonia. This also increases the pressure of the solution.

Material Supplying Phosphorus

Our phosphorus fertilizers come largely from Florida, where ancient oceans have left millions of years of accumulation of marine shell organisms. This rock phosphate ore is refined and ground to produce the rock phosphate of commerce. Rock phosphate is acidulated with sulfuric acid to make 20 per cent superphosphate and with phosphoric acid to produce 45 per cent triple superphosphate. (Figure 12.6)

FIG. 12.6. A natural deposit of rock phosphate in central Tennessee. Courtesy Tennessee Valley Authority.

Ordinary superphosphate is made by adding equal weights of rock phosphate and sulfuric acid (50°-55° Baumé concentration) in a mixer and thoroughly agitating it for from one to two minutes. The acid causes intense heat, which aids in the drying process. The mixture may be dumped in a pile and allowed to cure for several months, or it may be conveyed in a continuous curing operation. At the end of the curing period, the superphosphate must be blasted out, ground, and used either directly as a fertilizer or put into mixed fertilizers.

Upon treatment with acid, some of the tricalcium phosphate is changed to dicalcium phosphate and some to monocalcium phosphate. The average composition of granulated 20 per cent superphosphate is as follows:

Item	Per Cent
Gypsum	48
Monocalcium phosphate ($CaH_4(PO_4)2$)	30
Dicalcium phosphate ($Ca_2H_2(PO_4)2$)	9
Iron oxides, aluminum oxides, and silica	9
Tricalcium phosphate ($Ca_3(PO_4)2$)	2
Moisture	2
Total	100

Triple superphosphate is made by adding two parts by weight of rock phosphate to one part of 70 per cent phosphoric acid. The batch is mixed for three minutes, dried, ground, and used directly for field application or in mixed fertilizers.

A newer process, known as *nitric phosphates,* results in very high concentrations of nitrogen and phosphorus in chemical combination. A typical process consists of mixing rock phosphate, nitric acid, and phosphoric acid, then adding ammonia. The products can be varied, depending upon the proportion of the ingredients. An average analysis is 16-20-0. To these types of formulations can be added muriate of potash to produce a product such as 10-10-10.

Materials Supplying Potassium

Muriate of potassium is the principal fertilizer supplying potassium; second in importance is sulfate of potash. Of increasing significance is sulfate of potash-magnesia.

Muriate of potash is usually 95 per cent pure KCl, equivalent to 60 per cent K_2O. It is mined in New Mexico, Utah, and California; when mined, it contains approximately 40 per cent KCl. Purification increases the concentration to approximately 95 per cent KCl. (Figure 12.7)

Sulfate of potash is found also as a salt in areas near the KCl. Average purified sulfate of potash is 95 per cent K_2SO_4, equivalent to approximately 51 per cent K_2O.

FIG. 12.7. Mining potassium ore for refining to make muriate of potash fertilizer.

Courtesy American Mining Congress.

Sulfate of potash-magnesia is a naturally occurring double salt, found in the same general area with the other potash salts. It is a combination of potassium sulfate and magnesium sulfate. It analyzes approximately 18 per cent MgO and 22 per cent K_2O.

Secondary and Minor Elements

The secondary and minor elements which are sometimes added to fertilizer formulations or used as a fertilizer either singly or in mixtures include:

> Boron
> Calcium (usually applied as a lime)
> Copper
> Manganese
> Magnesium (often applied as a lime)
> Molybdenum
> Sulfur
> Zinc

To certain specialty fertilizers are added secondary and minor elements in varying amounts. For field-crop fertilization, the minor elements are often added separately after a known deficiency occurs. As soils are cropped more heavily, the need for adding more minor elements will no doubt increase (Figure 12.8).

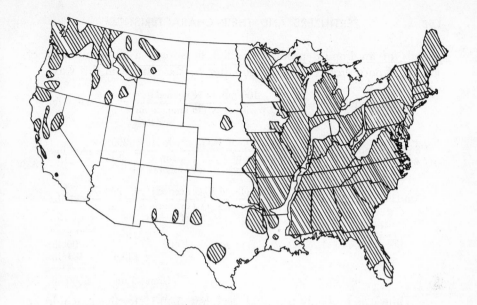

FIG. 12.8. Boron-deficiency symptoms have been reported on certain crops in the areas shaded.
Courtesy Pacific Coast Borax Co.

Formulation of Mixed Fertilizers

A complete fertilizer contains nitrogen, phosphorus, and potassium. The grade numbers in a complete fertilizer are the guaranteed analysis written as whole numbers. A 5-10-10 fertilizer is guaranteed to contain 5 per cent total nitrogen, 10 per cent available P_2O_5, and 10 per cent water-soluble K_2O. There is no actual P_2O_5 or K_2O in any fertilizer; these expressions are only the chemical equivalents of the actual chemical compounds in a fertilizer.

Calculations in the formulations of mixed fertilizers may be worthwhile as an example. Suppose that you were to mix a ton of a 5-10-10 fertilizer, using:

> 20% Superphosphate
> 21% Ammonium sulfate
> 60% Muriate of potash

A 5-10-10 would require per ton:

$$5\% \times 2000 = 100 \text{ lb. of N}$$
$$10\% \times 2000 = 200 \text{ lb. of } P_2O_5$$
$$10\% \times 2000 = 200 \text{ lb. of } K_2O$$

If we had pure N, P_2O_5, and K_2O, we would have our answer; but pure materials cannot be used to make a fertilizer. To compute the pounds of an impure product needed to supply a given number of pounds of pure product, divide the latter by the former, in this way:

$$\text{Ammonium sulfate needed} = \frac{100 \ (\text{lb. of N needed})}{\% \ \text{purity of N (in ammonium sulfate)}} = \frac{100}{.21} = 476 \ \text{lb.}$$

$$\text{Superphosphate needed} = \frac{200 \ (\text{lb. of } P_2O_5 \ \text{needed})}{\% \ \text{purity of } P_2O_5 \ (\text{in super-phosphate})} = \frac{200}{.20} = 1000 \ \text{lb.}$$

$$\text{Muriate of potash needed} = \frac{200 \ (\text{lb. of } K_2O \ \text{needed})}{\% \ \text{purity of } K_2O \ (\text{in muriate of potash})} = \frac{200}{.6} = 333 \ \text{lb.}$$

Total		1809 lb.
	Filler	191 lb.
Grand Total		2000 lb.

While it is probably true that very few 5-10-10 fertilizers would be mixed in this way, the principle of calculation is the same regardless of the method used. Modern fertilizers are usually made by ammoniating the superphosphate. As much ammonia as possible is used because it is cheaper than the solid nitrogenous fertilizers.

Examples of Open Formulas

An actual formulation to make a ton of 8-16-16 is shown in Table 12.1. This is called an "open formula." It can be seen that most of the nitrogen comes from a nitrogen solution, which is the cheapest form of N. Also, it can be observed that triple superphosphate supplies the largest part of the phosphorus. This is necessary in making high-grade fertilizers. A third important observation is that there is no filler because the relative amounts of the various materials are adjusted to equal exactly 2,000 pounds.

The ingredients necessary to make a ton of 14-14-14 are shown in Table 12.2. Three sources of nitrogen are used: ammonium sulfate, ammonium nitrate, and nitrogen solution. Triple superphosphate is used to supply all of the phosphorus, and muriate of potash supplies all of the potash. Clay is used at the rate of 60 pounds per ton to coat the granules of fertilizer so that they will not absorb so much water from the atmosphere.

Note that the mixture is guaranteed to be a 14-14-14, but that it is formulated to contain 14.27 per cent nitrogen, 14.24 per cent available P_2O_5, and 14.24 per cent water-soluble K_2O. These excess amounts of nutrients are added to the mixture to allow for some loss of nitrogen as ammonia, and to allow for possible errors in mixing and in segregation before the fertilizer reaches the consumer.

TABLE 12.1. Open Formula to Make a Ton of 8-16-16 Fertilizer *

Materials	Pounds of Material	Analysis %	Pounds per Ton				
			Nitrogen (N)	Phosphorus (P_2O_5)	Potassium (K_2O)	Magnesium MgO	Boron (B)
Nitrogen Solution	360	40.8 N	147	—	—	—	—
Ammonium Sulfate	100	20.8 N	21	—	—	—	—
Superphosphate, Triple	576	46.0 P_2O_5	—	265	—	—	—
Superphosphate, Normal	280	19.6 P_2O_5	—	55	—	—	—
Muriate of Potash	490	60.5 K_2O	—	—	296	—	—
Sulfate of Potash-Magnesia	110	22.0 K_2O 18.5 MgO	—	—	24	20	—
Borate	4	13.6 B	—	—	—	—	0.5
Sulfuric Acid	80	—	—	—	—	—	—
TOTAL	2000	—	168	320	320	20	0.5
Percentage in Mixture	—	—	8.4	16.0	16.0	1	—
Equivalent Acidity 450 lb. $CaCO_3$ per ton	—	—	—	—	—	—	—

* Henry Plate, Fertilizer Research Division, Eastern States Farmers Exchange, personal communication, Feb. 1956.

159

TABLE 12.2. Open Formula to Make a Ton of 14-14-14 Fertilizer *

Material	Pounds of Materials Per Ton	Analysis %	Percentage in Mixture		
			Nitrogen (N)	Phosphorus (P_2O_5)	Potash (K_2O)
Ammonium sulfate	149	20.8N	1.55	—	—
Ammonium nitrate	524	33.5N	8.78	—	—
Nitrate solution (Ammonium nitrate plus ammonia)	194	40.6N	3.94	—	—
Superphosphate, triple	606	47.0P_2O_5	—	14.24	—
Muriate of Potash	467	61.0K_2O	—	—	14.24
Clay to coat granules of fertilizer	60	—	—	—	—
TOTAL	2000	—	14.27	14.24	14.24

* Source: Lime and Fertilizer Branch, U. S. D. A.

Problems of Manufacturing Mixed Fertilizers

Perhaps a generation ago, many farmers mixed their own fertilizers with the use of carriers such as ammonium sulfate, superphosphate, and muriate of potash. No longer can farmers afford to do this. One reason is that labor costs are too high; the other reason is that modern fertilizers are not simple mixtures of dry materials. Fertilizers of today are the result of complex and costly methods which increase the concentration of the fertilizers and reduce their unit cost per pound of plant nutrients.

There are five basic ingredients in modern fertilizers. These are:

1. Carriers of N, P_2O_5, K_2O, and, at times, other materials.

2. Conditioners, such as ground vermiculite, tobacco stems, rice hulls, or other similar material.

3. Neutralizers of acidity, primarily dolomitic limestone.

4. Fillers, such as sand, to "make weight" when a fertilizer formulation does not equal the required weight. Most modern, high-grade fertilizers, however, do not contain fillers.

5. Materials for specialty fertilizers, such as insecticides, fungicides, or herbicides.

The biggest problem in making mixed fertilizers is to maintain a desirable physical condition. Most fertilizer plants are overcoming this difficulty by pelleting the fertilizer and by using certain clays and waxes to coat the pellets. Improper mixing and inadequate curing also contribute to an undesirable physical condition of the fertilizer.

Acidity or Basicity of Fertilizers

Since most fertilizers are used on acid soils, their acidifying properties are of great concern.

A glance at Table 12.3 establishes the fact that only the nitrogen fertilizers are acid; the potassium and the phosphorus fertilizers are physiologically neutral.

There is a tremendous difference in the acidifying properties of the nitrogen materials. Both sodium nitrate and cyanamid are alkaline, while the other nitrogenous carriers are acid. Listed in order of least acid-forming to most acid-forming per pound of N are:

Cyanamid
Sodium nitrate
Urea
Ammonium nitrate
Anhydrous ammonia
Ammonium sulfate

TABLE 12.3.   The Common Fertilizers and Their Acidity or Basicity

Material	N Per Cent	Equivalent Acidity		Equivalent Basicity	
		Per Pound of N	Per 100 Pounds of Material	Per Pound of N	Per 100 Pounds of Material
Sodium nitrate	16			1.8	29
Calcium cyanamid	21			2.9	61
Urea	46	1.6	74		
Ammonium nitrate	33	1.8	59		
Anhydrous ammonia	82	1.8	148		
Ammonium sulfate	21	5.2	109		
	K_2O Per Cent				
Muriate of Potash	60	Physiologically Neutral in Reaction			
Sulfate of Potash	50	Physiologically Neutral in Reaction			
	P_2O_5 Per Cent				
Superphosphate	20	Physiologically Neutral in Reaction			
Triple Superphosphate	45	Physiologically Neutral in Reaction			

Summary

The chemical fertilizer industry has grown during the past 100 years from nothing to become our largest chemical industry, selling each year more than 900 million dollars' worth of fertilizer. The proper use of fertilizers makes it possible for farmers to average three dollars from increased yields for each dollar invested in fertilizer.

The Hatch Act of 1887 setting up agricultural experiment stations, and the Smith-Lever Act of 1914 establishing Extension Services, were significant in promoting the widespread use of fertilizers.

The most common solid nitrogen fertilizers are nitrate of soda, cyanamid, ammonium nitrate, urea, and ammonium sulfate; the first two are alkaline and more expensive, and the others are acid but cheaper per pound of N. Most nitrogenous fertilizers are made with ammonia as the source of N. Nitrogen solutions for use in fertilizer formulations and for direct application to the soil have increased tremendously in recent years. There has also been a big increase in the direct use of anhydrous ammonia injected into the soil.

The principal material supplying phosphorus for commercial fertilizers is rock phosphate. Superphosphate is made by treating rock phosphate with sulfuric acid. Triple superphosphate comes from the acidulation of rock phosphate with phosphoric acid.

Potash salts are supplied by muriate of potash, sulfate of potash, and sulfate of potash-magnesia.

Problems encountered in the formulation of mixed fertilizers involve careful calculations of costs and efforts to overcome the hazard of a poor physical condition in the finished product.

Questions

1. Give three reasons for the rapid growth of the fertilizer industry.
2. When was the first patent issued for the manufacturing of a fertilizer?
3. Why are nitrate of soda and cyanamid being replaced by other nitrogenous fertilizers?
4. What material supplies most of the N for use in fertilizers?
5. Give some advantages of the direct use of anhydrous ammonia as a fertilizer.
6. Why are nitrogen solutions becoming increasingly popular?
7. What is the primary source of most of the phosphorus for use in fertilizers?
8. What is the principal material supplying potash?
9. Calculate the ingredients to make a ton of 8-16-16 fertilizer, using urea (45%N), triple superphosphate (46% P_2O_5), and muriate of potash (60% K_2O).
10. What are the main problems encountered in the manufacture of fertilizers?

References

Collings, Gilbearth, *Commercial Fertilizers, Their Sources and Use.* McGraw-Hill Book Co., Inc. New York. 1955.

Jacob, K. D., ed., *Fertilizer Technology and Resources in the United States.* Academic Press, Inc. New York. 1953.

Sauchelli, Vincent, *Manual on Fertilizer Manufacture.* Davison Chemical Co. Baltimore, Md. 1954.

13

Use of Fertilizers

Without commercial fertilizers, world populations would probably soon exceed their food supply. With fertilizers and other modern necessities, such as improved seed, better insecticides, and more effective fungicides, critical population pressures can be delayed perhaps indefinitely.

Based upon the records of production of fertilizers in the past, it is expected that the world production will increase approximately 6 per cent each year, or will double every 15 years. This rate of fertilizer production should be sufficient to help feed a growing population and to prevent starvation.

Fertilizer Consumption

During 1955 the nation consumed approximately two million tons of N. This represents an 80 per cent increase during the five-year period since 1950. Second in percentage increase during the same period was potassium, with a consumption of 1.9 million tons of K_2O, an increase of 40 per cent. Phosphorus consumption increased 20 per cent for the five-year period, to a total of 2.3 million tons of P_2O_5 in 1955.

A large part of the increased nitrogen consumption was due to an increase in the use of anhydrous ammonia and of ammonia in nitrogen solutions. Figure 13.1 identifies the total nitrogen consumed in relation to that of ammonia yearly since 1947.

In 1947 direct application of anhydrous ammonia to the soil was proved by Dr. W. B. Andrews at the Mississippi Agricultural Experiment Station, in co-operation with the Tennessee Valley Authority. The increased use of nitrogen solutions which contain ammonia, for formulating mixed fertilizers, is also a factor in explaining the rapid use of ammonia.

Although little ammonia was used commercially before 1947, the

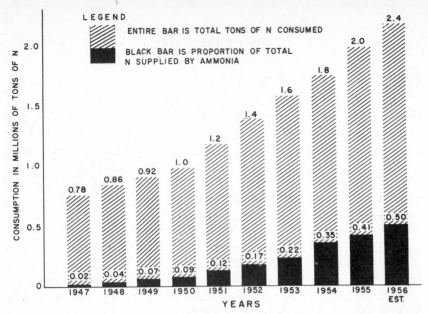

FIG. 13.1. The consumption of total nitrogen fertilizers by years, in relation to the proportion supplied by ammonia. (Source: U. S. D. A.)

consumption climbed to an estimated 0.5 million tons of N in 1956, which is 21 per cent of the total N consumed. (Figure 13.2)

FIG. 13.2. The use of anhydrous ammonia for direct application to the soil started in Mississippi in 1947 and has increased faster than any other method of applying fertilizer.
Courtesy Shell Chemical Corp.

Nutrients Removed by Crops

Crops sold from the farm remove nutrients that must be replaced. Sometimes soil minerals break down fast enough to release a large part of the nutrients found in crops, but this process is too slow to provide all nutrients for modern crop yields. Legumes are capable of fixing atmospheric nitrogen in amounts satisfactory for crop yields of ten years ago, but not sufficient for today's crop yields. The only logical conclusion for profitable farming is that most of the nutrients removed by high-yielding crops must be replaced by commercial fertilizers.

Pounds per acre of the primary nutrients removed by wheat, cotton, corn, and alfalfa are shown in Figure 13.3. Alfalfa removes more nitrogen, phosphorus, and potassium, while wheat removes the least, of the crops shown. Corn and cotton are intermediate in their chemical composition. Most of the nitrogen removed by alfalfa and other legumes is fixed by legume bacteria from atmospheric nitrogen.

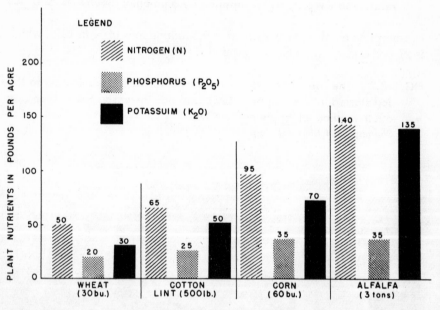

FIG. 13.3. Pounds per acre of nutrients removed by one crop of the size shown. (J. D. Romaine, "When Fertilizing, Consider Plant-Food Content of Crops," **Better Crops with Plant Food**, March, 1940.)

Time of Applying Fertilizers

It has been traditional to apply fertilizer to row crops just prior to or at the time of planting. This practice is still satisfactory if the efficient use of fertilizer is the only objective. But farmers are the busiest at this time of year, and fertilizer costs more when it must be supplied to everyone at the same time. *Fall* applications of fertilizers are a possibility in some areas.

Studies over the United States of fall-applied fertilizers in relation to leaching losses indicate that:

1. Phosphorus leaches out of the soil only in trace amounts. It is often fixed in some less soluble form, however, unless the soil pH is approximately 6.5 and there is an abundance of fresh organic matter present.

2. Potassium leaches from the soil in small amounts, but this is not serious enough to limit the practicability of applying potash fertilizers in the fall. Leaching losses of potassium can be reduced by maintaining a crop on the land at all times.

3. Nitrogen is readily lost in the water that percolates through the soil. The nitrogen lost in percolating waters is almost entirely in the nitrate form; loss in the ammonium form is negligible because clay and humus particles adsorb the ammonium ion and hold it in a non-leachable form.

The practicability of applying fertilizers in the fall therefore lies primarily in keeping the leaching losses of nitrogen to a minimum. This problem can be solved in two ways:

1. Keep the nitrogen in the ammonium form by applying it to a cold soil, and

2. Do not apply nitrogen fertilizers in the fall in areas where the percolation losses of water are great.

Nitrogen in the ammonium form is oxidized to the nitrate form quite rapidly when the soil temperature is above 50°F. Applying the ammonia to the soil in the fall after the soil gets no warmer than 50°F will help in reducing the transformation of ammonia to the nitrate form. In this way the losses of nitrogen by leaching will be reduced.

When there is no percolation of water through the soil, there can be no leaching losses of nitrates. Research at Temple, Texas, and Clarinda, Iowa, has shown that during the average year there are no percolation losses of water. This means that there can be no losses of nitrogen even though it is in the nitrate form. At La Crosse, Wisconsin, there is an average annual percolation loss of 2.3 inches of water. Here there will be a considerable loss of nitrates, and fall applications of ammonia should be made only when the soil temperature is below 50°F. By contrast, the water leached through the soil at Statesville, North Carolina, averages 16.7 inches a year. Add to this fact the factor of high soil temperatures, and the conclusion is reached that the application of ammonia to the soil in the fall under these conditions is not recommended.

There is one more factor to be considered in the question of applying ammonia in the fall. It has been shown by repeated research that when there is a vigorously growing crop on the land, leaching losses of nitrates will be nil because plant roots will then absorb the nitrates rapidly.

By way of summary, ammonia may safely be applied to the soil in the fall when:

1. There is no leaching, or
2. Soil temperatures stay below 50°F, or
3. A cool-season crop is growing vigorously.

Fertilizer Placement

Phosphorus and potash fertilizers move downward in the soil very slowly. For this reason it was thought that surface applications on sod crops were not effective. While these fertilizers do not move readily, plant roots move toward surface-applied phosphorus and potassium as long as the surface of the soil stays moist.

Ammonia must be applied in the soil deep enough to be absorbed

FIG. 13.4. Anhydrous ammonia can easily be applied by bubbling it into irrigation water.
Courtesy Shell Chemical Corp.

by the soil, usually at a six-inch depth. Ammonia can also be applied by bubbling it into irrigation water. Nitrates and other solid nitrogenous fertilizers are effective when applied on the surface because the next rain will leach them into the soil where plant roots are growing. (Figure 13.4)

For row crops, the mixed fertilizer is usually applied slightly below and to one side of the seed. Care must be used here, however, as potash and nitrogen fertilizers may be so close as to injure the sprouting seed. In sandy soils or with large amounts of nitrogen or potash, there is a real hazard of seedling injury. There is no such danger with phosphorus fertilizers.

A newer method of applying fertilizers is to put either a part or all of the fertilizer on the cover crop before it is turned under, prior to planting a row crop. In this way the nutrients are transformed by bacteria into the organic form, from which they are released at about the same rate as they are needed by the next crop.

Crop Increases from Fertilization

Almost everywhere that plants are grown, there is some kind of fertilizer practice that will increase crop yields. The principal exceptions to this rule are areas where water seriously limits growth, or in certain places during severe insect or disease damage.

Potential yields which are possible with adequate fertilization, in relation to average yields of the common crops during 1950, are indicated by regions in Table 13.1.

The outstanding potential-yield increases are, in descending order:

> Wheat in the South
> Corn in the South
> Hay in the North Central States
> Oats in the South
> Corn in the Northeast

Profit from Using Fertilizer

The use of fertilizers pays in many areas and with a wide variety of crops. The net profit in relation to the cost of the fertilizer is demonstrated in Figure 13.5 for the states of Washington and Ohio.

In Washington, when no fertilizer was used, a net profit of 5 dollars an acre was realized. When 8 dollars was spent for fertilizer, the net profit was 25 dollars. But when 16 dollars was spent on fertilizer, the net profit was 38 dollars.

Similar results were obtained in Ohio, where 20 dollars net per acre was realized when no fertilizer was used, 39 dollars when 10 dollars was

TABLE 13.1. The Potential Yield Increases Resulting from Full Fertilization of the Common Crops, by Regions *

| Crop | Average Yield per Acre, 1950 | | | Potential Yield Increases with Full Fertilization | | |
| | REGIONS | | | REGIONS | | |
	South	North Central	Northeastern	South %	North Central %	Northeastern %
Corn, grain	27 bu.	44 bu.	43 bu.	170	52	128
Sorghum, grain	23 bu.	24 bu.	—	40	33	—
Wheat	10 bu.	16 bu.	23 bu.	220	81	52
Oats	24 bu.	38 bu.	40 bu.	138	66	42
Soybeans	20 bu.	23 bu.	16 bu.	70	57	62
Cotton, lint	255 lb.	298 lb.	—	122	—	—
Potatoes	128 bu.	187 bu.	310 bu.	70	70	64
Hay	1.2 tons	1.3 tons	1.4 tons	75	154	100
Sugar beets	—	11 tons	—	—	46	—
Tobacco	1,271 lb.	2,457 lb.	1,215 lb.	18	39	35

* Fertilizer Use and Crop Yields. Agriculture Handbook No. 68. U. S. D. A. 1954.

spent on fertilizer, and 53 dollars per acre net profit when 21 dollars was
spent on fertilizer.

It seems that even more money could be spent for fertilizer so long
as the increased income continues to more than pay for the cost of the
fertilizer.

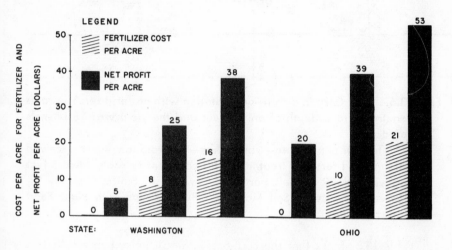

FIG. 13.5. The relationship between fertilizer costs and net profit per
acre. (Source: National Plant Food Institute, 1955.)

Fertilizers and Soil Moisture Efficiency

The proper use of fertilizers on soils of low natural fertility makes it
possible to grow a wider variety of crops. Widening the selection of
crops can result in the use of more vigorous, efficient, and more valuable
cropping systems. The net result of the liberal use of fertilizers is greater
efficiency in the utilization of land, labor, capital, and water.

An example of how a well-fertilized cropping system in Missouri
increased the efficiency of water will be cited.

In Missouri the year 1953 was classified as a drought year, since
only 60 per cent of the normal rainfall was received. A cropping system
of corn–oats with no fertilization was compared with a system of corn–
wheat–hay–hay which received adequate lime and fertilizers.

Corn with no fertilizer in the corn-oats rotation sent its roots down
only two feet, as compared with five feet for the roots of fertilized corn
in the four-year rotation (Figure 13.6).

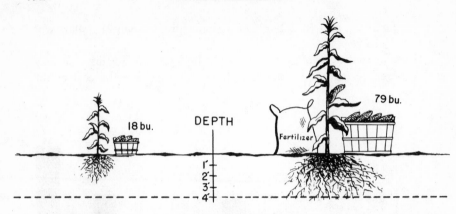

FIG. 13.6. **Left:** Corn in a corn—oats rotation with no fertilizer. The roots penetrated to a depth of only 2 feet and the yield was 18 bushels per acre.

 Right: Corn in a corn—wheat—hay—hay rotation which received full lime and fertilizer treatment. This corn sent its roots down 5 feet and yielded 79 bushels per acre. (Dwight D. Smith, "Fertility Increases Efficiency of Soil Moisture," **Better Crops with Plant Food Magazine,** June 1954.)

Table 13.2 shows that the corn-oats-no-fertilizer system resulted in an acre-yield of 18 bushels of corn and the use of 14 inches of water. This is an average of 0.8 acre-inches (22,000 gallons) of water per bushel of corn produced. By contrast, the corn in the four-year rotation yielded

TABLE 13.2. Full Fertilization Increases Water Efficiency and Corn Yields

Cropping System	Fertilization Per Acre (at beginning)	Yield of Corn in Bu./A.	Per Acre (inches)	acre-inches	gallons
			Water Used		
				Per Bu. of Corn	
Corn—Oats	None	18	14	0.8	22,000
Corn—Wheat—Hay—Hay	5 tons lime, 1/2 ton rock phosphate, 100 lb. KCL, 300 lb. 3-12-12, 100 lb. N (Subsequent fertilization made according to the results of a soil test)	79	16	0.2	5,500

79 bushels and used 16 inches of water. This is an average of 0.2 acre-inches (5,500 gallons) of water per bushel of corn. The net result is that only one-fourth as much water was required to produce a bushel of corn when the crops were rotated and properly limed and fertilized.

It is true that two more inches of water was used by the corn in the four-year rotation-plus-fertilization than in the corn-oats rotation. But slightly more than two additional inches of water soaked into the soil for use by the corn when the corn was in the four-year rotation.

FIG. 13.7.   Side placement of fertilizer for lima beans.
Courtesy U. S. D. A.

Summary

Commercial fertilizer is helping to keep a world population from outrunning its food supply. On a long-time average, fertilizer production is doubling every 15 years. The use of nitrogen fertilizer is increasing faster than the use of either potassium or phosphorus, with potassium second in percentage increase. The increased use of ammonia for direct application to the soil and of nitrogen solutions for use in mixed fertilizers accounts for most of the rapid increase in the use of nitrogen fertilizers.

Total nutrients removed by crops are in this order, from high to low:

Alfalfa $>$ Corn $>$ Cotton $>$ Wheat

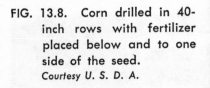

FIG. 13.8. Corn drilled in 40-inch rows with fertilizer placed below and to one side of the seed.
Courtesy U. S. D. A.

FIG. 13.9. Band placement of fertilizer for potatoes.
Courtesy U. S. D. A.

FIG. 13.10. Band placement of fertilizer
Courtesy American Potash Institute, Inc.

Ammonia fertilizers may be safely applied in the fall when there is no leaching, when the soil stays colder than 50°F after application, or when there is a vigorous cool-season crop growing.

Anhydrous ammonia must be applied approximately six inches in depth to insure adequate adsorption. Solid nitrogenous fertilizers are usually applied on the surface of the soil. Both nitrogen and potassium fertilizers are toxic in large concentrations and must therefore be placed away from the seed. Phosphorus fertilizers may be planted with seed without causing injury. Surface-applied phosphorus appears to be a satisfactory practice on perennial grasses and legumes.

Potential increases in the humid region with adequate fertilization varies from 220 per cent for wheat in the South down to 18 per cent for tobacco in the South. Fertilizers return approximately three dollars in increased yields for each dollar invested in fertilizer.

Adequate liming and fertilization permits a wider selection of valuable crops, which increase infiltration of water and result in a more efficient use of water.

Questions

1. How fast is world fertilizer use expanding?
2. Rank the major fertilizer elements in the order of their expanded use in the United States.
3. What two nitrogen materials have increased in use most rapidly?
4. What crop takes the most nutrients from the soil?
5. Under what conditions can anhydrous ammonia be applied in the fall?
6. Name three crops which have the highest yield potentials with adequate fertilization.
7. On the average, how much return can be expected from each dollar spent for fertilizer?

8. Explain how proper fertilization increases moisture efficiency.
9. Compare the root systems of corn in Missouri with and without fertilizers.
10. In Missouri, how much more efficient was the water on properly fertilized corn?

References

Page, H. J., *An Annual Review of World Production and Consumption of Fertilizers.* 1955. Food and Agriculture Organization of the United States. Rome, Italy. 1955.

Donahue, Roy L., *Our Soils and Their Management.* The Interstate. Danville, Illinois. 1955.

Collings, Gilbearth, *Commercial Fertilizers, Their Sources and Use.* McGraw-Hill Book Co., Inc. New York. 1955.

McVickar, Malcolm, *Using Commercial Fertilizer.* The Interstate. Danville, Ill. 1952.

Ignatieff, Vladimir, ed., *Efficient Use of Fertilizers.* Published for the Food and Agriculture Organization of the United Nations. Leonard Hill, Ltd. London, England. 1952.

14

Tillage

Soils must have the right proportion of air and water for plant roots to absorb adequate amounts of nutrients for luxuriant plant growth. Coarse-textured soils usually have good air and water relations but too small a capacity for supplying enough water and plant nutrients. Fine-textured soils normally have a satisfactory nutrient and water reserve but often contain too little air. (Figure 14.1)

FIG. 14.1. Plowing and cultivating fine-textured soils make them a better medium for plant growth and help to control weeds.
Courtesy New Hampshire Agricultural Experiment Station.

Plowing and cultivating coarse-textured soils do not seem to make them a better medium for plant growth. Tillage of fine-textured soils immediately improves the air-water relations for better plant growth.

On all soils, the primary purpose of tillage is to control weeds. But with the use of new herbicides for the control of weeds, this age-old reason for tillage must be re-examined. Tillage temporarily aerates the soil and controls weeds, but year by year it destroys desirable soil structure and eventually reduces aeration.

A virgin grassland soil is rich in organic matter and has a structure which is desirable for rapid plant growth. Under continuous tillage, the organic-matter level decreases and the soil structure deteriorates. Continuous tillage, especially with the use of heavy machinery, tends to compact the soil and thus make it a less desirable medium for plant growth.

FIG. 14.2. **Left:** A virgin soil that has developed under a tall-grass prairie. **Right:** The same kind of soil near by that has been cultivated for 50 years or more. (Texas)
Courtesy Texas Agricultural Experiment Station.

Tillage and Plant Growth

In the arid regions, the method of tillage is usually related to available moisture and to hastening organic decomposition for the release of nitrogen for plant growth.

The results of a ten-year experiment in Wyoming on the relationship between wheat yields and methods of tillage are summarized in Figure 14.3. Listing, plowing, and disking, in both early and late spring, were compared. With each method of land preparation, late spring tillage resulted in less wheat than did early spring tillage. Of the three methods, disking resulted in highest wheat yields.

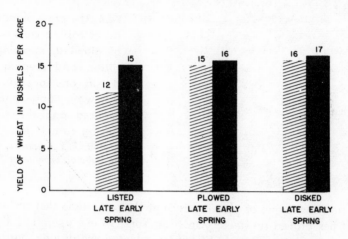

FIG. 14.3. The yield of wheat in relation to the method of tillage for the 10-year period, 1938-1947. (Av. ann. ppt., 16 inches.) (A. L. Nelson, **Methods of Tillage for Winter Wheat,** Wyoming Agr. Exp. Sta. Bul. 300, 1950.)

Experiments to find the minimum amount of tillage have been carried on in many places. Corn in Indiana has been grown successfully with only one cultivation. The system is to:

1. Spray old corn stalks with 2,4-D amine to kill weeds, 1¼ pints per acre. (The corn land is never plowed.)

2. Plant corn in early May between last year's stalks, with a special mulch planter that distributes fertilizer as the corn is planted.

3. In three weeks, the land is sprayed again with 2-4-D amine, ¾ pint per acre.

4. In a week, the corn is cultivated for the first time.

These four trips over the field are all that are made, except one more in the fall to harvest the corn. This system may not work satisfactorily in all regions, but with the use of modern methods of killing weeds, the use of fewer cultivations is the recommended practice everywhere.

FIG. 14.4. The plow-plant method of raising corn consists of plowing, applying fertilizer, and seeding corn, all in one operation. In this way, tillage pans are reduced and the cost of raising corn is less.
Courtesy R. B. Musgrave, Cornell Agricultural Experiment Station.

A new technique of planting corn at the same time that sod land is plowed has proved satisfactory in New York. In one operation, the sod land is plowed and corn is fertilized and planted. No disking, harrowing, or other land preparation is carried out. When the corn is knee-high, it receives its only cultivation. During this same operation, the corn can be side-dressed with nitrogen if desired. A third time over the field is necessary to harvest the corn. (Figure 14.4)

This plow-plant method was perfected in 1951 by Dr. R. B. Musgrave on hill land near Cornell University. Its principal advantages over the conventional method of growing corn are these:

1. Desirable soil structure is maintained instead of being destroyed by excess tillage.

2. Air-water relations are in better balance for more and deeper root growth.

3. Since the soil between the corn rows remains as rough, plowed ground until the corn is knee-high, more of the rainfall soaks into the soil for use by the corn.

4. Erosion is reduced because infiltration is increased.

5. Fewer corn roots are pruned by cultivation. A looser seed bed means that the corn roots are deeper than the normal depth of cultivation. Fewer roots are pruned also because there is only one cultivation instead of the usual five or six.

6. At least 10 dollars per acre is saved by the plow-plant method because of fewer trips over the field.*

Deep Tillage

Land that is plowed at the same depth for many years usually develops a compacted layer where the bottom of the plow slides over and compresses the soil. Compacted layers are formed at greater depths by the use of heavy machinery on moist, fine-textured soils. Some type of chiseling on such soils has often increased crop yields.

Chiseling in Indiana in connection with deep placement of fertilizers has increased corn yields approximately 30 per cent in some tests. The use of the chisel to a depth of 20 inches resulted in:

1. Temporary elimination of the plow sole and the heavy-machinery pan that was developed below the plow sole.

FIG. 14.5. Chiseling at a depth of 12 inches increased cotton yields in Mississippi almost 90 per cent over the conventional method of land preparation.
Courtesy Caterpillar Tractor Co.

* R. B. Musgrave, "Researchers Find Many Advantages in Plow-Plant Method," *Farm Research,* Vol. 22, 1956. Cornell Univ. Agr. Exp. Sta., Ithaca, N. Y.

2. An increase in plant roots in this layer as a result of chiseling and fertilization.

3. Greater movement of water into the soil and more water being stored for longer periods within reach of plant roots.

4. An increase in crop yields.

Breaking the soil with various implements was studied in Mississippi in relation to the yield of cotton. One series of plots was listed 8 inches deep (conventional method), another was chiseled 12 inches deep with the chisels spaced 20 inches apart, a third treatment consisted of plowing with a disk plow 12 inches deep, and a fourth treatment involved plowing 8 inches deep with a conventional plow to which was attached a chisel that shattered the soil 4 inches deeper.

The yields of seed cotton demonstrated that the disk plow and the moldboard plow plus chisel were equally effective in producing the highest yield, namely, 1800 pounds per acre. The next highest yield resulted from chiseling 12 inches deep, with 1700 pounds; and least effective was the conventional method of listing (middlebusting) to a depth of 8 inches, with a yield of 900 pounds of seed cotton per acre (Figure 14.6).

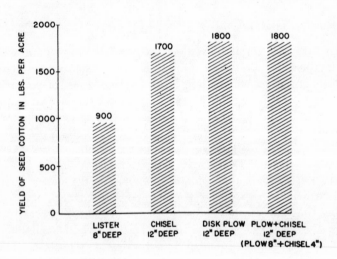

FIG. 14.6.   The effect of methods of breaking the land on the yield of cotton (Dubles fine sandy loam in Miss.). (W. A. Raney, et al., "The Effects of Deep Breaking on Miss. Soils," Inf. Sheet 492, 1954.)

This test demonstrated the desirability of tillage to a depth of 12 inches to shatter the tillage pan.

Tillage to Control Insects

The timely plowing under of crop residues is an effective means of controlling certain insects. The Hessian fly, which is serious in many wheat fields, can be controlled by plowing under infested wheat stubble and volunteer wheat. The wheat jointworm is held in check by destroying all volunteer grain. Plowing under corn stalks reduces next year's crop of European corn borers. Timely cultivation aids in reducing grasshopper infestations by drying out their eggs. The cotton boll weevil and the pink boll worm in cotton are held in check by the early destruction and plowing under of cotton stalks.

Tillage and Organic Matter

All forms of tillage in the spring help to warm and aerate the soil and to hasten the decay of organic matter. In any one season this is desirable because current crops benefit from nutrients released from the decomposing organic matter. If organic matter is not replenished, however, there will be a net loss over the years, sometimes with a serious reduction in crop yields.

Total organic matter lost during 65 years of continuous tillage in South Dakota was 40 per cent of the original organic matter.

Soil Moisture and Tillage

In arid and semiarid regions, either fall plowing or early spring plowing permits more water to be stored in the soil for use by crops than does late spring plowing. There is also more storage of water in the soil when no crop is grown for a year. This practice is known as *fallow*. But always the hazard of wind and water erosion must be equated against increases in crop yields.

The results of tillage research over a period of 18 years at three locations in western Kansas is portrayed in Figure 14.7. The average annual precipitation at these stations averages 20 inches.

Late plowing resulted in an average of 1 inch of available water at seeding time and an average yield of 8.4 bushels of wheat per acre. By contrast, early spring plowing allowed 1.8 inches of available soil water to be stored, which produced 11.5 bushels of wheat. A yield of 20.3 bushels of wheat per acre was obtained following a year of fallow when there was 5.9 inches of available water at seeding time.

Kinds of Pan Formations

Pan formations may be *natural*, caused by geological or pedological forces, or they may be *anthropic*, having been induced by man.

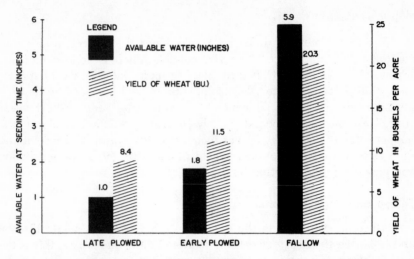

FIG. 14.7. The relationship between the time of plowing and fallow on available moisture at seeding time and the yield of wheat. (R. I. Throckmorton and H. E. Myers, **Summer Fallow in Kansas,** Kansas Agr. Exp. Sta. Bul. 293, 1941.)

Natural pans are of five types, depending upon the kind of cementation.

1. *Clay pans,* due to an accumulation of clay, usually in the B horizon.

2. *Silt pans,* caused by an excess of silt in or near the B horizon. These horizons are often called *fragipans.*

3. *Indurated horizons,* as a result of cementation by iron, silica, calcium carbonate, calcium sulfate, or humus.

4. *Dispersed horizons,* formed by the dispersing action of sodium on fine-textured soils.

5. *Compacted horizons,* due to the application of forces during geologic deposition. One theory of their formation is that they were compressed by the weight of the glacial ice.

Anthropic pans, induced by man, are of three general types:

1. *Tillage pans,* caused by the compaction of heavy implements or by compression at the bottom of a plow; the latter often are called *plow pans.*

2. *Surface crusts,* created by the impact of the falling raindrops on bare land.

3. *Pasture pans,* made by the packing action of grazing animals, especially on moist, fine-textured soils.

Tractor-Tire Compaction

Tillage pans created by the compression of a tractor tire extend below plow depth; for this reason, they cannot be eliminated by plowing at conventional depths.

Research results on the *depth* of tillage pans in relation to soil moisture are given in Figure 14.8. A dry Cecil clay was compacted by a conventional tractor tire to a depth of 13 inches. When moist, the same soil was compacted to a 16-inch depth; when wet, to a 17-inch depth.

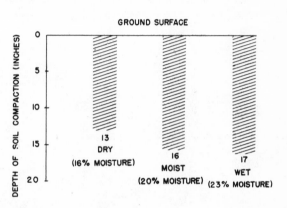

FIG. 14.8. The depth of soil compaction of a tractor tire in relation to the soil-moisture content of Cecil clay. (Vernon C. Jamison, "Heavy Machinery— New Problem in Soil Management," **What's New in Crops and Soils,** October, 1952.

The *amount* of compaction in relation to soil moisture may be seen in Figure 14.9. The dry Cecil clay was compacted to 20 per cent less than its original volume; moist clay was compacted 53 per cent, and wet clay 49 per cent. It is of interest to note that moist clay compacted more than did wet clay.

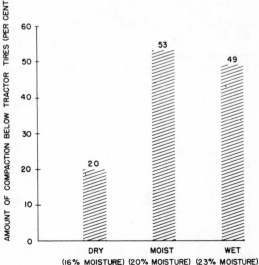

FIG. 14.9. The relationship between the percentage of soil compaction by a tractor tire and the soil-moisture content of Cecil clay. (Vernon C. Jamison, "Heavy Machinery— New Problem in Soil Management," **What's New in Crops and Soils,** October, 1952.)

Detrimental effects of compaction caused by the wheels of a loaded truck are similar to those created by tractor tires. In Massachusetts, second-cutting yields in an area compacted by dual truck wheels were less than 800 pounds, whereas between the truck tires the yields averaged nearly 2500 pounds of dry forage per acre.

Plow Pans and Infiltration Rates

The bottom of a plow sliding along the soil at the same depth year after year soon compacts the soil into a plow pan. This compacted layer restricts root penetration, decreases permeability, and reduces the infiltration of water.

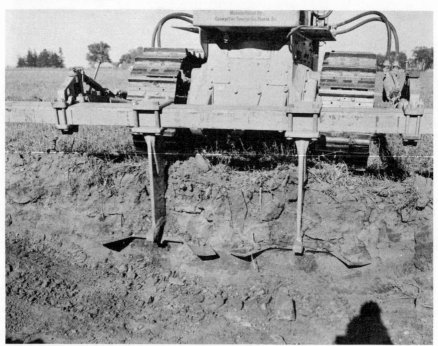

FIG. 14.10. Tillage pans can be broken by some type of chisel. Note the greatest soil compaction at and below plow depth.
Courtesy Caterpillar Tractor Co.

The effect of a plow pan on the rate of infiltration in the Southern Great Plains was studied. Thirty-five years of cropping to grain sorghums reduced the infiltration rate to 0.2 inches of water per hour. Below the plow pan, the infiltration was 9 inches per hour, or 45 times faster.

Probably the best cure for the plow pan is chiseling to at least 12 inches in depth, to be followed by perennial grasses and legumes in a regular cropping system. (Figure 14.10)

Cropping Systems and Soil Structure

Perennial grasses are probably the best vegetation for improving soil structure; continuous tillage seems to be the worst land-use for maintaining desirable structure. Since the farmer usually makes more money from cultivated crops, there must be a compromise between continuous grass and continuous tillage.

FIG. 14.11. In Oklahoma, tillage since 1914 has compacted the soil to the point where grain sorghum roots do not develop below the tillage pan.

Courtesy L. F. Locke, Southern Great Plains Field Experiment Station.

The influence of various cropping systems on soil structure in Illinois is reported in Table 14.1. The cropping system of corn—oats—2 years of alfalfa—bromegrass resulted in 54 per cent soil aggregation and 68 bushels of corn per acre. Corn—oats—alfalfa was next most desirable in maintaining soil structure and corn yields. Other rotations, in order of effectiveness, were: corn—oats (sweetclover); corn—oats; and 10 years of continuous corn.

Soil density as measured by the weight of dry soil per cubic foot is another way to report indirectly the results of cropping systems or other land-use on the physical conditions of the soil. Figure 14.12 graphically shows the weight of virgin soil per cubic foot as compared with soil continuously cropped for 40 years. The surface foot of virgin soil averages 66 pounds while cropped soil averages 82 pounds, on an oven-dry basis.

TABLE 14.1. The Relationship Between Cropping System, Percentage Aggregation of the Soil, and Yields of Corn (No fertilizer was used. Soil was dark-colored, level, clay.) *

Cropping System	Percentage of Plow Layer Aggregated	Corn Yield Per Acre (Bu.)
Corn-Oats-2 years of Alfalfa plus Bromegrass	54	68
Corn-Oats-Alfalfa	53	59
Corn-Oats (Sweetclover)	45	47
Corn-Oats	40	39
Continuous Corn for 10 years	23	22

* R. S. Stauffer, *Tilth of Corn-Belt Soils.* Illinois Agr. Exp. Sta. Circular 655, 1950.

The second-foot comparisons are 70 and 87, while the third-foot comparisons are 77 and 91 pounds per cubic foot, for virgin and cultivated soil, respectively.

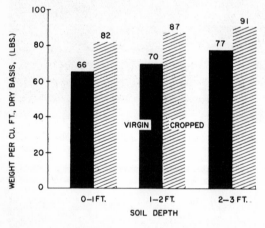

FIG. 14.12. A comparison of the weight per cubic foot of cropped and virgin soil. (Nappanee silt loam in Ohio cropped for 40 years.) (Source: Ohio Extension Bul. 175, 1941.)

The 40 years of continuous cropping resulted in a soil compaction of more than 24 per cent in the surface two feet and 18 per cent in the third foot.

Factors Restricting Root Growth in Compact Horizons

Several soil scientists have discovered that normal root growth is severely restricted in fine-textured soil horizons when the bulk density is greater than 1.4, and in coarse-textured soils of bulk density above 1.6.

FIG. 14.13. Tillage pans restrict corn root penetration, probably because of a reduction in soil oxygen and because there are too few
crevices through which the roots can grow.
Courtesy Caterpillar Tractor Co.

Compact horizons may restrict root growth for several reasons:

1. There may not be enough channels through which roots can grow.

2. Oxygen may not be in sufficient concentration at all times for normal root respiration or for translocation of nutrients. (Figure 14.13)

3. Sufficient available water may not be present for each day of the growing season.

4. Available nutrients may be in too low a concentration.

5. Toxic substances may be present, such as a high concentration of manganese or of carbon dioxide.

Summary

Soils are cultivated to aerate and warm the soil and to control weeds. With the wise use of herbicides, tillage to control weeds is not now so essential as it was a few years ago.

In semiarid regions, early spring tillage is conducive to the storage of more available water and to higher crop yields. Disking was superior to listing and plowing as a method of land preparation for wheat.

Deep tillage, especially when combined with the establishment in the cropping system of perennial grasses and legumes, results in more desirable soil structure and greater crop yields.

Timely tillage is important in the control of certain insects, such as the Hessian fly, wheat jointworm, European corn borer, grasshoppers, boll weevil, and pink boll worm.

There are five types of natural pan formations and three types of anthropic pans. The natural pans are clay pans, silt pans (fragipans), indurated horizons, dispersed horizons, and compacted horizons. Anthropic pans are tillage pans, surface crusts, and pasture pans.

The normal use of a tractor results in the creation of compacted layers as deep as 17 inches and as compressed as 53 per cent less than original soil volume. Plow pans decrease the infiltration rate of water as much as 45 times.

Continuous corn may have only 23 per cent of the surface soil aggregated, while a good cropping system consisting of corn—oats—two years of alfalfa plus bromegrass may have 54 per cent of the surface soil aggregated. Continuous tillage for 40 years was responsible for compacting the surface two feet of soil more than 24 per cent; and the third foot was 18 per cent heavier as a result of tillage compaction.

Questions

1. Why is it necessary to cultivate less now than formerly?
2. In the semiarid region, why is early tillage desirable?
3. Why does deep tillage often result in increased crop yields?
4. How does tillage often control insects?
5. Why does organic matter decrease with tillage?
6. State the advantages and disadvantages of tillage.
7. Name the five natural pans.
8. Explain the formation of anthropic pans.
9. How deep and how much soil compaction is possible from a tractor tire?
10. How much compaction would you expect in Ohio in the first two feet of soil as a result of continuous tillage?

References

Raney, W. A., T. W. Edminster, and W. H. Allaway, "Current Status of Research in Soil Compaction," *Soil Sci. Soc. of Amer. Proceed.* 19:4, 1955.

Shaw, Byron T., ed., *Soil Physical Conditions and Plant Growth.* Agronomy Monographs II. Academic Press, Inc. N. Y. 1952.

Soils and Men. The 1938 Yearbook of Agriculture. U. S. Dept. of Agriculture.

15

Water Conservation

The United States Geological Survey estimates that our nationwide daily use of water is now 200 billion gallons. By 1975 the amount is expected to be double this quantity. Add to this statement the fact that our center of population is rapidly shifting westward where there is less water, and the only possible conclusion is:

Water will become one of the most important factors limiting the progress of our nation.

The amount and intensity of limitation to our progress brought about by a deficiency of water will depend upon:

1. How much we understand the water problems.
2. What we do about the problems of a restricted water supply.

In this chapter we are concerned primarily with the source of water, storage of water in the soil, and the principles and methods of reducing runoff by increasing infiltration.

The Hydrologic Cycle

Water moves in a continuous cycle from ocean to clouds to earth to ocean, and from liquid to solid to vapor to liquid—always in response to physical and chemical laws of nature. These movements of water are known as the *hydrologic cycle.*

Figure 15.1 portrays the hydrologic cycle. Moist air from the ocean moves over land and is deflected upward. As the moist air mass rises, it cools and its ability to hold water vapor decreases. Vapor then condenses into raindrops which fall to earth. Some of the rain is intercepted by the leaves of plants, some runs off into streams, and some enters the soil. Of the water that enters the soil, some is used immediately by plants, some

FIG. 15.1.   The hydrologic cycle. The sun evaporates
water from the sea and land to form clouds; then
rain falls. Part of the rainfall is intercepted by
plants, part is used immediately for plant growth,
part is held by the soil as a reserve for later use,
part goes to underground reservoirs to sustain

THE HYDROLOGIC CYCLE

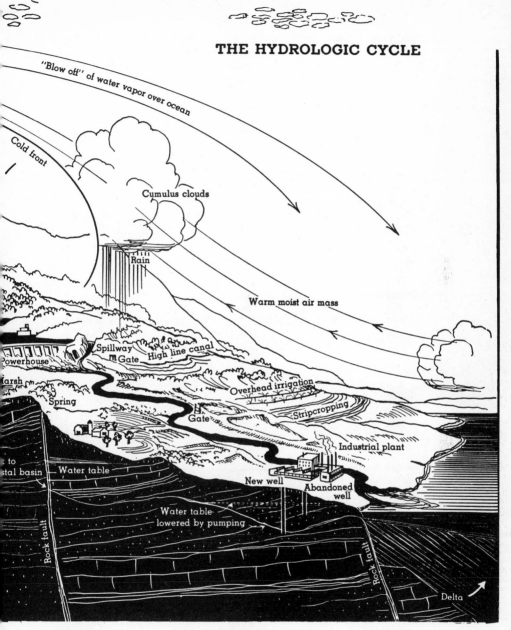

"Blow off" of water vapor over ocean

Cold front

Cumulus clouds

Rain

Warm moist air mass

Spillway Gate

High line canal

Powerhouse

Overhead irrigation

Marsh

Spring

Gate

Stripcropping

Industrial plant

to stal basin

Water table

New well

Abandoned well

Rock fault

Water table lowered by pumping

Rock fault

Delta

wells, springs, and streams, and part runs off to form rivers which do their work as they return to the sea. (Source: **A Water Policy for the American People.** Vol. I, **The Report of the President's Water Resources Policy Commission, 1950.**)

is stored in the soil for later use by plants, and the remainder moves downward to replenish the water table. The water table becomes the source of water for springs and wells.

Water is lost from the soil in four ways:

1. Surface runoff.
2. Movement downward of drainage waters.
3. Evaporation into the atmosphere from the surface of the soil.
4. Transpiration into the atmosphere through the leaves of plants.

In water conservation the primary objective in humid regions is to encourage as much water as possible to enter the soil and thereby reduce runoff to a minimum. In arid regions where dryland crops are grown, the objective is the same as that in humid regions; but where water is impounded for irrigation, the main objective is to encourage as much runoff as possible without harm to the watershed.

Precipitation

Precipitation in the United States averages 30 inches a year, with a variation of from under 10 to more than 80 inches (Figure 15.2).

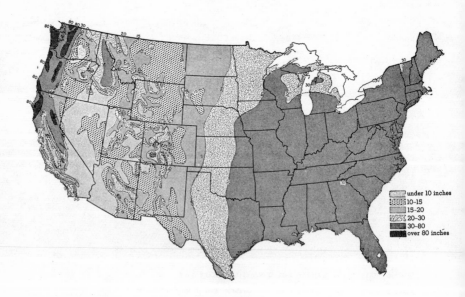

FIG. 15.2. Average annual precipitation in the United States. (Source: **A Water Policy for the American People. Vol. I, The Report of the President's Water Resources Policy Commission, 1950.)**

From the Great Plains eastward, the precipitation is from 30 to 80 inches. The Great Plains receives from 20 to 30 inches; west of the Plains to the Rocky Mountains, from 15 to 20 inches; and in the lowlands of the Intermountain Region, from 10 to 15 inches. In Nevada, southeastern California, and southwestern Arizona, the precipitation is under 10 inches a year, the least in the nation. On the West Coast, precipitation is the highest in the United States, averaging more than 80 inches in places.

It is not the average annual precipitation that determines how much water is available for the growth of plants; it is the amount of water which enters the soil and is held there at between one-third and 15 atmospheres of tension. It is difficult to measure infiltration. As an indirect measure of infiltration, the average annual runoff is subtracted from the average annual precipitation.

There are two omissions in this measure of infiltration. One is the water intercepted by the leaves which never touches the soil, and the other is the water lost by evaporation from the surface of the soil. Intercepted water, water lost by evaporation, and runoff do not contribute to available soil water. Of the three sources of water that is lost, runoff is usually the largest in amount and the most damaging.

Runoff

Runoff in the United States is exemplified in Figure 15.3 as varying from less than 1 to more than 10 inches a year. It is of interest to note

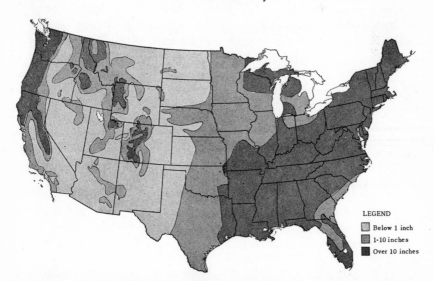

LEGEND

Below 1 inch

1-10 inches

Over 10 inches

FIG. 15.3. Average annual runoff in inches depth in the United States. (Source: **A Water Policy for the American People.** Vol. I, **The Report of the President's Water Resources Policy Commission,** 1950.)

that the less the average annual precipitation, the greater the percentage of runoff. From a water-conservation standpoint, it means that arid and semiarid regions have a doubly critical situation: not only do these regions receive less precipitation, but a larger part of that which is received is lost as runoff.

In some areas of the arid and semiarid region, runoff is encouraged as a means of obtaining larger supplies behind dams for use in irrigation. In many cases, however, the runoff is so rapid and the watershed is so poorly protected by vegetation that soil erosion is very serious.

Storage of Water in the Soil

Sandy soils are capable of holding about one inch of rain per foot of soil depth. Clay soils often hold four inches per foot. In between these extremes are the loams and silt loams, which are capable of holding from two to three inches of water per foot.

Since most plants extend their roots approximately four feet down, the total amount of water held in the root zone is between 4 and 16 inches, depending upon soil texture and organic content. Only about half of this is available to plants; some is lost by evaporation and some is held so tightly by the soil that plants cannot get it. Water that plants cannot get is held with a force greater than 15 atmospheres.

Virgin forest soils have an organic accumulation on the surface that acts as a sponge to increase the infiltration of water. Research in eastern Tennessee indicates that the leaf litter in hardwood forests serves as an excellent medium for storing water. In August, the average amount of hardwood litter on the forest floor was 4.2 tons, with a field capacity of 135 per cent. This is equivalent to a water-holding capacity of 0.5 inch of rain. Following fresh leaf-fall in December, the leaf litter totalled 5.2 tons, equal to a water-holding capacity of 0.6 inch of rain. During flood periods, it is of tremendous benefit to have this much water held back on the land by the leaf litter rather than to have it contribute to the increasing of flood crests.* Much of the water stored in the humus becomes available to growing plants. (Figure 15.4)

Terracing for Water Conservation

For water conservation, the ridge terrace is the type that is recommended. In constructing a ridge terrace, the main object is to build a high ridge and a wide channel to impound as much water above the terrace as possible.

* Frank E. Blow, "Quantity and Hydrologic Characteristics of Litter under Upland Oak Forests in Eastern Tennessee," *Journal of Forestry*, 53:3, 1955.

FIG. 15.4. Hardwood leaf litter is an excellent medium for storing water. Approximately 1/2 inch of water can be so stored.
Courtesy U. S. Forest Service.

In regions of approximately 20 inches of annual precipitation, terraces are constructed with high ridges, no grade in the channel (level), and with closed ends. These terraces are designed to hold *all* of the water that falls on a field until it soaks into the soil.

Research in the 20-inch rainfall belt of Texas has shown that closed-end, level terraces impound more water and result in a 60 per cent in-

FIG. 15.5. Closed-end, level terraces in the 20-inch rainfall belt in Texas increased cotton yields an average of 60 per cent over a 26-year period, as compared with no terraces.
Courtesy Soil Conservation Service.

crease in the yield of cotton as compared with cotton grown on land not terraced. These are average yields over a 26-year period.* (Figure 15.5)

Contour Tillage to Conserve Water

"Contour tillage" means the operation of all farm implements across the slope. By strict definition, the tillage should be exactly on the level, but in practice this condition is only approximated. (Figure 15.6)

FIG. 15.6.　Aerial view of contour strips, Clayton County, Iowa.
Courtesy Soil Conservation Service.

Contouring is not new. In 1813 Thomas Jefferson, a good farmer as well as statesman, wrote:

We now plow horizontally, following the curvature of the hills and hollows on dead level, however crooked the lines may be. Every furrow thus acts

* Earl Burnett and C. E. Fisher, "The Effect of Conservation Practices on Runoff, Available Soil Moisture, and Cotton Yield," *Soil Sci. Soc. of Amer. Proceedings,* 1954.

as a reservoir to receive and retain the waters; . . . scarcely an ounce of soil is now carried off. . . . In point of beauty nothing can exceed that of the waving lines and rows winding along the face of the hills and valleys.

The effect of contour tillage on runoff losses is given in Figure 15.7 for several crops in six states. In every instance, runoff is reduced by contour tillage. The greatest percentage reduction of runoff as a result of contouring is on Houston clay soil supporting cotton.

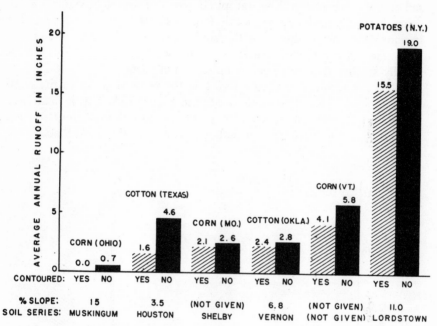

FIG. 15.7.   The Effect of contour tillage on runoff losses. (J. H. Stallings, **Effect of Contour Cultivation on Crop Yield, Runoff, and Erosion Losses.** Soil Conservation Service, Unnumbered Publication, 1945.)

Benefits from contour farming may be summarized in this way:

1. Available soil moisture is increased.
2. Soil erosion is reduced.
3. Wind erosion is less.
4. Crop yields are increased.

Forests and Water Conservation

In humid regions, one objective of forest management is to reduce runoff and thereby reduce flood hazards. On the other hand, in arid regions, a primary objective is to obtain as much runoff water as possible, mainly for irrigation purposes.

Forest trees, like all other plants, transpire large amounts of water as a vapor through their leaves and into the atmosphere. Forests also intercept considerable quantities of rain or snow and permit it to be evaporated back into the atmosphere before the water ever reaches the soil. Both transpiration and evaporation are often desirable losses in humid regions but are undesirable in semiarid areas.

By removing a part of the forest cover, more water will strike the soil and less per acre will be transpired. Another source of water loss appears, however, and may be a fairly large amount. The more cutting that is done in a forest, the more the sunlight strikes the ground and the more the evaporation of water from the soil surface. But this loss is usually smaller than has been realized in the past.

The net result of cutting a forest on the yield of water in the semiarid region of Colorado is demonstrated in Figure 15.8. This is in an area where the objective in water conservation is to obtain as much runoff water as possible for irrigation without damage to the watershed.

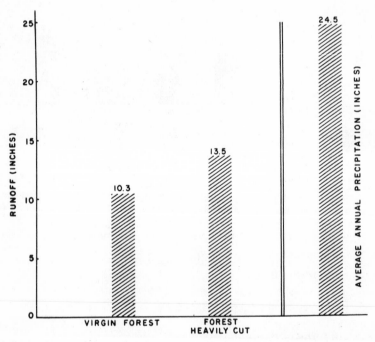

FIG. 15.8. The relationship between inches of runoff per acre in a virgin forest and in a heavily cut forest in Colorado. The average annual precipitation is shown for comparison. (H. G. Wilson, "Forests and Water," **Trees:** the 1949 Yearbook of Agriculture, p. 599.)

Of the 24.5 inches of average annual precipitation, a virgin forest permitted a runoff of 10.3 inches per acre. On an adjoining plot, heavy cutting resulted in 13.5 inches of runoff per acre. This is a net gain of 3.2 inches of water for each acre that was heavily cut. On this basis, the increased yield of water from 10 acres of a heavily cut forest would be sufficient to irrigate an acre of sugar beets. But always the value of the increased water yield must be weighed against the possible deterioration of the watershed. Too little cutting results in more infiltration and less runoff; too much cutting, and there is not sufficient protection to control soil erosion.

Plants as Luxury Consumers of Water

Transpiration is a necessary function of plants. Under conditions of excess soil moisture, however, transpiration is a wasteful process.

Figure 15.9 illustrates the amount of water transpired by saltgrass in relation to the depth of the water table. When the water table stood at 4 feet saltgrass transpired 13 acre-inches of water a year. In contrast, 43 inches of water was transpired when the water table was only one foot deep.

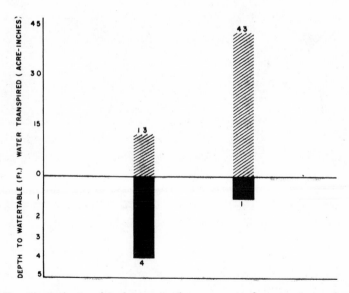

FIG. 15.9.   The relationship between the amount of water transpired by saltgrass and the depth to the water table (Southern California). (Herbert C. Fletcher and Harold B. Elmendorf, "Phreatophytes—A Serious Problem in the West," **Water: the Yearbook of Agriculture,** 1955, p. 425.)

FIG. 15.10. Properly grazed grasslands encourage the infiltration of nearly all of the rain, as shown above. Below, the range has been overgrazed, and, as a result, the grasslands became a desert.
Courtesy Soil Conservation Service.

Luxury transpiration is characteristic of nearly all plants, but especially of these plants: *

> Saltgrass—*Distichlis spicata*
> Greasewood—*Sarcobatus vermiculatus*
> Salt-cedar—*Tamarix gallica*

* Herbert C. Fletcher and Harold B. Elmendorf, "Phreatophytes—A Serious Problem in the West," *Water:* The Yearbook of Agriculture, page 424, 1955.

Cottonwoods—*Populus species*
Baccharis—*Baccharis glutinosa*
Willows—*Salix species*
Mesquite—*Prosopis juliflora*

One practical application of the luxury consumption of water by certain plants was used on a ranch in Santa Clara County, California. The rancher sprayed and killed the woody plants around a spring, and, with no additional rain, within a week the *increased* flow amounted to 28,000 gallons, or approximately one acre-inch of water. The plants were mostly willow, bay, white oak, and live oak.

Land-Use to Conserve Water

Proper land-use is probably the most important factor in water conservation. It is also a factor within the control of the farmer.

Grasslands or any dense soil covers increase infiltration and thereby reduce runoff. Much of the water that moves into the soil later becomes available to plants. Proper land-use is therefore equivalent to an increase in rainfall. (Figure 15.10)

Figure 15.11 portrays the results from five erosion experiment sta-

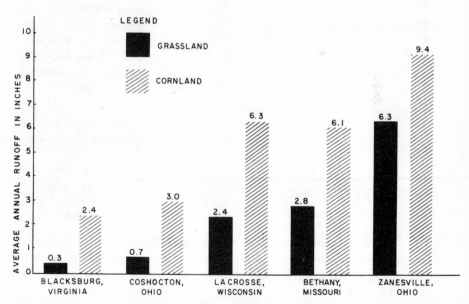

FIG. 15.11.   A comparison of the runoff from grassland and cornland in the humid region. (Lloyd L. Harrold, "Effect of Increasing Grassland on Water Yields in Humid Areas," **Proceedings**, International Grassland Congress, 1952, pp. 1071-1075.)

tions comparing the runoff in inches from grasslands and cornlands. The saving in water through the use of grasslands varied from 2.1 to 3.9 inches, when compared with cornland.

Infiltration rates of water in South Carolina were studied in relation to soils under continuous cotton and soils under a cropping system of cotton-wheat-Kobe lespedeza (Figure 15.12). Water moved into the soil with continuous cotton at a rate of 0.3 inch per hour, but into the soil under a rotation at the rate of 1.63 inches per hour. This is more than a fivefold increase in infiltration due to the crop rotation.

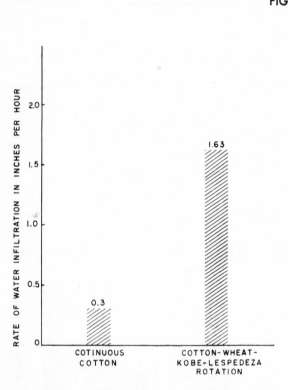

FIG. 15.12. Infiltration rates in a soil with continuous cotton as compared with cotton in a wheat-Kobe-lespedeza rotation for a period of 10 years, 1945-1954. Determinations made in 1954. (T. C. Peele and O. W. Beale, "Laboratory Determination of Infiltration Rates of Disturbed Soil Samples," **Soil Science Society of America Proceedings,** 19:4, 1955.)

Notes: (1) Soil was a Cecil sandy loam at Clemson, South Carolina.

(2) The infiltration rate was measured after 1 hour of simulated rainfall.

A surface mulch also aids in increasing infiltration and in extending the depth of moisture penetration. Figure 15.13 compares the depth of moisture penetration following a 2.8-inch summer rain in the 20-inch rainfall belt in Texas.

With no mulch, the water moved downward 15 inches; with 16 tons of mulch per acre, water penetrated twice this depth. Four- and eight-ton applications of mulch per acre gave intermediate results.

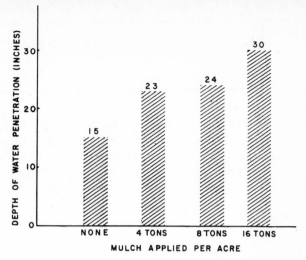

FIG. 15.13. Average depth of moisture penetration following a 2.8-inch rain in relation to the amount of mulch applied (20-inch rainfall belt in Texas). (Earl Burnett and C. E. Fisher, **Agronomy Abstracts**, 1955, p. 46.)

Problems of Frozen Soils

Many spring floods in the northern part of the United States are caused by the fact that water cannot move downward fast enough into the soil and therefore must flow over the surface and into streams. The cause is frozen, impermeable soils, and the result is damaging floods.

The problem of frozen soils is restricted to the northern one-third of the United States (Figure 15.14). Outside of this area, soil freezing does

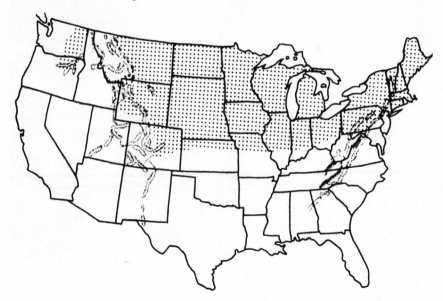

FIG. 15.14. The shaded areas represent that part of the United States where the freezing of the soil greatly affects infiltration, runoff, and erosion.

occur, but it is largely intermittent and of slight consequence as a factor in making soils impermeable to water.

On first thought, it may seem that the question of frozen soils is academic; that nothing can be done about it. This is not true.

Not all frozen soils are impermeable; some of them absorb water almost as fast when frozen as when not frozen. It is mainly a question of the amount of organic matter in the soil and the use of the land.

There are four principal kinds of frozen soil:

1. Concrete-like
2. Honeycomb
3. Stalactite
4. Granular

Concrete-like Soils: Bare soils, soils low in organic matter, and pasture soils that have been heavily grazed usually freeze into a concrete-like, impermeable mass. These soils freeze to greater depths than do soils in any other type of land-use. (Figure 15.15)

FIG. 15.15. Soils low in organic matter freeze into a dense, **concrete** type of structure.
Courtesy U. S. Forest Service.

Honeycomb: Soils high in organic matter, such as those in a well-managed forest or those that have been artificially mulched, usually freeze into a loose, porous, honeycomb type of structure. (Figure 15.16)

Stalactite: Honeycomb structure that thaws on top for about an inch

FIG. 15.16. Soils rich in coarse organic matter freeze into a very porous **honeycomb** structure.
Courtesy U. S. Forest Service.

and then re-freezes often forms stalactite structure. Here many icicles push upward to lift the surface crust as much as six inches. Stalactite structure is permeable to water. A similar type of freezing takes place when plants are heaved out of the ground. (Figure 15.17)

FIG. 15.17. Alternate freezing and thawing of soils high in organic matter produce a **stalactite** type of structure that is porous.
Courtesy U. S. Forest Service.

Granular: Soils high in organic matter that freeze only to a shallow depth usually are of a granular structure. Continued freezing often changes the granular structure to a honeycomb structure. Granular structure permits water to move into it freely. (Figure 15.18)

Any type of land-use that adds organic matter, either living or dead, results in a soil that is open, porous, and easily penetrated by water even when frozen. Planting trees, leaving crop residues, adding manure, and planting sod crops all contribute to some type of porous structure when the soil freezes.

FIG. 15.18. Soils high in organic matter that freeze only to shallow depths are usually **granular** and permeable.
Courtesy U. S. Forest Service.

Summary

The pressure of our growing population and its shift westward into areas of less rainfall makes water one of our most critical resources. Understanding water problems will aid in their solution.

Water moves in a never-ending cycle from ocean to clouds to earth to ocean, and from a solid to a liquid to a gas, without loss. This is the hydrologic cycle.

Precipitation varies over the United States from less than 10 inches to more than 80 inches. Runoff can be reduced by planting trees, adopting a good crop rotation system, mulching, terracing, and contour tillage and by grazing range and pasture land moderately.

If it is available, most plants transpire more water than they need for normal growth. One practical application of these findings is to destroy shrubs around water courses and thereby increase the amount of water available for the growth of palatable grasses and for other purposes.

If adequate organic matter is present, soils which freeze are still permeable to water during the winter.

Questions

1. Why is water becoming increasingly critical?
2. Briefly tell about the hydrologic cycle.
3. What is the general pattern of precipitation in the United States?
4. Describe three ways to reduce runoff.
5. How do forests help to prevent floods?
6. Describe a terrace system recommended to increase infiltration of water in arid and semiarid regions.
7. How does contour tillage increase the amount of water available for plant growth?
8. How can proper forest-cutting practices be used to increase water supplies for Western irrigation?
9. What is meant by a "luxury consumption" of water?
10. What can be done to make soils capable of infiltration even when frozen?

References

"A Water Policy for the American People." The Presidents' Water Resources Policy Commission. Volume I, General Report. Washington, D.C. 1950.

Climate and Man, The Yearbook of Agriculture, 1941. U.S.D.A.

Donahue, Roy L., *Our Soils and Their Management.* The Interstate. Danville, Ill. 1955.

Donahue, Roy L., Everett F. Evans, and L. I. Jones, *The Range and Pasture Book.* Prentice-Hall, Inc. Englewood Cliffs, N. J. 1956.

Trees, The Yearbook of Agriculture, 1949. U.S.D.A.

Water, The Yearbook of Agriculture, 1955. U.S.D.A.

16

Soil Conservation

The impact of the falling raindrop on bare soil is the major factor in starting the process of soil erosion. When plant cover, either living or dead, is present, the kinetic energy of the falling raindrop is dissipated by the springy organic carpet. As a result, the raindrop strikes the organic matter, the organic matter gives with the blow, and the raindrop slides harmlessly downward to soak into the soil for use by growing crops. (Figures 16.1, 16.2)

FIG. 16.1.   The impact of the falling raindrop on bare soil is the major factor in starting the process of water erosion.
Courtesy Soil Conservation Service.

FIG. 16.2. Luxuriant vegetation breaks the impact of the falling raindrop and thereby keeps erosion from starting.
Courtesy Soil Conservation Service.

Untamed winds moving across unprotected soil will absorb surface moisture, break down soil granules, and carry, roll, or skip soil particles along with the wind. A plant cover, either living or dead, reduces surface wind velocities, maintains surface soil moisture, and prevents destructive wind erosion.

Both water and wind erosion are serious factors tending to destroy our economy; both can be reduced to insignificance if the land is managed on the basis of scientifically proved practices.

Soil erosion is present at higher elevations all over the United States, regardless of the amount of precipitation received.

The Nature of Water Erosion

Soil erosion by water may be divided into (1) splash erosion, (2) erosion by surface flow, and (3) erosion by channelized flow.

Splash Erosion. One acre-inch of water weighs approximately 220,000 pounds, but is capable of exerting splash erosion with a force of three million foot-pounds of kinetic energy, or almost 14 times its own weight.

The raindrop falls with an approximate speed of 30 feet a second (20 miles an hour). When raindrops strike bare soil, they beat it into flowing mud which splashes as much as two feet high and five feet away.

The soil textures most readily detached by raindrop erosion are fine sands and silts. Coarser particles are not shifted about much because of their greater size and weight. Most soils of finer texture, such as clays and clay loams, are not readily detached because of the strong forces of cohesion which keep them aggregated.

During a heavy rain, the soil aggregates are disrupted, splashed, shifted about, and packed together more closely. As the muddy water flows down through natural openings, the sediment plugs the channels. The result is a sealed surface which, upon drying, forms a crust slowly permeable to air and water. Water which would have moved downward during the rain now must move over the surface, carrying soil particles with it.

Surface Flow. Runoff water is also a factor in soil erosion. Runoff water moves soil by (1) surface creep, (2) vaultation, and (3) suspension. *Surface creep* means movement of soil downhill by a rolling or dragging action of the water. *Vaultation* results when turbulent waters cause soil particles to hop or skip as they move downward. Soil particles which never touch the soil surface as they are moved along are carried by *suspension.*

Channelized Flow. As water moves over the surface of the soil, some of it concentrates in low places to form channels. Continued flow develops minor rills, and later large gullies may be formed by the scouring action of ever-increasing volumes of muddy water. (Figures 16.3, 16.4)

FIG. 16.3.   Channelized flow of water results in rills, then gullies.
Courtesy Soil Conservation Service.

FIG. 16.4. Unchecked rills develop into gullies.
Courtesy Soil Conservation Service.

Rainfall and Erosion

A study of records for the nation reveals that there is not a good correlation between mean annual or mean monthly rainfall and erosion. More important than mean rainfall is the intensity of the rain and whether the soil has a protective cover.

In an 11-year study of erosion in the Texas Blacklands, of the 1,055 rains received, only 141 of them resulted in any runoff. On the most erosive plot, 3 rainstorms caused 27 per cent of the erosion losses of soil, while 14 storms were responsible for 52 per cent of the erosion. More often than not, one storm a year usually caused more than half of the soil loss. April and May were the months of greatest loss because the soil was bare as a result of having been prepared for planting crops at that time.

Water Erosion a Selective Process

Research in Wisconsin has demonstrated that, while loss of soil by erosion is serious, the problem is more critical when one considers that the most productive soil is lost.[*] Soil eroded from experimental plots in

[*] H. F. Massey and M. L. Jackson, "Selective Erosion of Soil Fertility Constituents," *Soil Sci. Soc. of Amer. Proceed.* 16:4, 1952.

four locations in Wisconsin were analyzed and compared with soil not eroded. The eroded soil contained:

    (1) 2.1 times more organic matter
    (2) 2.7 times more nitrogen
    (3) 3.4 times more available phosphorus
    (4) 19.3 times more available potassium

In general, the erosive processes are more selective when total soil losses are low.

Depth of Topsoil and Crop Yield

As water continues to carry away the topsoil, the productivity of the land declines. This fact is shown graphically in Figure 16.5. The relationship between depth of topsoil and the yield of wheat in Washington, corn in Missouri, and cotton in Georgia, is given in this figure.

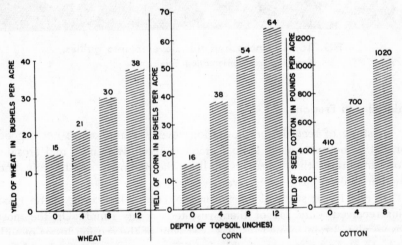

FIG. 16.5. The relationship between the depth of topsoil and the yield of wheat in Washington, corn in Missouri, and cotton in Georgia. (Source: T. P. 98, 1950. U. S. Department of Agriculture.)

Decreasing thickness of topsoil results in decreased wheat yields. Thirty-eight bushels of wheat was the average where the topsoil was 12 inches deep. With all topsoil gone, wheat yields were 15 bushels to the acre.

Corn responded on an even greater scale to increased thickness of topsoil. Corn grown where the topsoil was 12 inches thick yielded 64 bushels per acre, but with no topsoil, the yield was 16 bushels to the acre.

Cotton yields were influenced in a similar manner. On 8 inches of topsoil, cotton gave 1020 pounds of seed cotton, but 410 pounds was the yield on no topsoil.

Cropping Systems to Reduce Soil Losses

If a luxuriant crop covers the surface of the soil when the rains are most intense, there is almost no chance for the soil to erode. Keeping the surface protected and making a good living from the crops grown require scientific management.

Twenty years of experimental results on the relationship between cropping systems and soil-erosion losses are identified for Missouri in Figure 16.6. Continuous bluegrass protected the soil and permitted only a trace of soil erosion. Next in order was a rotation of corn—wheat—red clover—timothy, which permitted 10 tons of soil loss per acre per year. The poorest protection was given by continuous corn, which resulted in a loss of 50 tons of soil per acre each year.

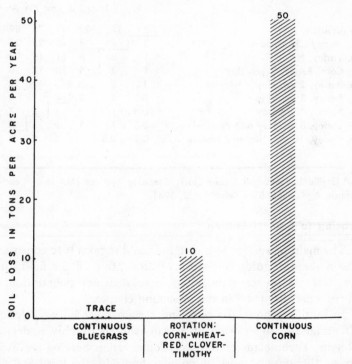

FIG. 16.6.   Soil losses in relation to cropping system in Missouri. (Dwight D. Smith, Darnell M. Whitt, and M. F. Miller, "Cropping Systems for Soil Conservation," Mo. Agr. Exp. Sta. Bul. 518, 1948.)

Any cropping system which allows more than three tons of soil loss per acre per year is not to be recommended.

The anticipated soil loss from various cropping systems in Wisconsin is given in Table 16.1. Soil losses for slopes from 3 to 24 per cent are shown for nine cropping systems, all of which include corn. The "safe" cropping systems on various slopes are those which result in no more than three tons of soil loss per acre each year. The rotation offering the most soil protection is corn—barley—ten years of hay and pasture. This cropping system is considered "safe" for slopes no greater than 16 per cent.

TABLE 16.1   Expected Soil Losses in Tons Per Acre Per Year from Cropping Systems on Moderately Eroded Slopes (72-Foot Length of Slope) *

Cropping System	Per Cent Slope							
	3	6	9	12	15	16	18	24
	Tons Soil Lost Per Acre							
Corn Annually	5	12	22	44	76	89	117	242
Corn, Barley (Sweetclover)	2	4	8	16	28	33	44	90
Corn, Barley, Hay	1	3	6	11	19	22	29	60
Corn, Corn, Barley, 3 yrs. Hay	1	3	5	10	17	20	26	54
Corn, Barley, 2 yrs. Hay	1	2	3	6	11	13	17	35
Corn, Barley, 3 yrs. Hay	0.5	1	2	4	7	8	10	22
Corn, Barley, 4 yrs. Hay	0.5	1	2	3	6	7	9	19
Corn, Barley, 6 yrs. Hay and Pasture	0.5	1	1	2	3	5	7	14
Corn, Barley, 10 yrs. Hay and Pasture	0.2	0.5	1	1	2	3	4	8

* Orville E. Hays and Noble Clark, *Cropping Systems That Help Control Erosion*, Wisconsin Agri. Expt. Sta., Bulletin 452, 1941.

Terracing to Control Erosion

The main reason for terracing in humid regions is to construct a ridge across a slope to guide the surplus water safely off the field. In dryland areas, terraces are constructed to increase water penetration. Dryland terraces were discussed in the preceding chapter.

In humid regions, the terracing system must be well designed and built under the supervision of a man who thoroughly understands the problems. Technicians of the Soil Conservation Service are available to carry on this type of work, in co-operation with the local Soil Conservation Districts.

Terraces are usually recommended only on intensively used cropland. Land in a good grass cover seldom needs terracing for proper water

FIG. 16.7. In humid regions, terraces are recommended on intensively cultivated fields, but they must be maintained at all times.
Courtesy Texas Extension Service.

control. Tillage parallel with the terraces is always a safe practice. When the field is plowed, the crest of the terrace should be the back-furrow. Terraces usually need annual maintenance to keep them useful.

The Problem of Wind Erosion

Some wind erosion occurs in nearly every state on unprotected sandy soils. But wind erosion is very serious on many soils in the Great Plains Region (Figure 16.8). Twice during the last 25 years parts of the Great Plains have earned the unenviable name of "The Dust Bowl." On the average, approximately once in 20 years the Southern Great Plains has had a serious drought and severe wind erosion.

FIG. 16.8. The Great Plains region, where the most serious wind erosion takes place.

Most soil blowing starts on poor land which normally has a scant vegetative cover for protection. The Soil Conservation Service estimates that 14 million wind-erosion susceptible acres in the Great Plains which are now raising cultivated crops should be put in permanent grass to reduce wind erosion. (Figure 16.9)

FIG. 16.9.   High winds on unprotected, dry soils cause the soil particles to hop, skip, jump, and roll along the ground before coming to rest.
Courtesy Agricultural Research Magazine, U. S. D. A.

Wind Erosion a Selective Process

A few years ago, soil material was blown from Texas and Oklahoma and analyzed at Clarinda, Iowa, a distance of more than 500 miles from its source. This windblown soil, as compared with the soil from whence it came, was:

19 times higher in phosphorus
10 times higher in organic matter
1.5 times higher in potassium

A mechanical analysis showed this dust to contain no sand but 97 per cent silt-plus-clay. Soil material deposited 300 miles away from its source

FIG. 16.10. It is no pleasure to live in an area where the wind is constantly blowing sand about.
Courtesy Soil Conservation Service.

contained 4 per cent sand, 68 per cent silt, and 25 per cent clay. This indicates that sand can be carried 300 miles but not 500 miles under these conditions.* (Figure 16.10)

Controlling Wind Erosion

Foremost in wind-erosion control is to put the 14 million wind erosion-susceptible acres now in cultivation back to grass. Most of these areas cannot successfully be seeded to grass until a wet season occurs.

Stubble mulches are always recommended to control soil blowing. Crop residues on the surface help to hold winter snows, protect the soil from violent winds, improve soil structure, and increase the infiltration of rainwater.

Stubble mulches for reducing wind erosion have been encouraged by partial payments to farmers and ranchers for this practice. The Agricultural Conservation Program has reported that, from 1936 to 1954, landowners carried out stubble-mulch management to the extent of a cumulative total of approximately 61½ million acres.

* J. H. Stallings, "Soil Fertility Losses by Erosion," *Better Crops with Plant Food Magazine,* October, 1951.

FIG. 16.11. Stubble mulches help hold winter snows, improve soil structure, increase the infiltration of water, and reduce wind erosion.
Courtesy Soil Conservation Service.

Many sloping fields also should be terraced, contour-furrowed, sub-
soiled, and tilled with subsurface implements that leave crop residues
on the surface. (Figure 16.11)

Subsoiling for increased water absorption has been practiced on more
than 11 million acres. This is a cumulative total from 1936 to 1954 as a
partial-payment practice of the Agricultural Conservation Program.

On rangelands, the best practices to control wind erosion are:

1. Always leave a large percentage of the forage for reserve and
residue. From 20 to 50 per cent should remain, depending on circumstances.

2. Livestock numbers (stocking) per unit area must be carefully adjusted to current rainfall and available grass.

3. Provide additional watering places for the livestock so that they
will not overgraze areas adjacent to water.

4. Place salt boxes to encourage more uniform grazing. Livestock do
not need salt near water.

5. Water spreading, gully control, brush eradication, and reseeding
desirable grasses are other practices designed to reduce wind erosion.

Proof that many of the recommended practices for controlling wind erosion are scientifically sound may be seen from a release from the United States Department of Agriculture.*

Wind tunnels have been constructed in Texas and one in Nebraska to study wind erosion. Wheat following wheat, with fall plowing, eroded at the rate of 60,000 pounds of soil per acre. By contrast, leaving the wheat stubble protected the soil and reduced wind-erosion losses to 280 pounds per acre.

In Kansas, it was discovered that the direction of the rows of grain sorghum was a very important factor. Soil losses were three times greater when the rows were parallel to the prevailing winds than when the rows were at right angles to the wind.

Summary

Raindrops striking bare soil are the primary cause of water erosion. Drying winds moving over unprotected soil start the process of wind erosion. The control of both water and wind erosion is achieved by providing protective cover for the soil. No part of our nation escapes erosion.

Most erosion is caused by only one or two torrential rains or dust storms a year, which come at a time when the soil is least protected by crops. Both water erosion and wind erosion are selective processes, eroding the most productive parts of the surface soil. Yields of crops at any one location are greater when more topsoil is present.

The most protective cover is a healthy stand of trees or grass. Next in effectiveness is a cropping system which includes perennial grasses and legumes.

Terraces to reduce water erosion are recommended practice on many gently sloping cropland acres. The terraces must be laid out by a technician and carefully maintained. Terracing grasslands is usually wasted effort.

Wind erosion on the Great Plains is a very serious problem. It has been estimated that 14 million acres of cropland in this region should be planted to perennial grasses to reduce the hazard of wind erosion. The use of stubble mulches, terracing, contour furrowing, subsoiling, and subsurface tillage are some of the practices used to reduce wind erosion.

* *Important Recent Achievements of Department of Agriculture Scientists.* Document No. 6. Rev. Nov. 15, 1951. U. S. D. A.

Questions

1. What is the primary cause of water and wind erosion?
2. Where is erosion most serious in our nation?
3. Describe splash erosion.
4. What is the relationship between rainfall and erosion?
5. "Water and wind erosion are selective processes." Explain this statement.
6. Describe the ideal cropping system for erosion control.
7. How can terraces control water erosion?
8. What should be done in the Great Plains to control wind erosion on 14 million acres of cropland that are susceptible to wind erosion?
9. In general, what can you do to control wind erosion?
10. Describe stubble-mulch management.

References

A *Water Policy for the American People.* Vol. I, General Report. The President's Water Resources Policy Commission. Washington, D.C. 1950.

Soils and Men, The 1938 Yearbook of Agriculture. U. S. D. A.

Water, The 1955 Yearbook of Agriculture. U. S. D. A.

17

Irrigation Practices

The West was explored by men in search of gold. The West was settled by men who found water and learned how to use it efficiently. Water was the principal barrier to the settlement of the West, and today it is still the main factor restricting the development of the region.

Indians in New Mexico and Arizona were using crude irrigation practices when the Spanish explorers came upon them. But the first Anglo-Saxons to establish scientific irrigation practices were the Mormons. In 1847 the Mormons started to irrigate their crops near Salt Lake City, Utah. Today these people are leaders in irrigation agriculture.

When Theodore Roosevelt became President in 1901, one of his first acts was to establish an expanded program for conservation of soil and water in the West. As a result of this legislation, the Roosevelt Dam was started on the Salt River in Arizona in 1909. The impounded waters were used for making electricity, for providing recreation, and for irrigating.

From its beginnings in 1847, irrigation agriculture grew in the 17 Western states to a 27.5 million-acre business in 1953. While this represented only 3.5 per cent of the total land in farms in these Western states, the crops harvested from irrigated land had a value of 35 per cent of all crops harvested in the region.

In the East, expansion in irrigation has been rapid. Irrigation is concentrated in the rice belts of Texas, Louisiana, and Arkansas and in the vegetable areas in central and southern Florida. All other states in the humid region practice irrigation to some extent, but especially those near New York City, Chicago, and other large centers of population (Figure 17.1).

No one doubts the need for irrigation in the West. Recent work in North Carolina may give some indication of the future need in humid regions. In an area receiving an average annual precipitation of 40 inches,

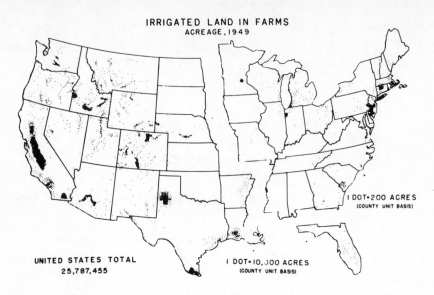

IRRIGATED LAND IN FARMS
ACREAGE, 1949

I DOT·200 ACRES
(COUNTY UNIT BASIS)

UNITED STATES TOTAL
25,787,455

I DOT·10,000 ACRES
(COUNTY UNIT BASIS)

FIG. 17.1.   Irrigated land in farms in the United States in 1949. (Source: U. S. Bureau of the Census.)

as many as 50 days of drought may occur one year in five. This indicates that, even though the average precipitation seems to be adequate for crop production, irregularities in the distribution may make irrigation profitable.

Water Quality

Water for irrigation must not only be plentiful throughout the growing season, but also it must be of the right quality. The quality of water is determined by four characteristics:

1. The total concentration of soluble salts.
2. The amount of sodium in relation to calcium-plus-magnesium.
3. The amount of bicarbonate.
4. The presence of boron in amounts which may be toxic.

The soluble salts in irrigation waters are mainly the cations, calcium, magnesium, and sodium. Anions consist of sulfate, chloride, and bicarbonate.

The soluble salts in Eastern surface waters are seldom in sufficiently high concentration to be harmful. In Western surface waters, however, salt content is usually too high. Western waters vary from 70 to 3,500 parts per million of soluble salts. The higher the salt concentration in irrigation waters, the greater the hazard of toxic accumulations in the soil. (Figure 17.2)

FIG. 17.2. This California field has a high concentration of water-soluble salts on the surface. The field needs leveling.
Courtesy U. S. D. A.

Ground waters in the East are free of harmful salt concentrations; but in Western areas, ground waters may be as high or higher in total salts than surface waters.

In irrigation language, there is a saying, "Hard water makes soft land and soft water makes hard land." The explanation of this statement is that calcium and magnesium, the two principal cations making water hard, help in creating desirable soil structure. Sodium, the dominant cation in soft water, disperses clay and humus and creates an undesirable structure.

When there is a large amount of sodium in the irrigation water and a low percentage of calcium and magnesium, the sodium is readily absorbed on the clay and humus particles. The sodium disperses the soil and makes it less able to absorb water. If the same amount of sodium is present but there is a larger quantity of calcium and magnesium, less sodium is absorbed, and therefore a better soil structure is maintained. It is therefore the amount of sodium in relation to calcium and magnesium that is important in judging the quality of irrigation waters.

The bicarbonate ion is toxic, especially to apple trees, beans, and dallisgrass. Specific toxicity of the bicarbonate ion may be found on other plants as more research is conducted in this field. It has been demonstrated that the bicarbonate ion accumulates in the soil and interferes with the uptake of iron in plants. This condition causes *iron chlorosis.*

Boron is present in nearly all western irrigation waters. A boron concentration as high as three parts per million is satisfactory only for such boron-tolerant crops as asparagus, sugar beets, alfalfa, and cabbage. This concentration of boron is toxic for the sensitive crops, such as navy beans and almost all tree fruits.

Consumptive Use of Water

"Consumptive use" is defined as the sum of the water transpired by plants and the water evaporated from the surface of the soil.

Factors influential in determining the consumptive use for any crop are:

1. Length of growing season.
2. Temperature.
3. Daytime hours.

Other factors of minor importance are relative humidity and wind movement.

TABLE 17.1.   Annual Consumptive Use of Water for Selected Crops in South Dakota *

| Crop | Annual Consumptive Use of Water | | |
	Supplied by Rain (Inches)	Supplied by Irrigation (Inches)	Total Consumptive Use (Inches)
Alfalfa	12	15	27
Grass, Hay, or Pasture	12	12	24
Sugar Beets	12	10	21
Corn	9	10	19
Flax	9	10	19
Potatoes	9	10	19
Small Grains	9	7	16
Dry Beans	9	5	14

* Leonard J. Erie and Niel A. Dimick, *Soil Moisture Depletion by Irrigated Crops Grown in South Dakota.* South Dakota Agr. Exp. Sta. Cir. 104. 1954.

The annnal consumptive use of water was determined for eight crops in South Dakota and is shown in Table 17.1. The consumptive use varies from 27 inches for alfalfa to 14 inches for dry beans. The water supplied by rain varies from 9 to 12 inches, depending on the length of time the crop is growing. Perennial crops, such as alfalfa and long-season annuals like sugar beets, benefit more from natural rain than will shorter-season crops. The column "Supplied by Irrigation" is an average value determined for a period of years at 32 locations in South Dakota.

The kind of grass makes a big difference in the efficiency of use of water. Some grasses produce a large amount of dry matter per acre-inch of water; other grasses, even though closely related, are more wasteful. Figure 17.3 illustrates this statement. Coastal Bermuda-grass, a giant hybrid, produced one ton of dry matter for each six acre-inches of water. In contrast, it took nine acre-inches of water for Pensacolagrass and Bahiagrass and 14 acre-inches for each ton of dry matter of common Bermuda-grass. The common Bermuda-grass, therefore, used two and one-third times as much water per unit of dry matter as did Coastal Bermuda-grass.

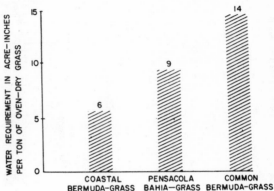

FIG. 17.3. A comparison of the water requirement (consumptive use) of three Southern grasses. (Glenn W. Burton, E. H. De Vane, and Gordon M. Prine, **Agronomy Abstracts,** 1955, p. 59.)

Daily consumptive-use values have been determined for cotton and for grain sorghums on the High Plains (Panhandle) of Texas. The research was carried out on Pullman clay loam. Cotton uses the largest amount of water around July 15, the average date of the first bloom. At this time the consumptive use of water for cotton is approximately 0.25 inch of water per day. Grain sorghum needs a maximum of 0.33 inch of water daily just prior to "booting." *

Studies have also been made of the daily consumptive use of water for forests. From June 1 to July 15, the consumptive use of water for fully stocked forest stands in Arkansas was 0.19 inch per day. Water depletion was determined weekly to a depth of 60 inches. Measurements were made on even-aged and all-aged hardwoods (southern red oak, post oak, and sweetgum), and even-aged and all-aged softwoods (loblolly pine and shortleaf pine). The consumptive use of water was the same, regardless of the composition of the forest.**

* E. L. Thaxton, Jr., "Irrigating Cotton and Grain Sorghum," *Texas Agricultural Progress,* 2:2, March-April, 1956. Texas A. & M. College System, College Station, Texas.

** *Soil Moisture Depletion Equal under Pines or Hardwoods,* 1955 Annual Report, Southern Forest Experiment Station, pp. 29.

Water-Holding Capacity of Soils

The depth of penetration in the soil of a specific amount of infiltrated water depends upon the water-holding capacity of the soil. This, in turn, is influenced mainly by soil texture.

In Figure 17.4 it may be seen that three inches of water, either as rain or irrigation, wets each soil texture to definite soil depths. For example, three inches of water wets a clay soil to a one-foot depth, but a loam to two feet and a sand to a four-foot depth.

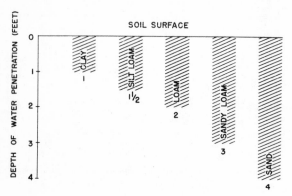

FIG. 17.4. Three inches of water will wet each soil texture to the depth shown. (Data from various sources.)

Normal Irrigation Depth for Crops

The depth to wet the soil for the best response of crops will vary with the depth of rooting of each crop. Probably the best rule is to irrigate to a depth where 90 per cent of plant roots are growing.

Figure 17.5 gives the normal irrigation depth for several crops. For most vegetables, a depth of one and one-half feet is satisfactory, while for alfalfa five feet is the recommended depth to irrigate. Other crops should be irrigated to intermediate depths.

Amount and Frequency of Irrigations

Based upon the consumptive use of the crop, the rooting habit of the crop, and the water-holding capacity of the soil, the amount of water to apply when there is no rain during the growing season can be determined for each crop in each field.

As an example of how to calculate the amount of water to apply, look at Table 17.1. These data show that corn has a consumptive use of 19 inches. Assuming that the corn is growing in a silt loam soil, Figure 17.4 indicates that three inches of water will wet the soil to a depth of one and one-half feet. Then Figure 17.5 shows that the normal irrigation depth for corn is three feet. To wet a silt loam soil to three feet requires

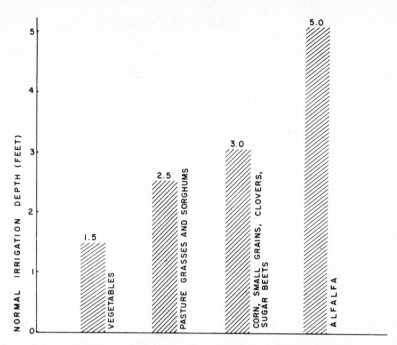

FIG. 17.5. The normal irrigation depth of some common crops in Colorado. (A. J. Hamman and W. E. Code, in "Irrigation Guide for Colorado," Agr. Extension Service and Experiment Sta. Bul. 432-A, 1954.)

six inches of water. Starting with dry silt loam soil, any irrigation water in excess of six inches would soak below three feet and would therefore be wasted.

Since the total consumptive use for corn is 19 inches, this amount should be added as needed during the growing season. Each time water is added, a soil probe should be used to check the depth of wetting so as to stop irrigating when the soil is wet to a depth of three feet.

At first thought it would seem as if we could divide the consumptive use (19) by the amount of water required to wet the soil to the three-foot depth (six inches) to obtain the number of times needed to irrigate. This would be true if the soil were allowed to become air-dry each time water is applied. But we know that plants would wilt before the soil became that dry. As a rule of thumb, it is practical to irrigate when the soil is 50 per cent depleted of moisture. In our example, this would mean that watering should be started when the soil, to a three-foot depth, contains three inches of water. At this point, three inches of water should be supplied by irrigation. On this basis, 19 divided by 3 equals $6\frac{1}{3}$; or roughly six irrigations of three inches of water each will be required during the growing season.

By way of a general summary, the relationship between soil texture and the interval between irrigations to a desired depth is shown in Figure 17.6.

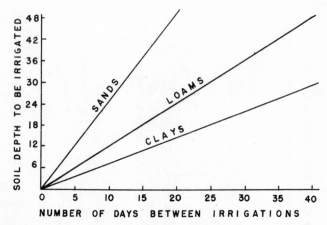

FIG. 17.6. The relationship between soil texture and the interval between irrigations to desired soil depths. (Source: **Water:** The Yearbook of Agriculture, 1955, p. 467.)

From Figure 17.6 it may be readily observed that sands must be irrigated more frequently than clays when both are wetted to the same depth. When all soils are irrigated to a depth of 24 inches at each application, a sand would have to be irrigated every 10 days, a loam every 20 days, and a clay every 35 days.

Sprinkler Irrigation

The sprinkler irrigation system consists of pumping water through a pipe and through rotating heads so as to apply water to the soil in a manner similar to that received by natural rainfall. This is the most popular system in humid regions. (Figure 17.7)

The advantages of the sprinkler system are that:

1. Land-leveling is not necessary.
2. Drainage problems are decreased.
3. Erosion is kept to a minimum.
4. Fewer special skills are required.

Some disadvantages of the sprinkler system are:

1. The initial investment is high.
2. Power costs are higher.
3. More labor is required to move the pipe.

FIG. 17.7. The sprinkler irrigation system is best adapted to sloping land or sandy soils.

Courtesy Sprinkler Irrigation Association.

4. Wind prevents a uniform distribution, making it often necessary to irrigate at night.

5. Evaporation losses of water are higher than with other methods of irrigation.

Furrow Irrigation

Furrow irrigation is the oldest kind of irrigation system. In this method, water flows by gravity from a main ditch and down each furrow. On top of the furrows the crop has been planted before water is applied.

Field crops such as corn and potatoes have a furrow to carry water between all rows. Crops that are planted in double rows or beds are irrigated by directing the water between the beds. Crops planted in a wide spacing, such as berries, grapes, and orchards, usually have two furrows for irrigation between each two rows of plants.

In general, soil erosion is excessive when the furrow method of irrigation is used on rows that have a slope of more than two per cent (Figure 17.8). An aim should be to keep the slope of the furrows less than one-fourth of one per cent. Running the rows on the contour helps to reduce erosion.

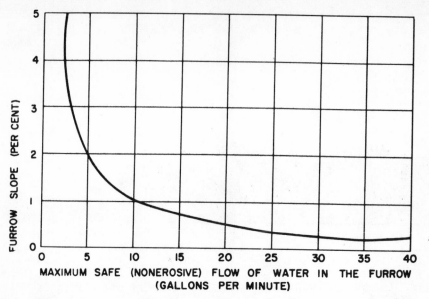

FIG. 17.8. The relationship between per cent slope and the maximum safe flow of water in the furrow. (George A. Lawrence, **Furrow Irrigation**. U. S .D. A. Leaflet 344, 1953.)

The aim of the irrigator should be to obtain the maximum flow of water down each furrow without causing excessive erosion. In this way, water will soak into the soil at a fairly uniform rate all along the furrow. As a rule of thumb, if it takes four hours to add sufficient water to a furrow, then the water should be turned into the furrow in such volume that it will flow to the end of the furrow in one hour (one-fourth of the elapsed time). (Figure 17.9)

FIG. 17.9. Row irrigation of cotton, showing plastic siphon tubes in use for moving water from the main ditch to each furrow.
Courtesy Drue W. Dunn, Oklahoma Extension Service.

The common methods of controlling the distribution of water in furrow irrigation are as follows:

1. Field lateral ditch with small equalizing ditch leading directly to each furrow.

2. Field lateral ditch with siphon tubes leading to each furrow.

3. Field lateral ditch with spiles (small straight pipes) leading directly to each row.

4. Irrigation pipe with large openings (gates) emptying into each furrow.

5. Buried pipe to carry the water to the field, with risers emptying into each furrow or series of furrows.

Corrugation Irrigation

The corrugation method of irrigation consists of running water down many small furrows for the irrigation of non-row crops such as alfalfa, grasses, and the small grains. (Figure 17.10)

FIG. 17.10. Laying out small furrows on the contour in preparation for corrugation irrigation.   *Courtesy U. S. D. A.*

This method is adapted to slopes up to five per cent, to fine-textured soils, and to soils that are inclined to bake when the flooding system of irrigation is used. A diagram showing the usual field layout is displayed in Figure 17.11.

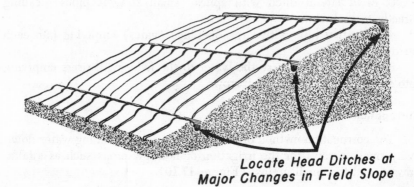

*Locate Head Ditches at
Major Changes in Field Slope*

FIG. 17.11. Generalized suggested layout of the corrugation method of irrigation. (Source: William R. Stanley, **Corrugation Irrigation.** U. S. D. A. Leaflet 343, 1954.)

Border Irrigation

The border method of irrigation is used on gentle slopes. Narrow strips of land are leveled, a low ridge built around them as a border to hold water, and each strip is irrigated by flooding. (Figure 17.12)

FIG. 17.12. The field has been prepared for border irrigation by building small levees around each leveled area; then the areas are flooded to irrigate them.
Courtesy Texas Extension Service.

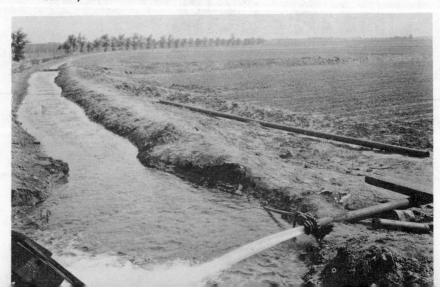

Border irrigation is most satisfactory under these conditions:

1. When the surface soil is deep enough to permit the land to be leveled without leaving areas of unproductive soil.

2. When the infiltration rate of the soil is intermediate. Sandy soils would not permit a uniform depth of water penetration, while on impervious clay soils an excessive amount of water would be lost by evaporation before it soaked into the soil.

3. When the slope is satisfactory to permit the construction of borders with a slope of two per cent or less. Land to remain in sod crops can be steeper without causing excessive erosion.

4. When the land is planted to crops which are not injured by temporary flooding.

Summary

Irrigation practices are spreading rapidly in nearly every state in our nation; even humid regions have frequent drought periods when irrigation pays.

Water for irrigation must be low in soluble salts, sodium, bicarbonates, and boron. Alfalfa has a high consumptive use, corn is intermediate, and small grains and beans have a low consumptive use of water. Three inches of irrigation water will wet a dry sandy soil to approximately 4 feet but a clay soil only 1 foot. Alfalfa should be irrigated to a depth of 5 feet, corn to 3 feet, grasses to 2.5 feet, and vegetables to 1.5 feet. A crop should be irrigated when one-half of the available soil water has been depleted. Sandy soils will require more frequent irrigations than fine-textured soils.

The sprinkler irrigation system is adapted especially to rolling topography and is the most popular system in the humid region. Furrow irrigation is the oldest method known and is adapted to row crops on fairly level land. Corrugation irrigation is used mostly on sod crops growing on fairly steep slopes. The border irrigation system is well adapted to soils of intermediate infiltration capacity, such as sandy loams.

Questions

1. How important is irrigation to the arid areas?
2. Why is irrigation increasing also in the humid areas?
3. Describe a good quality of water for irrigation.
4. "Hard water makes soft land and soft water makes hard land." Explain.
5. What is meant by the "consumptive use" of water?
6. On the average, how deep will three inches of water soak into a dry loam?
7. How deep should the soil be wetted for corn?

8. Which texture requires the most frequent irrigations—sand, loam, or clay?
9. What are the advantages and disadvantages of the sprinkler system of irrigation?
10. Why is furrow irrigation the oldest system known?

References

Climate and Man: The Yearbook of Agriculture, 1941.

Diagnosis and Improvement of Saline and Alkali Soils. U. S. Salinity Lab. Staff. U. S. D. A. Agriculture Handbook No. 60, 1954.

Thorne, D. W., and H. B. Peterson, *Irrigated Soils,* 2nd ed. The Blakiston Co. New York. 1954.

Water: The Yearbook of Agriculture, 1955.

18

Drainage Systems

Drainage systems of some type have been used since man first began to till the soil. Cato, in 234-149 B.C., recommended the following system for draining fields in Rome:

If the land is wet it should be drained with trough-shaped ditches dug three feet wide at the surface and one foot at the bottom, and four feet deep. Bind these ditches with rock. If you have no rock, then fill them with green willow poles braced crosswise. If you have no poles, fill them with faggots. Then dig lateral trenches three feet deep and four feet wide in such a way that the water will flow from the trenches into the ditches.

Drainage in the United States

The Dismal Swamp area in North Carolina and Virginia was surveyed for drainage by George Washington in 1763. Early drainage enterprises were also organized in Georgia, South Carolina, Maryland, New Jersey, Delaware, and Massachusetts.

As the present Corn Belt and Gulf Coast were being settled, thousands of acres were bypassed because they were too wet. A greater density of population and the coming of modern machinery made it possible to drain many productive acres that were formerly too wet to raise crops.

The first Census of Drainage, taken in 1920, reported approximately 65½ million acres in organized drainage enterprises. Each succeeding decade showed increases in artificially drained acres, until in 1950 the acreage was 103 million, more than 57 per cent greater than that in 1920 (Figure 18.1). The greatest increases in drained acres were in Louisiana, Florida, and Texas, in the order named.

237

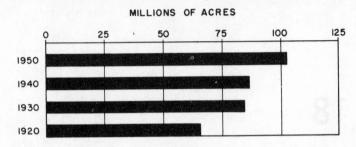

AGRICULTURAL LAND IN DRAINAGE ENTERPRISES, FOR THE UNITED STATES: 1920—1950

MILLIONS OF ACRES

FIG. 18.1. The changes in acreages of artificially drained land, by decades, 1920-1950. (Source: U. S. Bureau of the Census.)

During the period from 1936 to 1954, the Agricultural Conservation Program assisted in establishing drainage systems by paying the farmers a part of the cost for draining more than 34 million acres.

Present areas in drainage enterprises are indicated on the map in Figure 18.2. The figure indicates that the artificial drainage is concentrated in Michigan, Ohio, Indiana, and Illinois; the Mississippi Valley; the Louisiana and Texas Gulf Coast; southern Florida; Northeastern North Dakota; and in scattered areas throughout the West, mostly in conjunction with irrigation projects.

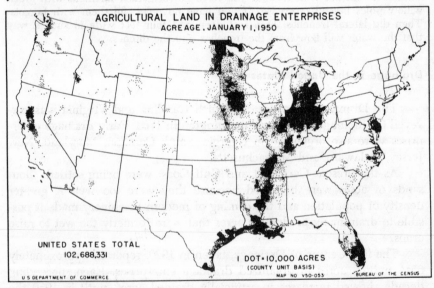

FIG. 18.2. Map of the United States showing the location of land that is artificially drained, as of Jan. 1, 1950. (Source: U. S. Bureau of the Census.)

Benefits from Drainage

Artificial drainage of wet soils lowers the water table and results in these benefits:

1. Wet soils are usually the most fertile soils on the farm. Drainage permits them to be used.

2. Properly drained soils warm earlier in the spring, thus permitting crops to be planted early enough to mature. It takes five times the heat to raise the temperature of water one degree as is required for dry soil.

3. Drainage increases the amount of oxygen in the soil. Often a deficiency of oxygen results in a chemical reduction in iron and manganese which may be toxic to plant growth.

4. Drainage decreases the losses of nitrogen from the soil by denitrification.

5. Drainage increases the percentage of crude protein in plants. The percentage of potassium, chlorine, and magnesium in plants is also increased by drainage.

6. Drained soils are freer from certain diseases such as black rot of strawberries, fusarium root rot of sugar beets, and cereal root rots.

7. Drained pastures are healthier pastures because more parasites are killed by desiccation.

8. Soil structure is improved by drainage. The increase in wetting and drying, and the greater root growth, earthworm activity, and accelerated growth of bacteria and fungi aid in creating desirable soil structure.

9. Land which has been drained is adapted to a wider variety of more valuable crops.

10. Drainage permits a deeper penetration of plant roots; this increases the amount of nutrients available to growing plants and results in greater crop yields. Deeper roots also make the plants more drought resistant (Figure 18.3).

11. Drainage carries away excess surface water. This reduces the losses of plants due to the "heaving" action resulting from freezing and thawing of the soil.

12. Plants growing on well-drained soils utilize lime and fertilizers more efficiently.

Soils That Require Drainage

A soil may need artificial drainage for one of two reasons:

1. When there is a high water table that should be lowered, or
2. When excess surface water cannot move downward fast enough to keep from suffocating plant roots.

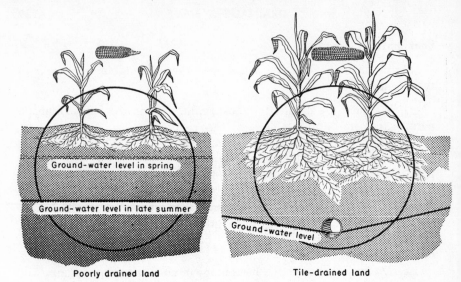

Poorly drained land | Tile-drained land

FIG. 18.3. **Left:** On poorly drained land, the plant roots are shallow because of excess water near the surface in the spring of the year. As the water level drops in the summer, the crop suffers from a lack of water.

Right: The same soil properly tile-drained permits an extensive root system which obtains water and nutrients from a larger volume of soil.

(Lewis A. Jones, **Farm Drainage.** U. S. D. A. Farmers' Bul. 2046, 1952.)

High water tables are common in most peat and muck soils and in some low-lying sandy soils. More commonly, however, level upland soils need artificial drainage because of excess surface water. Soils that permit only a slow movement of water downward may need ditching. Repeated experiments in areas of high rainfall have shown that fine-textured soils with a massive structure are most in need of artificial drainage. Much can be learned about the internal drainage of the soil by digging into the soil. Digging post holes, trench silos, or foundations will reveal some subsoil characteristics that indicate soil permeability. Permeability is the capacity of a soil to allow movement of air and water through it. A permeable soil seldom needs artificial drainage, except when the soil has a high water table. Slowly permeable soils often need artificial drainage, especially when the land surface is level and rainfall is high.

Permeable soils that do not require drainage are uniform in color throughout the profile. The color may vary from brown to red. Yellow subsoils indicate intermediate permeability, especially when the texture is a clay. Subsoils that are mottled with red, yellow, and gray are more

FIG. 18.4. Peat and muck soils require drainage because of a high water table. This is a mole drainage machine in operation. (Florida) *Courtesy Soil Conservation Service.*

FIG. 18.5. This soil requires drainage to get rid of the excess surface water. (Louisiana)
Courtesy Soil Conservation Service.

slowly permeable than are yellow subsoils. Gray clay subsoils in humid regions indicate very slow permeability and a probable need for artificial drainage. (Figures 18.4, 18.5)

Drainage Capacity of Soils

It is often difficult to determine whether a soil will drain rapidly enough to permit the use of some form of subsurface drainage. With a potential investment so large, it usually pays to make some field and laboratory determinations to find what drainage system is best suited to any particular soil.

One way to obtain reliable data is to determine the field capacity, bulk density, and particle density. From the bulk density and particle density, the total pore space can be calculated. Then from this value is subtracted the per cent of pore space occupied by water at one-third atmosphere of tension. (The per cent moisture at one-third-atmosphere tension is the same numerical value as the per cent pore volume at the same tension, because one gram of water occupies 1 c.c.) The result represents the pore spaces through which water will move through the soil toward an underground drain. Such a value is known as *drainage capacity.*

To obtain total pore space, this simple equation is used:

$$\% \text{ total pore space} = 100 - \frac{\text{Bulk density}}{\text{Particle density}} \times 100$$

Pore spaces which hold water at the field capacity are not available for transmitting water through a soil in the field. These pore-space volumes may be readily obtained from field-capacity determinations. Moisture held at one-third atmosphere of tension closely approximates the moisture obtained from a field determination of field capacity.

Drainage capacity, as a percentage, is then found in this way:

% drainage capacity = % total pore space − % pore space occupied by water at the field capacity.

An example may help to further explain drainage capacity.

In Mississippi, the surface soil of Memphis silt loam (developed from loess) has a total pore space of 59 per cent. The pore volume at one-third-atmosphere tension (field capacity) is 20 per cent. The drainage capacity is therefore 59 − 20 = 39 per cent. For contrast, the drainage capacities are displayed for two other Mississippi soils in Table 18.1.

TABLE 18.1. Total Pore Space, Pore Volume at 1/3-Atmosphere Tension, and Drainage Capacity of Three Mississippi Soils *

Soil Type	Depth (Inches)	Total Pore Space (Per Cent)	Pore Volume at 1/3 Atmosphere of Tension (Field Capacity) (Per Cent)	Drainage Capacity (Per Cent)
Memphis silt loam	0-6	59	20	39
Bosket sandy loam	0-8	51	39	12
Sharkey clay	0-6	51	81	0

* W. M. Broadfoot and W. A. Raney, "Properties Affecting Water Relations and Management of 14 Mississippi Soils," Miss. Agr. Exp. Sta. Bul. 521, 1954.

From Table 18.1 it may be seen that Memphis silt loam, with a drainage capacity of 39 per cent, will drain readily. Bosket sandy loam will drain fairly readily, with a drainage capacity of 12 per cent. On the other hand, since its moisture at one-third atmosphere is greater than the total pore space, *Sharkey clay will not drain* through tile drains. This soil must be drained only by surface ditches, since water will not flow through it into tile drains.

Surface Drainage

Soils which have a low drainage capacity must be drained by surface ditches. These open drains should be large enough to be crossed by machinery, if the fields are to be managed efficiently. (Figure 18.6)

FIG. 18.6. Some soils can be drained only by open ditches because water will not flow through the soils fast enough for a tile drainage system. (South Carolina)
Courtesy Soil Conservation Service.

Drainage ditches may be laid out by eye, leading from wet spot to wet spot, and finally into a protected grassy or wooded area. Too often such a system of drainage becomes a maze of gullies which prevent the efficient use of the land.

The best system of surface drainage consists of drainage-by-beds, sometimes known as "turtlebacks" (Figure 18.7). This system is best adapted to nearly level, fine-textured soils.

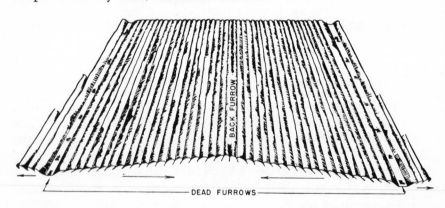

FIG. 18.7. A system of drainage-by-beds, showing how it is maintained by the direction of plowing. The center or crest should be the back furrow and the ditches should be the dead furrows. The width of the beds varies from 50 to 150 feet. (Source: A. M. Goodman, **Farm Drainage**, Cornell Extension Bul. 875, 1953.)

Tile Drainage

Satisfactory layout of a tile drainage system requires considerable planning and a lot of experience. Technical assistance in layout and installation of a tile drainage system can be obtained from the local Soil Conservation Service.

A tile drainage system will be satisfactory for a century or more if properly planned, adequately constructed, and carefully maintained. The depth and spacing at which to lay the lines of tile will vary with the crops grown and the type of soil. Soils with slow downward movement of water should have shallower placings of the lines of tile, and the lines should be laid closer together. Drainage to be established for alfalfa or orchards needs a depth of tile of about four feet. Corn needs intermediate depths, and the grasses and small grains can get along best with the tile lines placed about two feet deep. Spacings may vary from 40 to 300 feet between lines of tile, depending upon soil drainage capacity, which is related to soil texture and soil structure.

In clay and clay loam soils, the depth of the tile should not exceed three feet and the spacing no more than 70 feet. Tile lines in silt loam soils can be placed four feet deep and 100 feet apart. The respective maximum depth and spacing allowed in sandy soils is four and one-half and 300 feet.

Outlets for tile lines should be screened to prevent rodents from plugging them. Outlets should also be encased in cement, with a suitable apron to prevent undercutting by flowing water. Also, the last ten feet of tile back from the outlet should be cemented at the joints. Other tile in the lines are placed end to end so as to permit water seeping between each two sections of tile.

Trees near tile lines should be cut so that the roots cannot grow into the cracks between the joints of tile. A hole in the soil above a tile line indicates that one of the sections has been broken or displaced. This should be repaired before the whole tile system is ruined. Occasionally the outlet will become plugged by "mud dobber" nests, birds' nests, or rodents living in the tile. Sometimes also, an outlet will erode and render useless the whole drainage system. All of these maintenance jobs pay big dividends in extending the useful life of a tile drainage system.

Tile drains operate more effectively when a good cropping system is followed. Deep-rooted legumes and grasses are especially effective in helping to improve the drainage capacity of the soil. The land should be kept in close-growing crops as long in the rotation as possible to extend the effective life of the tile drainage system.

Heavy machinery operating on a wet soil reduces its drainage capacity by creating tillage pans. These reduce the effectiveness of the tile drainage system. The feet of grazing cattle on a wet soil pack the surface inches into a pasture pan and also lower the efficiency of the drainage system.

Summary

Drainage systems have been in use since early Roman times. In our country, George Washington helped to establish a drainage enterprise in 1763. During the past 30 years, acres in drainage systems have increased approximately 57 per cent.

Drained soils are warmer in the spring, more efficient for the use of fertilizers, are healthier for livestock, and have a more desirable structure and a wider adaptation for a greater variety of crops.

Soils with a fairly high drainage capacity can be tile-drained; those with a low drainage capacity must be drained by open ditches. Some soils need to be drained because of a high water table; others require drainage because of excess surface water flowing onto them. Any drainage system should be laid out by a person trained to do the work and built by experienced machinery operators. Careful and regular maintenance extends the life of a drainage system for many decades.

Questions

1. How old is the science of drainage?
2. Explain the rate of growth of drainage enterprises in the United States.
3. Why do drained soils warm more rapidly in the spring?
4. Why are drained pastures healthier pastures?
5. Explain the improvement of soil structure following drainage.
6. Why are drained soils less droughty?
7. A soil may require drainage for one of two reasons. Name these reasons.
8. Explain the term "drainage capacity."
9. How does the drainage capacity of a soil determine what type of a drainage system should be installed?
10. How should a tile drainage system be maintained?

References

Broadfoot, W. M., and W. A. Raney, *Properties Affecting Water Relations and Management in 14 Mississippi Soils.* Miss. Agr. Exp. Sta. Bul. 521. 1954.

Goodman, A. M., *Farm Drainage.* Cornell Extension Bul. 875. 1953.

Jones, Lewis A., *Farm Drainage.* U.S.D.A. Farmers' Bul. 2046. 1952.

Water, The 1955 Yearbook of Agriculture. U.S.D.A.

19

Manure, Compost, Sewage Sludge, and Sawdust

Under constant tillage, our soils are losing organic matter faster than it can be replaced. A decrease in soil organic matter results in compact soils, shallow roots, increased droughtiness, and crusty and cloddy soils. In addition to using more sod crops in rotation, farmers can maintain soil organic matter by making more efficient use of farm manure, compost, sewage sludge, and sawdust.

Composition of Cow Manure

An average ton of cow manure plus bedding contains 500 pounds of organic matter, 10 pounds of N, 5 pounds of P_2O_5, and 10 pounds of K_2O. Water makes up most of the remaining 1475 pounds, or almost three-fourths of the ton of manure (Figure 19.1).

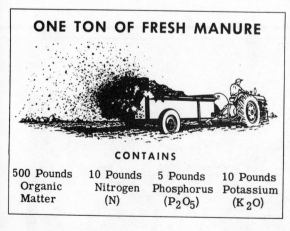

ONE TON OF FRESH MANURE

CONTAINS

| 500 Pounds Organic Matter | 10 Pounds Nitrogen (N) | 5 Pounds Phosphorus (P_2O_5) | 10 Pounds Potassium (K_2O) |

FIG. 19.1. Average composition of one ton of fresh manure including solid, liquid, and bedding. (C. M. Linsley, "Manure Is Worth Money, It Deserves Good Care," Illinois Agr. Extension Service Cir. 595, 1953.)

Approximately 50 per cent of the nitrogen is in the solid portion and the other 50 per cent is in the liquid part of the manure. By contrast, nearly all of the phosphorus (99 per cent) is in the solid portion. Eighty-four per cent of the potash is in the liquid and only 16 per cent is in the solid part (Figure 19.2).

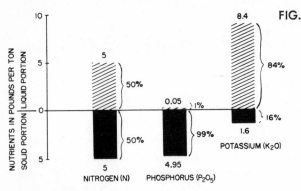

FIG. 19.2. Pounds of N, P_2O_5, and K_2O in one ton of manure from dairy cattle (includes bedding). (Firman E. Bear, Willis A. King, and Carl B. Bender, "The Cow as a Conserver of Soil Fertility," New Jersey Agr. Exp. Sta. Bul. 730, 1950.)

The Care of Manure

Manure is difficult to use without waste because it is bulky and perishable. Water-tight gutters, adequate bedding, and reinforcement with superphosphate all aid in reducing losses of nutrients from manure. Of special importance in the care of manure is keeping it protected from the weather until it is spread on the field. (Figures 19.3, 19.4)

FIG. 19.3. To conserve as many plant nutrients as possible, manure should be spread daily.
Courtesy New Idea Farm Equipment Co.

FIG. 19.4. Aproximately half of the fertilizing value of manure is lost when it is handled in this way.
Courtesy New Hampshire Agricultural Experiment Station.

Figure 19.5 presents graphically that approximately one-half of the fertilizing value of manure is lost during several months of exposure to the weather.

FIG. 19.5. Approximately half of the nutrients in fresh manure is lost by weathering before it is spread on the land. (C. M. Linsley, "Manure Is Worth Money, It Deserves Good Care," Illinois Agr. Extension Service Cir. 595, 1953.)

Reinforcing Manure

Superphosphate is used to reinforce manure for three primary purposes:

1. To reduce losses of nitrogen as ammonia.
2. To increase the percentage of phosphorus in manure to make it a better-balanced fertilizer.
3. To increase the efficiency of phosphorus utilization in soils that tend to tie up phosphorus.

It is recommended that two pounds of 20 per cent superphosphate be applied per day in the gutter behind each cow. If this is not done, 50 pounds of superphosphate per ton of manure can be added after the manure is on the spreader. Hydrated lime, ground limestone, and borax are added to manure to reduce odors and to control flies. (Figure 19.6)

FIG. 19.6. Cow manure is low in phosphorus. To make manure a better-balanced fertilizer, apply 2 pounds of 20 per cent superphosphate per cow per day in the gutter. The manure chelates the phosphorus and thereby reduces fixation by the soil.
Courtesy U. S. D. A.

Many soils have a very high capacity for making phosphorus fertilizer quickly unavailable to plants. One way to reduce this fixation is to apply the phosphorus fertilizer to manure. The organic matter in the manure supplies citrates, tartrates, oxalates, and other similar compounds which combine with iron and aluminum compounds more readily than phosphorus. The result is a tie-up of iron and aluminum by the organic materials and an increase in availability of phosphorus. These substances are known as *chelates*.

An application of this principle is presented graphically in Figure 19.7. Superphosphate mixed with the soil, the manure being applied later, produced 7 grams of dry weight of tomato plants per pot. But when the superphosphate was mixed with manure and then applied to the soil, 30 grams of dry weight resulted. The organic matter in the manure combined with soluble iron and aluminum, thus reducing a tie-up of iron and aluminum with phosphorus. As a consequence, more phosphorus was available for plant growth. This research was conducted in Vermont.

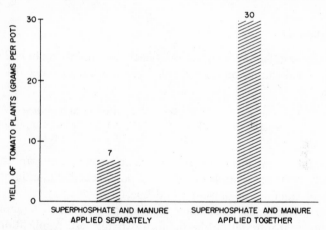

FIG. 19.7.   The yield of tomato plants when superphosphate was applied separately as compared with the yield when superphosphate and manure were applied together. (All superphosphate was applied at the rate of 200 pounds of P_2O_5 per acre, and manure at the rate of 20 tons per acre.) (A. R. Midgley and David E. Dunklee, "The Availability to Plants of Phosphates Applied with Cattle Manure," Vermont Agr. Exp. Sta. Bul. 525, 1945.)

Nutrients in Feed and Manure

From her feed, the dairy cow returns a large percentage of plant nutrients to the manure. When corn is fed, approximately 75 per cent of the N, 80 per cent of the P_2O_5, and 90 per cent of the K_2O is returned in manure (Figure 19.8).

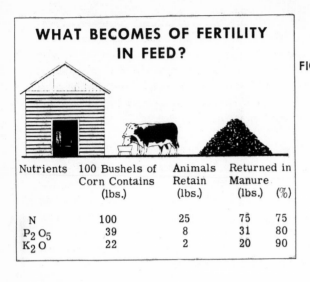

WHAT BECOMES OF FERTILITY IN FEED?

Nutrients	100 Bushels of Corn Contains (lbs.)	Animals Retain (lbs.)	Returned in Manure (lbs.)	(%)
N	100	25	75	75
P_2O_5	39	8	31	80
K_2O	22	2	20	90

FIG. 19.8. From 75 to 90 per cent of the N, P_2O_5, and K_2O in corn is returned to the soil in manure. (C. M. Linsley, "Manure Is Worth Money, It Deserves Good Care," Illinois Agr. Extension Service Cir. 595, 1953.)

Poultry Manure

The average laying hen produces each year approximately 33 pounds of manure, calculated on an oven-dry basis. Without litter, the manure analyzes: *

NITROGEN (%N)	PHOSPHORUS (%P_2O_5)	POTASSIUM (%K_2O)	CALCIUM (%$CaCO_3$)	MAGNESIUM (%$MgCO_3$)	BORON (p.p.m.B)
1.47	1.15	0.48	2.5	0.4	5

A hen in a year therefore produces manure containing approximately 0.5 pounds of N, 0.4 pounds of P_2O_5, 0.2 pounds of K_2O, and appreciable amounts of calcium, magnesium, and boron.

Most laying houses in winter have a strong odor of ammonia. This is evidence that nitrogen in the manure is being lost. Applications on the litter of two pounds per day of superphosphate per 100 birds will reduce nitrogen losses approximately one-half.

Other materials have been used for reducing losses of ammonia from poultry manure. In order of effectiveness, from most to least, these are: superphosphate, quicklime, gypsum, and peat moss.†

On an oven-dry basis, fresh turkey manure has an average chemical composition as follows: **

* Stanley Papanos and B. A. Brown, *The Care and Use of Poultry Manure,* Storrs Agr. Exp. Sta., INF-13, 1950.
† Wasley, Yushok, and Firman E. Bear, *Poultry Manure,* New Jersey Agri. Exp. Sta. Bul. 707, 1943.
** J. W. White, F. J. Holben, and A. C. Richer, *Production, Composition, and Value of Poultry Manure,* Pennsylvania Agr. Exp. Sta. Bul. 469P, 1944.

| NITROGEN | PHOSPHORUS | POTASSIUM |
(%N)	(%P$_2$O$_5$)	(%K$_2$O)
1.31	0.71	0.49

A mature turkey each year produces approximately 40 pounds of manure. On the basis of the analysis given here, each year a turkey produces manure containing 0.5 pound of N, 0.3 pound of P$_2$O$_5$, and 0.2 pound of K$_2$O. For comparison, the manure produced by hens and turkeys contains the same number of pounds of N and K$_2$O per bird per year, but hen manure contains more phosphorus.

Both hen manure and turkey manure are low in potash. When used on land to be seeded to legumes or root crops, manure should be reinforced with approximately 25 pounds of K$_2$O per ton.

Rabbit Manure

Rabbit manure is a valuable fertilizer, analyzing higher in percentage of N, P$_2$O$_5$, and K$_2$O than any other common manure.

In a year, a doe with her four litters produces approximately 90 pounds of manure, calculated on an oven-dry basis. Without straw or hay refuse, the manure will analyze as follows: *

| NITROGEN | PHOSPHORUS | POTASSIUM |
(%N)	(%P$_2$O$_5$)	(%K$_2$O)
2.4	1.4	0.6

On this basis, manure produced by a doe and her young during a year contains 2.2 pounds of N, 1.3 pounds of P$_2$O$_5$, and 0.5 pound of K$_2$O. A dry doe or herd buck produces approximately one-half of these amounts.

Manure as a Mulch on Corn

In a three-year test in Ohio, ten tons of manure per acre as a surface mulch increased the yield of corn an average of ten bushels more per acre than did the same amount of manure plowed under. The increased yield resulting from the mulch was attributed to (1) a protection of the soil from beating raindrops, (2) more water entering the soil for use by the corn, (3) a better structure that permitted corn roots to obtain more oxygen, and (4) a cooling effect of the mulch.

Manure and Available Water

At the Rothamsted Experiment Station near London, England, 14 tons of barnyard manure per acre per year was applied for 100 years. A similar plot received no manure. The results show that the plow layer of

* George S. Templeton, *Value and Use of Rabbit Manure,* United States Dept. of Agr. A. H. D. No. 89, 1946.

the manured plot is capable of supplying 0.7 more inches of available water for crops than the plot which received no manure.

Manure and Crop Yields

Such crops as corn and alfalfa respond readily to applications of manure, both in humid regions and in arid regions under irrigation.

Corn that received 5 tons per acre of manure in Michigan produced 46 bushels, as compared with 35 bushels per acre with no manure. An application of 10 tons of manure gave 49 bushels and 15 tons resulted in a corn yield of 51 bushels on each acre. The first 5-ton application was the most efficient per ton of manure (Figure 19.9).

Under irrigation in the state of Washington, 6 tons of manure per acre resulted in an increase of 9 bushels of corn. Reinforcement of the manure with superphosphate gave an increase of 17 bushels per acre over the check plot.

Irrigated alfalfa responded to manure in a manner similar to corn.

BUSHELS OF CORN PER ACRE

FIG. 19.9. Yield of corn in relation to the amount of manure applied. (L. M. Turk and A. G. Weidemann, "Farm Manure," Mich. Agr. Extension Bul. 300, 1949.)

Approximately a 1,000-pound increase in alfalfa was due to a manure treatment of 6 tons per acre. Manure reinforced with superphosphate resulted in yields over the check plot of 3,000 pounds of alfalfa hay.*

Dollar Value of Manure

The average value of the increase in crop yields was computed for several long-time rotations in Minnesota. With rates of 6 to 10 tons of manure per acre, a rotation of barley—hay—hay—potatoes resulted in crop increases valued at $7.30 per ton of manure applied. In a rotation of corn—wheat—barley—hay, the increase in crops was valued at only $2.00 per ton of manure used. Five other rotations gave increases in between

* L. E. Dumm and L. C. Wheeting, *Utilization of Barnyard Manure for Washington Soils*, Wash. Agr. Ext. Bul. 267, 1941.

these figures. The average increase in value of crops per ton of manure applied for seven rotations was $4.20.*

Organic Matter and Soil Structure

As organic matter decomposes, certain glue-like substances are released which tend to create more water-stable aggregates in the soil. This is desirable.

The aggregating influence of sawdust, cow manure, alfalfa hay, and wheat straw is presented by a line graph in Figure 19.10. These organic substances were incubated with a loam soil for a period of 200 days and their ability to stabilize soil aggregates larger than 50 millimeters in diameter was measured.

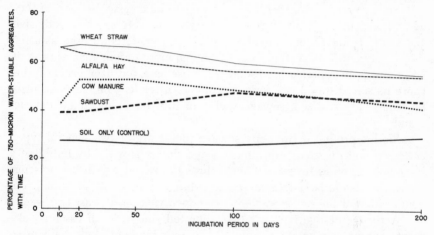

FIG. 19.10.   The effect of certain organic materials on aggregation of Declo loam. (Each organic material was applied in concentrations of 2 per cent.) (J. J. Doyle, "Organo-Clay Relationships in Soil Aggregate Formation." Ph.D. Thesis, Ohio State University, 1952.)

Wheat straw was most efficient in soil aggregation, followed by alfalfa, cow manure, and sawdust.

Compost

A desirable, weed-free substitute for well-rotted manure can be made and will be ready for use within a year. Grass clippings, garden weeds, hay, garbage, tree leaves, sawdust, and peat, together with soil, sod, lime, and fertilizers, can be used in making a compost pile.

* Harold E. Jones, *Barnyard Manure*, Minnesota Agr. Extension Folder 168, 1954.

Alternate layers of various organic materials should be piled in six-inch depths until a height of five feet is reached. The best width is four feet. As the various layers of organic materials, soil, fertilizers, and lime are applied, the sides of the pile should be as vertical as possible and the top depressed to absorb the rain.

As alternate layers of organic materials are put in the pile, lime and fertilizers are added to hasten decomposition and to reinforce the compost. The recommended amounts per ton of dry organic material are:

Dolomitic limestone	60 lb.
Ammonium nitrate	40 lb.
Superphosphate	30 lb.

Sewage Sludge

Most countries consider human wastes to be an essential part of their agriculture; in the United States even the idea often seems repulsive. Especially in the Orient human excreta (night soil) is all used as a fertilizer; without it, starvation would be much more serious than at present.

Sewage in America has found some use as a fertilizer primarily because its safe disposal is a serious problem. After its value as a fertilizer becomes fully realized, sewage will probably be in much greater demand.

Sludge produced from city sewage plants are of two general types, *activated* and *digested*. Activated sewage sludge is made by bubbling a large volume of air for several hours through raw sewage in the presence of aerobic bacteria. Digested sewage sludge consists of anaerobic decomposition of the raw sewage in large open vats for at least two weeks.

Activated sludge is richer than digested sludge in all essential elements except manganese (Table 19.1). Both kinds of sludge are especially high in percentage of zinc. There is almost no potassium in either kind of sludge, because it is leached out by the large quantities of water used in their processing.

Sawdust

There are millions of tons of sawdust that could be used as a mulch, bedding material, compost, or for direct application to the soil. Although some sawdust is now being used for these purposes, a greater knowledge of its properties will result in its expanded use.

As a fertilizing material, sawdust ranks very low. A comparison of its nutrient content with that of wheat straw and alfalfa is given in Table 19.2. Sawdust contains 4 pounds of N, 2 pounds of P_2O_5, and 4 pounds of K_2O per ton of material, on an oven-dry basis. Sawdust is richer than wheat straw only in its calcium content. Alfalfa is from 5 to 15 times as plentifully supplied with the essential elements as is sawdust.

TABLE 19.1.   Essential Elements in Activated and Digested Sewage Sludge *

Kind of Sludge	Nitrogen (N) %	Phosphorus (P$_2$O$_5$) %	Potassium (K$_2$O) %	Zinc (Zn) ppm	Copper (Cu) ppm	Manganese (Mn) ppm	Boron (B) ppm	Molybdenum (Mo) ppm
Activated	5.6	5.7	Trace	2,500	916	134	33	16
Digested	2.4	2.7	Trace	2,459	643	262	9	6

* M. S. Anderson, "Composition of Sewage Sludge as Influenced by Type of Disposal System." A Paper Presented Before the Soil Science Society of America, Davis, California, 1955.

TABLE 19.2.   The Principal Plant Nutrients in Sawdust, Wheat Straw, and Alfalfa Hay in Pounds Per Ton of Dry Material *

Organic Material	Nitrogen (N) (Lb.)	Phosphorus (P_2O_5) (Lb.)	Potassium (K_2O) (Lb.)	Calcium ($CaCO_3$) (Lb.)	Magnesium ($MgCO_3$) (Lb.)
Sawdust	4	2	4	11	1
Wheat Straw	10	3	12	7	2
Alfalfa Hay	48	10	28	50	15

* F. E. Allison and M. S. Anderson, *The Use of Sawdust for Mulches and Soil Improvement,* U. S. D. A. Cir. 891, 1951.

Sawdust as a mulch is usually a good practice if certain precautions are used. Blueberries and strawberries especially are benefited by a sawdust mulch. To decrease the tie-up of available soil nitrogen, approximately 25 pounds of N should be mixed with each ton of dry sawdust used.

As a bedding material to absorb liquids, sawdust is a satisfactory product. Depending on its fineness, sawdust is capable of absorbing from two to five pounds of water per pound of sawdust. This compares with three pounds of water absorbed for each pound of chopped hay.

Sawdust is often used in a garden to make fine-textured soils more easily worked. This is a desirable practice if weathered sawdust is used and if at least 25 pounds of N per ton of sawdust is first added. Sometimes it is desirable to use small amounts of a phosphorus fertilizer to overcome the possible tie-up of phosphorus by the decomposing bacteria. Sawdust has very little influence on soil acidity. (Fig. 19.11)

FIG. 19.11.   Wood chips can be economically made in some areas; they can be used in ways similar to sawdust. (New Hampshire) *Courtesy Soil Conservation Service.*

Wood chips are available in some areas and can be used in a way similar to that for sawdust.

Summary

Manure contains the greatest fertilizing value when it is fresh; this means that manure should be applied to the land as soon as possible after it is produced. When it can't be spread immediately, manure should be stored in a compact, moist pile under shelter until it is used.

Losses in storage are higher in the summer because of increased bacterial activity. It is therefore more urgent to spread manure daily in warm weather than it is in cool weather.

Nitrogen is lost readily as ammonia when manure is improperly stored. Losses of ammonia can be reduced by adding superphosphate to manure. The recommended amount is two pounds of 20 per cent superphosphate in the gutter per cow per day. If the superphosphate is added to the manure pile or to manure after it is loaded on the manure spreader, approximately 50 pounds of superphosphate per ton is recommended.

In addition to reducing losses of ammonia, the superphosphate reinforces the manure to make it a better-balanced plant nutrient and decreases phosphorus tie-up by the soil.

Greater efficiency per ton of manure is obtained when manure is applied in small amounts and more often. Approximately ten tons per acre on every acre each year will result in greater increases in crop growth than will 20 tons per acre every other year.

The returns per ton of manure are higher when manure is used on infertile and eroded soils than when used on the best soils. By contrast, commercial fertilizers usually respond best on good soils.

The use of manure and other organic materials improves soil structure, increases the available water capacity of soils, and increases crop yields.

Compost, sewage sludge, and sawdust are good sources of organic matter, and their use will increase in proportion to the information available concerning their value.

Questions

1. What is the average chemical composition of cow manure?
2. When manure is exposed to the weather for a few months, approximately what per cent of its nutrients are lost?
3. Explain the three reasons for reinforcing manure with phosphorus.
4. Compare the chemical composition of hen manure, turkey manure, and rabbit manure.
5. Explain the use of manure as a mulch.
6. Why do organic materials improve soil structure?

7. What determines the dollar value of manure?

8. Describe the construction of a compost pile.

9. How does the chemical composition of sewage sludge compare with that of hen manure?

10. Why is it necessary to add nitrogen and sometimes phosphorus fertilizer to sawdust before it is used?

References

Lyon, T. L., H. O. Buckman, and N. C. Brady, *The Nature and Properties of Soils.* The Macmillan Co. New York. 1950.

Millar, C. E, and L. M. Turk, *Fundamentals of Soil Science.* John Wiley and Sons, Inc. New York. 1951.

Our Land and Its Care. The National Plant Food Institute. Washington, D.C. 1955.

Soils and Men, The Yearbook of Agriculture for 1938. United States Department of Agriculture.

20

Management of Mineral Soils in Humid Regions

Good soil management in humid regions includes these practices:

1. Liming the soil according to the results of a soil test. The ideal conditions are assumed to be a pH of 6.5, an exchangeable base saturation percentage of 80, and an exchangeable hydrogen percentage of 20. The exchangeable bases are recommended to consist of 65 per cent calcium, 10 per cent magnesium, and 5 per cent potassium.

2. Selecting a cropping system that will give the soil a rest from cultivation for as long a period as possible. This system should include perennial legumes and grasses that are productive as well as protective. Alfalfa, birdsfoot trefoil, bromegrass, and orchardgrass are good examples of excellent legumes and grasses for protecting the soil, building desirable structure, and producing excellent yields of nutritious forage.

3. Preserving all organic residues by leaving them on the surface of the soil for as long as possible. The residues from tall-growing crops, such as corn stalks, should be either shredded or disked down close to the surface of the soil. Being closer to the soil, cornstalks will offer more protection from beating raindrops.

4. Spreading all manure over the fields as soon as possible after it is produced. If this is not feasible, pack the manure in a sheltered manure pit and spread as soon as possible.

5. Keeping livestock and machinery off wet, fine-textured soils to reduce soil compaction. Pasture pans and tillage pans restrict the movement of water and plant roots and result in lowered crop yields.

Cropping Systems and Soil Conditions

The best soil structure is maintained when land is kept in continuous grass. In some places, a farmer can make a good living from the land when it is used only for the production of grass; at other places, he must raise such cultivated crops as cotton and corn. Cultivation always destroys desirable soil structure, causing soil compaction and a decrease in beneficial water relations in the soil. As a consequence, crop yields decline. Practical management provides some cropping system that permits cultivated crops to be grown in rotation with sod crops. (Figures 20.1, 20.2)

FIG. 20.1.   Both soils were in a good rotation of corn—wheat—hay for 10 years. Two years before these photos were taken, the soil in photo "b" was planted to corn—soybeans, while the soil in photo "a" remained in the corn—wheat—hay rotation.
Courtesy Edward Strickling, Maryland Agricultural Experiment Station.

FIG. 20.2. Soil from various long-time cropping systems in Illinois: No. 1, virgin sod; No. 2, rotation of corn—oats—clover—wheat (clover); No. 3, rotation of corn—corn—corn—soybeans.
Courtesy Illinois Agricultural Experiment Station.

TABLE 20.1. The Effect of Cropping Systems on Yield of Corn, Density of the Plow Layer, and the Percolation Rate *

Cropping Systems	Yield of Corn (Bu. per Acre)	Density of the Plow Layer (Lb. per Cu. Ft. Oven-Dry Basis)	Percolation Rate of Water (Inches per Hour)
Continuous Grass	—	69	8.4
Corn—Oats—Clover—Wheat (Clover)	59	80	3.2
Corn—Corn—Corn—Soybeans	44	87	0.2

* C. A. Van Doren and A. A. Klingebiel, "Effect of Management on Soil Permeability," *Soil Science Society of Amer. Proceed.* 16, 1952.

Table 20.1 gives the results in Illinois of cropping systems on the yield of corn in relation to the density of the plow layer and the percolation rate of water through the soil.

The plow layer under continuous bluegrass weighed 69 pounds per cubic foot, on an oven-dry basis. This is in contrast to 80 pounds for the soil planted to corn—oats—clover—wheat (clover), and 87 pounds per cubic foot for the soil in the corn—corn—corn—soybeans rotation. The two cropping systems result in an increase in soil density of more than 16 and 26 per cent, respectively.

Water moved through a column of soil under continuous grass at the rate of 8.4 inches per hour. Through the soil supporting the corn—oats—clover—wheat (clover) rotation, water moved at the rate of 3.2 inches per hour. Through the soil supporting a corn—corn—corn—soybeans rotation, water moved only 0.2 inch per hour.

Cropping Systems and Losses of Nitrogen

In a 24-year study of soil nitrogen levels in relation to cropping systems, Missouri reports that continuous rye turned under caused a loss of soil nitrogen (Table 20.2). A corn—wheat—clover rotation produced a gain of 20 pounds of N per acre during the 24-year period. The greatest gain of N was with a system of continuous red clover, with no forage removed; here the soil increased 660 pounds of N per acre.

TABLE 20.2   Changes in the Nitrogen Content of Surface Soils During a 24-Year Period Under Different Cropping Systems * (1917-1941)

Cropping Systems	Pounds of N Lost Per Acre During 24 Years	Pounds of N Gained Per Acre During 24 Years
Rye, turned under	640	———
Corn—Wheat—Clover	———	20
Corn—Wheat—Clover, manured	———	140
Rye—cowpeas, turned under	———	280
Red Clover, taken off	———	340
Alfalfa, taken off	———	440
Bluegrass sod, nothing taken off	———	500
Red Clover, turned under	———	660

* M. F. Miller, *Studies in Soil Nitrogen and Organic Matter Maintenance,* Missouri Agr. Exp. Sta. Bul. 409, 1947.

Legumes in Rotation

In southeastern Kansas, near Columbus, the average annual precipitation is 42 inches, with May and June as the months with the highest rainfall. Experiments have been conducted on fertility and crop rotation since 1924. A 24-year average of crop yields following a legume are compared with relative yields of the same crops following a nonlegume. The experimental results are reproduced graphically in Figure 20.3.

Oats following a legume produced 6 per cent higher yields; wheat, 9 per cent higher; corn, 32 per cent higher; and flax, 44 per cent more

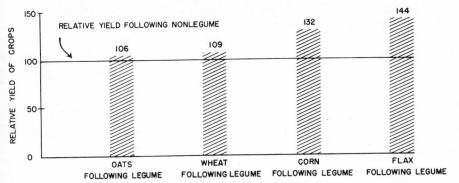

FIG. 20.3. The relative yield of crops following a legume compared with yields following a nonlegume (Kansas). (Average annual precipitation, 42 inches.) (F. W. Smith, F. E. Davidson, and V. H. Peterson, "Soil Fertility Investigations at Columbus Experimental Field, 1924-1954," Kan. Agr. Exp. Sta. Bul. 372, 1955.)

yield after a legume. These data substantiate the results of many experiments which indicate that corn and flax are excellent crops to follow legumes in the rotation.

Fertilizer and Lime Needs of Potato Soils

Irish potatoes are a short-season crop that require a very high state of fertility. Research on the fertility needs of potatoes in northern Maine (Aroostook County) helps us to understand some of the problems encountered in the production of a crop that has been heavily fertilized for many years. Under these conditions it was found that phosphorus and potassium had accumulated to a level approximately six times that in the original forest soil. But even with this build-up, annual applications of phosphorus and potassium continue to give satisfactory increases in the yield of potatoes.

Table 20.3 presents the results of research in Maine on the fertility status of potato soils in relation to the original forest soils. Approximate fertilizer, lime, and cropping systems are recommended, confirmed by field experiments.

Readily soluble phosphorus in potato soils has been increased almost six times the level found in the original forest soil. But even with this build-up, phosphorus applications of 160 pounds of P_2O_5 (800 pounds of 20 per cent superphosphate) per acre per year is the general recommendation for maximum potato production.

TABLE 20.3.   The Comparative Fertility Status of Potato Soils
and the Original Forest Soils, and the Approximate Fertilizer
Recommendations (Aroostook County, Maine) *

Nutrient	Major Use of Land	Amount in Surface 6 Inches (Lb. Per Acre)	Approximate Recom. for Maximum Yields of Potatoes. (Lb. Per Acre Per Year)
Readily Soluble Phosphorus (P_2O_5)	Potatoes	198	160
	Forest	34	——
Exchangeable Potassium (K_2O)	Potatoes	386	200
	Forest	68	——
Exchangeable Calcium (CaO)	Potatoes	1974	None
	Forest	1136	——
Exchangeable Magnesium (MgO)	Potatoes	183	None
	Forest	137	——
PH	Potatoes	5.06	None
	Forest	4.76	——
Organic Matter	Potatoes	5.15%	Rotate potatoes with oats, clover, and timothy.

* Arthur Hawkins, Joseph A. Chucka, and A. J. MacKenzie, *Fertility Status of Potato Soils of Aroostook County, Maine, in Relation to Fertilizer and Rotation Practices,* Maine Agr. Exp. Bul. 454, 1947.

Exchangeable potassium levels in potato soils has also increased to nearly six times the potassium in original forest soils. In spite of this reserve, approximately 200 pounds of K_2O per acre per year is recommended.

Both the exchangeable calcium and exchangeable magnesium in potato soils are only slightly greater than those in the nearby forest soils. Neither has the pH increased appreciably. Because of the hazard of potato scab, it is not desirable to lime the soil when the pH is above 5.0, as is the case under these conditions.

The organic matter in potato soils averaged 5.15 per cent. This appears very high for organic-matter levels in cultivated fields over the

United States, but it is not high for fine-textured soils in northerly latitudes. To maintain the organic matter content and the desirable soil structure, it is recommended to rotate potatoes with oats, clover, and timothy.

Long-Time Fertility Trends

Many field experiments of long duration give a good indication of what happens to the productive ability of a soil over the years. Research on two contrasting soils for 35 years in Illinois is of extreme interest.

The relative amounts of the nutrients supplied by the soil and by man on two contrasting soils is diagrammatically shown in Figure 20.5.

FIG. 20.4. An aerial view of the oldest agricultural experiment in the world, the Broadbalk Field in the Rothamsted Experiment Station, Harpenden, England. Parts of this field have been growing wheat continuously since 1843. Yields per acre of wheat have averaged as follows: No fertilizer, 13 bu.; manure, 32 bu.; complete fertilizer, 34 bu.

Used with written permission.

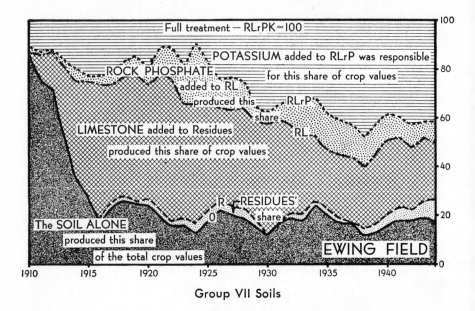

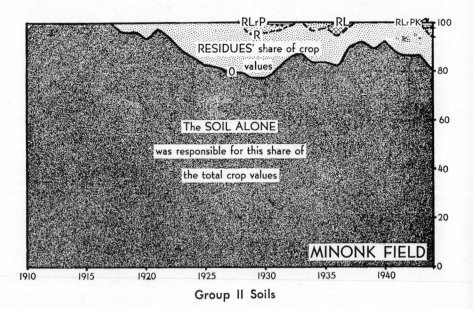

Legend: R—Crop residues; L—Limestone; rP—Rock phosphate; K—Potassium.

FIG. 20.5.   The relative amounts of nutrients supplied to all crops from native and applied sources by an infertile soil (**above**) and a fertile soil (**below**) in Illinois. (F. C. Bauer et al., "Effects of Soil Treatment on Soil Productivity," Illinois Agr. Exp. Sta. Bul. 516, 1945.)

An infertile soil, classified as Group VII, is compared in its crop-producing ability with the soil in Group II, a productive soil.*

During the 35 years of the experiment, three facts were significant:

1. Over the years, the infertile soil contributed a progressively smaller share of nutrients for crops, while crop residues, lime, and commercial fertilizers contributed an increasing share. After the first five years of tillage, the poor soil contributed only about 20 per cent of the total nutrients needed for crop production. After the first 15 years, potassium fertilizers became increasingly important.

2. During the first five years, the good soil alone was responsible for the total crop. No lime or fertilizers were necessary. From the fifth year, crop residues supplied from 10 to 20 per cent of the total nutrients needed by crops. At no time during the 35-year period did lime or fertilizers contribute more than 5 per cent toward total crop production.

Summary

To maintain desirable productivity in humid regions, the soils for most crops should be limed to approximately a pH of 6.5, a cropping system should be selected that includes perennial legumes and grasses, all organic residues and manures should be preserved, and livestock and heavy machinery should be kept off fine-textured soils when they are wet.

Continuous grass maintains the best soil structure. Soil nitrogen can be maintained when legumes and grasses occupy the land at least two-thirds of the time. Crops such as corn and flax appear to be able to utilize legume residues better than oats and wheat can.

On potato soils in Maine, even though the present soil is approximately six times as great in phosphorus and potassium as the original forest soil, annual applications of these fertilizers continue to result in increased yields of potatoes.

A productive soil is capable of supplying as much as 80 per cent of all essential needs for the growth of plants for as long as 35 years of cropping. An infertile soil supplied these essentials for a period of only five years:

Questions

1. Name the essentials of good soil management in humid regions.
2. What are the results of continuous tillage on soil conditions?

* Group II are fertile soils and are very dark-colored, fine-textured soils, with moderately permeable subsoils and with calcium carbonate existing at a shallow depth. Group VII are infertile soils. They are gray and strongly leached, with very slowly permeable subsoils and with an occasional slick spot.

3. How much reduction in percolation rate can be expected under a rotation of corn—corn—corn—soybeans?

4. What seems to be a desirable cropping system to maintain soil nitrogen?

5. What crops respond best after legumes?

6. What crops respond the least following legumes?

7. Approximately how much increase in phosphorus and potassium was found in Maine potato soils?

8. With a build-up in phosphorus and potassium reserves, why are annual applications of these fertilizers still recommended?

9. What is the hazard of liming potato soils when the pH is above 5.0?

10. Compare the long-time results of using a productive and a nonproductive soil in Illinois.

References

Climate and Man, The 1941 Yearbook of Agriculture.

Millar, C. E., *Soil Fertility*. John Wiley and Sons. New York. 1955.

Soils and Men, The 1938 Yearbook of Agriculture.

21

Management of
Peat and Muck Soils

The total acreage of peat and muck soils in the United States is approximately 79 million. These organic soils are found scattered over most of the nation, but large bodies exist in the Southeast, the Great Lakes region, and the Pacific Coast region. The largest continuous area of organic soils lies adjacent to Lake Okeechobee in the Florida Everglades.

There is no common agreement among soil scientists regarding a definite criteria for determining whether a soil is classified as a mineral soil, a peat, or a muck. In general, it is assumed that at least one foot of organic matter must be present for it to be classified as an organic soil. In broad terms, a *peat* consists of recognizable plant remains; but if the organic matter is decomposed beyond recognition, it is called a *muck*.

Origin of Peats and Mucks

Peat and muck soils have accumulated in place from centuries of plant remains that have been preserved because they were covered with water. The condition of continuous saturation with water resulted in a deficiency of oxygen for rapid decomposition.

Peat and muck soils usually start forming around the edges of shallow lakes. Water hyacinths commonly grow as floating vegetation; then in water four to five feet deep, water lilies develop from a large, fleshy root anchored in the mud but with long upright stems extending to the water surface, where the leaves float. In water two or three feet deep, such plants as cattails grow and continue to fall into the water to add to the total organic matter for making a peat or muck soil. In even shallower water, shrubs like the button willow, black willow, cypress, and tupelo

271

FIG. 21.1. In the North, sphagnum moss is responsible for the creation of many acres of peat soils. (New York)

Courtesy Cornell Agricultural Experiment Station.

gum are common. A hardwood forest may then appear on sites that are better drained.

This plant succession is common throughout the southern part of our nation. Along the northern border, a common succession of plants, from deep to shallow water are:

Leatherleaf and bog rosemary—sphagnum moss—black spruce—yellow birch—hemlock—upland hardwoods and conifers. (Figure 21.1)

Classification of Peat

There are three principal kinds of peat, based upon the origin of the plant residues. These kinds are:

Sedimentary Peat—derived from such plants as water lilies, water hyacinths, and cattails.

Fibrous Peat—derived mainly from sedges and mosses.

Woody Peat—derived mostly from the roots, stems, and branches of trees and shrubs.

Organic Soils of the Florida Everglades

The Florida Everglades is primarily a saw grass peat marsh and covers 4,000 square miles; it is probably the largest body of organic soils in the world. In general, the peat deposits vary from a few inches to approximately 10 feet in depth, and most of them rest on limestone.

Many acres of the peat soils of the northern Everglades are used intensively to produce sugar cane and vegetable crops. Under cultivation are 85,000 acres, one-fourth of which is in sugar cane and three-fourths of which is planted to such vegetables as onions, cabbage, tomatoes, peppers, and beans. There are an additional 20,000 acres in the southern Everglades, approximately one-fourth of which are planted to citrus orchards, including oranges, lemons, and grapefruit.

Soils in the Everglades have been derived from several kinds of organic materials and are underlaid by porous limestone. The soils are classified into three major soil types, as follows:

1. Okeechobee muck.
2. Okeelanta peaty muck.
3. Everglades peat (Table 21.1 and Figure 21.2).

TABLE 21.1.   The Principal Organic Soils of the Florida Everglades and Their Characteristics *

Soil Type	Characteristics	Organic Matter %	Native Vegetation
Okeechobee muck	Dark gray to black mixture of decomposed organic matter and mineral matter over brown, felty fibrous peat	30-65	Custard apple
Okeelanta peaty muck	Dark gray to black, finely fibrous, well-decomposed organic matter over black, colloidal, plastic muck over brown, fibrous peat	65-85	Sawgrass, willow, and elder
Everglades peat	Black, finely fibrous, well-decomposed organic material over brown, felty, fibrous peat	85-92	Sawgrass

* *Soils, Geology and Water Control in the Everglades Region,* Florida Agr. Exp. Sta. Bul. 442, 1948.

A cubic foot of Everglades peat has an oven-dry weight of approximately 15 pounds, or one-fourth the weight of water.

The Uses of Peat

Besides its use as a field soil for raising such crops as onions, cabbage, cranberries, carrots, and other specialized crops, peat has many other uses. When dug out and dried, certain kinds of peat are desirable for use in nurseries and greenhouses, mainly because of its property of holding water in amounts as much as ten times its dry weight. Where the

FIG. 21.2. Most peat and muck soils in Florida are shallow over porous limestone.
Courtesy Florida Agricultural Experiment Station.

cost is competitive with other materials, peat is also used as a bedding for livestock, a poultry litter, and a mulch for certain flowers, shrubs, and vegetables.

Peat consists of plant remains which have been preserved because water has reduced the rate of aerobic decomposition. Under the right conditions of a slow rate of decomposition in combination with pressures within the earth, peat is gradually changed to lignite, lignite to bituminous, and bituminous to anthracite coal.

To only a limited extent in the United States, but in large amount in many European countries, peat is used as a fuel. Ireland, Belgium, England, Holland, and Germany burn considerable quantities of peat for heating their homes.

Adapted Crops

When peat and muck soils exist in large areas, are satisfactorily drained, and are properly limed and fertilized, excellent yields of many crops can be obtained on them. An excellent quality of many kinds of grasses for hay, such as reed canarygrass and bromegrass, can be grown on some peat and muck soils. Irish potatoes, onions, celery, cabbage,, carrots, and peppermint are the principal crops grown on organic soils in the northern areas of the United States. In Florida, the main crops are sugar cane, onions, cabbage, tomatoes, peppers, and beans. When properly managed, the crop yield per acre is usually higher on peats and mucks than on adjacent mineral soils.

Fertilization and Liming

Most peat and muck soils are extremely low in potassium and somewhat deficient in phosphorus. For this reason, a 0-10-30 fertilizer is in common use.

Acid peats and mucks are also usually deficient in calcium, magnesium, boron, copper, and zinc. Calcium and magnesium are usually supplied as dolomitic limestone, boron as borax or borate, copper as copper sulfate, and zinc as zinc sulfate.

Alkaline organic soils often need additional manganese, boron, copper, and zinc. Manganese is usually applied as manganese sulfate, copper and zinc as their sulfates, and boron as borax or borate. When the soils are strongly alkaline, sulfur will make them less alkaline. Sulfur deficiency has also been reported on some muck soils.

Crops growing on organic soils commonly respond to an application of 500 pounds of common salt (sodium chloride) per acre.

Even though there is approximately two per cent total nitrogen in muck soils, which releases ammonia and nitrates upon decomposition, early crops on muck soils often need a nitrogen fertilizer. This condition may be explained by the fact that muck soils are wet and cold in the spring and they warm very slowly. As a result, bacterial decomposition of the muck is very slow at this season and a soluble nitrogen fertilizer is usually needed to hasten growth.

Water Control

Almost all organic soils need artificial drainage as well as subsurface irrigation to make them most productive. The usual procedure is to install gates on the main drainage ditches and thereby maintain a specified level of the water table. A water table maintained at an average depth of two feet is desirable for most crops. To maintain the water table at this depth, tile lines should be approximately four feet deep and the water level in the open ditches maintained at about three feet. The explanation is that peats and mucks drain so slowly that between the drainage lines, the water table is a foot or more nearer the surface.

Subsidence

Most organic soils are artificially drained before they are used for growing crops. Lowering the water table causes shrinkage and speeds the decomposition; the result is a settling or subsidence of the surface. The rate of subsidence is approximately the same whether the soil is virgin land or land cropped to sugar cane, vegetables, or forage crops.

Subsidence of organic soils in Florida and Indiana is summarized in Figure 21.3. Subsidence is directly related to the height of the water table. The reason for this relationship is that water reduces aeration and, hence, retards decomposition.

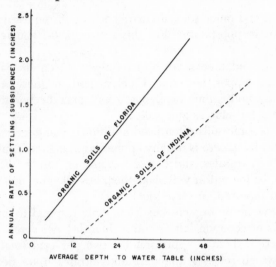

FIG. 21.3.   The relationship of the annual rate of settling (subsidence) to the depth of the water table in organic soils in Indiana and Florida. (Source: **Water:** Yearbook of Agriculture, 1955, p. 706.)

When the water table is maintained at a depth of 12 inches, the average rate of subsidence in Indiana peat is 0.1 inch a year, and in Florida peat, 0.75 inch a year. With a 24-inch water table, the rates are 0.6 inch and 1.5 inches, respectively. A 36-inch water table has average subsidence rates of 1.1 inches a year in Indiana and 2.25 inches in Florida.

Tillage Compaction

Most peat and muck soils are too loose and open to make the best seed bed. Some surface compaction is necessary to improve the germination of seeds. On the other hand, continuous tillage compacts the soil as deep as a foot and often results in a water table too close to the surface for the best root development.

Figure 21.4 indicates the amount and depth of compaction caused by 14 years of tillage as compared with a virgin soil. The pounds of oven-dry soil per cubic foot in the 1- to 6-inch layer of the virgin soil were 9.4. After 14 years of tillage, the weight was 23.0 pounds, or nearly 2½ times as dense. At a depth of 7-12 inches, the virgin soil weighed 6.9 pounds and the cultivated soil 14.4 pounds, or more than 2 times as heavy. Below the 12-inch depth, there was no significant difference in the density of the peat.

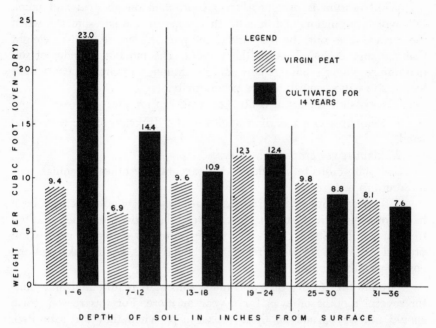

FIG. 21.4. Compaction of Everglades peat due to tillage of virgin soil for 14 years. (B. S. Clayton, et al., "Water Control in the Peat and Muck Soils of the Florida Everglades," Fla. Agr. Expt. Sta. Bul. 378, 1942.)

Because of the lowering of the surface by decomposition and tillage compaction, tile lines may need to be dug out and laid at a lower depth. Sometimes, also, the main ditches must be dug deeper every few years.

Special Problems of Management

It is true that crop yields are usually higher on peats and mucks than on mineral soils, but the problems of management are also greater. In addition to the need for drainage, irrigation, liming, and fertilizing with special nutrients, organic soils also must have extra protection from frost, wind erosion, and ground fires.

Cold air always flows downhill, as does water, and settles in the lowest basins. In these basins the organic soils occur. For that reason, peats and mucks are always subject to more frost hazards than are soils on nearby slopes. The usual method of overcoming frost hazards is to plant such hardy crops as onions, cabbages, lettuce, peppermint, and carrots. The use of smudge pots and special fans to reduce frost damage is not a very common practice on muck soils.

Wind erosion is usually a serious problem on all peat and muck soils which are maintained in cultivated crops. In the late summer, when the surface dries out, the peat and muck particles are so light in weight that the slightest wind moves them about. The moving particles of soil may injure young seedlings and may fill drainage ditches. A continuous loss of soil will seriously reduce productivity.

The possible means of control of wind erosion are:

1. Plant row crops at right angles to the direction of the prevailing wind.

2. Plant cover crops such as rye.

3. Rotate crops to include reed canarygrass or other perennial, sod-forming crops.

4. Use windbreaks at strategic locations. The windbreak may be a hedge of willow trees, scotch pine, white cedar, privet, or other adapted trees or shrubs. Strips of rye at varying intervals also give good wind protection. Wood-slat snow fences are effective as windbreaks, but the cost is usually prohibitive.

Ground fires in dry peat and muck soils start readily and may burn for several months or even for a year or more. For this reason, trash should not be burned on these soils except when they are saturated. Hunters, fishermen, campers, picnickers, and smokers should be warned against the hazard of campfires and the careless use of tobacco in the vicinity of dry organic soils. Once a peat or muck fire has gotten a good start, the only way to stop it is to flood the area by closing the drainage system.

Summary

There are approximately 79 million acres of organic soils in the United States, mostly in the Great Lakes and the Southeast regions. The largest body of peats and mucks lies in the Florida Everglades. These soils have formed from generations of plants which have died and have been preserved by a high water table. Peats are classified into sedimentary, fibrous, and woody.

Organic soils in the Florida Everglades are shallow and are underlain mainly by porous limestone. Sugar cane, onions, cabbage, tomatoes, peppers, and beans are the main crops. Peats and mucks are used for growing many specialized crops. Dried materials are used for their water-absorbing properties in nurseries, greenhouses, poultry houses, and barns. Peat is also used as a mulching material and as a source of fuel.

Peat and muck soils are usually deficient in potassium and some-times in phosphorus, calcium, magnesium, boron, copper, zinc, and manganese.

Nearly all organic soils need both drainage and some form of irri-gation. Usually flood gates are installed in the drainage ditches and subsurface irrigation is practiced.

When organic soils are drained, the surface subsides significantly each year because of oxidation. To reduce excess settling, the water table should be maintained at a depth of approximately two feet. Till-age also tends to lower the level of the surface because of compaction within the first foot of soil.

Organic soils are subject to the hazard of frosts, wind erosion, and ground fires.

Questions

1. Approximately how much land in the United States is classified as peat and muck?
2. Where are most of the organic soils located?
3. How is peat classified?
4. Describe a peat or muck in the Florida Everglades.
5. What are the principal uses of peat?
6. What crops are especially adapted to peat and muck soils?
7. What nutrients are sometimes deficient in organic soils?
8. Of what importance is it to reduce subsidence?
9. How much compaction can be expected from tillage machinery?
10. How can a field be protected from wind erosion?

References

Albert, A. R., and O. R. Zeasman, *Farming Muck and Peat in Wisconsin.* Wis-consin Extension Cir. 456. 1953.

Clayton, B. S., J. R. Neller, and R. V. Allison, *Water Control in the Peat and Muck Soils of the Florida Everglades.* Florida Agr. Exp. Sta. Bul. 378. 1942.

Jones, Lewis A., *Soils, Geology, and Water Control in the Everglades Region.* Florida Agr. Exp. Sta. Bul. 442. 1948.

Lyon, T. L., H. O. Buckman, and N. C. Brady, *The Nature and Properties of Soils.* The Macmillan Co. New York. 1950.

Soils and Men: The Yearbook of Agriculture for 1938. U. S. Department of Agriculture.

Uyl, Daniel Den, *Windbreaks for Protecting Muck Soils and Crops.* Indiana Agr. Exp. Sta. Cir. 287. 1943.

Waksman, Selman A., et al., *The Peats of New Jersey and Their Utilization.* New Jersey Department of Conservation and Development Bul. 55—Part B. 1943.

22

Management of Soils in Arid and Semiarid Regions

This chapter deals with the management problems of soils in arid and semiarid regions. For convenience, the Lime Line in Figure 22.1 will be used to separate the humid from the arid and semiarid regions.

FIG. 22.1. The "Lime Line." Because of low rainfall, soils west of this line accumulate lime in the soil profile; soils east of the line are losing lime by leaching because of high rainfall. In the high-rainfall areas of western Washington, western Oregon, and northwestern California, the soils are similar to those in the East.

The Lime Line was originally drawn by C. F. Marbut, formerly Chief of the Division of Soil Survey, United States Department of Agriculture. In most areas west of this line, lime accumulates in the soil profile; while east of the line, lime tends to leach out of contact with plant roots. As a consequence, most soils east of this line are acid and need lime for the production of many crops. West of the line, frequently so much lime and soluble salts are contained in the soils as to be detrimental to plant growth.

It should be pointed out that many soils west of the Lime Line have developed under humid conditions and are as free of harmful quantities of lime and soluble salts as any in the East. Soils on the western mountain slopes in Washington, Oregon, and California are similar to those in the humid East.

Variation in total annual precipitation along the Lime Line is of interest. In western Minnesota, where the climate is cool, the Lime Line coincides with the 20-inch belt of precipitation. The Lime Line parallels the 25-inch precipitation line in Nebraska and the 30-inch belt in Texas. The explanation of this variation in precipitation along the Lime Line is probably that 20 inches of precipitation in the cool North is as effective in leaching lime downward as is 30 inches in the hot, dry Southwest.

Soils in Arid and Semiarid Regions

Many soils in arid and semiarid regions need only water to make them productive for most crop plants. Supplying water to soils is discussed in Chapter XVII, "Irrigation Practices." Other soils in the West may be *saline* or *alkali* and require special treatment to make them productive.

Saline and alkali soils have been classified by the scientists at the United States Salinity Laboratory in Riverside, California, into *Saline, Alkali,* and *Saline-Alkali* soils.

Saline Soils. Soils are classified as saline if the solution extracted from a saturated soil paste has an electrical conductivity value of 4 or more milli reciprocal ohms per centimeter, usually written as 4 mmhos/cm. at 25°C. This information is obtained on a special salt bridge, patterned after a common Wheatstone bridge. The amount of exchangeable sodium in saline soils is low, being less than 15 per cent; as a consequence, the pH is below 8.5.

For many years saline soils were called *white alkali* by soil scientists as well as by most farmers; now the term is gradually changing to *saline* soils.

Saline soils usually have a surface crust of white salts, especially in the summer, when the net movement of soil moisture is upward. Salts dissolved in the soil water move to the surface, where they are left as a crust when the water evaporates. These white salts are mostly chlorides, sulfates, and carbonates of calcium and magnesium. Owing to the small amount of sodium present, saline soils are in a flocculated condition, and consequently the excess salts can readily be leached below the root zone with irrigation water.

Alkali Soils. The percentage of exchangeable sodium saturation in alkali soils is greater than 15; as a result, the pH is between 8.5 and 10.0. The saline content is below 4 mmhos/cm. at 25°C, as measured on a salt bridge. The former name of these soils was *black alkali,* because they usually are black, owing to the effect of the high sodium content and the dispersal of organic matter. Locally, many of the areas are known as *slick spots,* because, when the soil is plowed slightly wet, it turns over in slick, rubbery furrow slices.

Because of the high sodium content, both the clay and the organic matter are dispersed, and the result is close packing of the soil particles. The close packing of the particles reduces the size and the amount of pore spaces, and as a consequence, water and air will not move through the soil readily. Poor aeration and high sodium content, which is often toxic, make alkali soils difficult to reclaim.

Saline-Alkali Soils. The term "saline-alkali" applies to soils which are both saline and alkali. For example, they have:

1. A conductivity of the saturated extract greater than 4 mmhos/cm. at 25°C.

2. Exchangeable sodium in excess of 15 per cent.

3. A variable pH, depending upon the relative amounts of exchangeable sodium and soluble salts. When soluble salts are leached downward, the pH will rise above 8.5; but when the soluble salts again accumulate, the pH may again fall below 8.5.

Reclamation of Saline and Alkali Soils

Saline soils are relatively easy to reclaim for crop production. The main problem is to leach the salts downward and out of contact with subsequent irrigation water.

Frequently the saline soils have a high water table, a dense gypsum layer, or are fine-textured. These conditions reduce the movement of irrigation water downward and therefore make it difficult to leach the salts to the desired depth. In salty soils with a high water table, artificial drainage is necessary before the excess salts can be removed. Deep chiseling or deep plowing is sometimes used on soils with impervious layers in order to open the soil for the desired downward movement of salt.

The reclamation of alkali soils is another story. In alkali soils, the exchangeable sodium is so great as to make the soil almost impervious to water. But even if water *could* move downward freely in alkali soils, the water alone would not leach out the excess exchangeable sodium. The sodium must be replaced by another cation and then leached downward and out of reach of plant roots.

By cationic exchange, calcium is often used to replace sodium in alkali soils (Figure 22.2). Of all calcium compounds, calcium sulfate (gypsum) is considered the best for this purpose. (Figure 22.3)

1 Too much sodium attached to clay particles tends to make the particles pack together in such a way that water cannot get through.

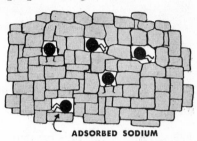

2 Sulfur materials furnish soluble calcium, which replaces the ex-. cess adsorbed sodium.

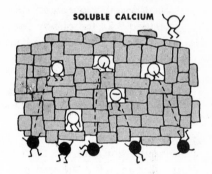

3 This replacement allows the soil particles to group themselves so that larger pore spaces are formed.

Then when the soil is flooded, the water can pass through and wash out excess salts, including sodium.

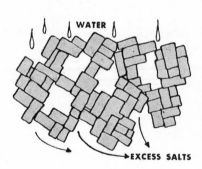

FIG. 22.2.   How soluble calcium reclaims black-alkali soils. (Source: Daniel G. Aldrich, Jr., and W. R. Schoonover, "Gypsum and Other Sulfur Materials for Soil Conditioning," Calif. Agr. Exp. Sta. Cir. 403, 1951.)

FIG. 22.3. Alkali soils contain so much sodium that some of it must be replaced before crops can be grown. Gypsum has frequently been used for this purpose. The center plot received no gypsum and yielded 0.24 ton of hay per acre. Plots on each side received 6 tons of gypsum per acre, and the forage yield was 1.44 tons per acre. In the no-gypsum plot, water moved downward only 7 inches, while in the gypsum-treated plots water moved downward 12 inches. (Nevada)

Courtesy Nevada Agricultural Experiment Station.

Applications of 18 tons of gypsum per acre in Nevada increased water infiltration and increased the depth of water penetration. Three years after applying the gypsum, the water penetrated to a depth of 19

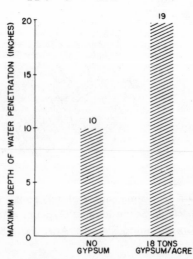

FIG. 22.4. Gypsum increases the infiltration of water in soils. Maximum depth of water penetration from six irrigations. (Clyde E. Houston, et al., "Gypsum for Improving Alkali Soils," Nevada Agr. Exp. Sta. Cir. 7, 1955.)

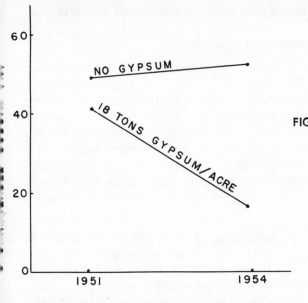

FIG. 22.5. Gypsum reduces the percentage of exchangeable sodium in soils. (Soil was sampled to a 30-inch depth.) (Clyde E. Houston, et al., "Gypsum for Improving Alkali Soils," Nevada Agr. Exp. Sta. Cir. 7, 1955.)

inches in the soil receiving the gypsum, and to 10 inches in the soil which received no gypsum (Figure 22.4). This resulted in a reduction of exchangeable sodium percentage from 42 to 18 per cent during the three-year period. At the same time, the no-gypsum plot gained in exchangeable sodium from 50 to 53 per cent (Figure 22.5). Yields of hay were increased from 0.05 tons to 1.02 tons per acre per year as a result of the application of gypsum (Figure 22.6).

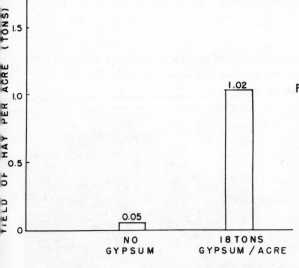

FIG. 22.6. Gypsum increases the yield of hay. (One application three years previously.) (Clyde E. Houston, et al., "Gypsum for Improving Alkali Soils," Nevada Agr. Exp. Sta. Cir. 7, 1955.)

Plants as Indicators of Saline and Alkali Soils

Of the early American soil scientists, Hilgard [*] was among the first to study the intimate relationships between plant response and soil characteristics. Some of his classical work points out the differences in shape and size of loblolly pine in Mississippi growing on "flatwoods," and on well-drained upland soils. Later, in California, Hilgard initiated scientific studies of plant growth in relation to saline and alkali soils.

More recent work in the West has pointed out more relationships between plants and soil properties, especially as indicators of saline and alkali soils. In applying these findings, certain precautions should be taken, as follows:

1. Certain plants have a wide range of adaptation. Some are able to tolerate a high percentage of salt in the soil but also grow in soils low in salt content. Alkali sacaton, saltgrass, and shadscale are good examples of plants able to grow on saline as well as on nonsaline soils.

2. Soils under pure stands of a particular species should be sampled, rather than soils under mixed stands of plants. In mixed stands of plants, the relationship between soils and plants is not so clear-cut.

3. The soil sample for study must be taken with wisdom and care. Large differences may occur in soils in sites only a few feet apart.

Some of the most common indicator plants are as follows:

Mesquite (Prosopis juliflora) (Figure 22.7)
    Usually found on nonsaline soils suitable for agriculture.

[*] E. W. Hilgard, *Soils: Their Formation, Properties, Composition, and Relations to Climate and Plant Growth.* The Macmillan Co., New York, 1911. First copyrighted in 1906.

FIG. 22.7.   Mesquite bushes are found on nonsaline soils that are usually suitable for agriculture when water is available. (Texas)
Courtesy Soil Conservation Service.

Creosotebush (Larrea tridentata)
　　Where stands are good, the soils are usually suitable for crop production.
Sagebrush (Artemisia tridentata)
　　Soils usually adapted to farming.
Shadscale (Atriplex confertifolia)
　　Usually indicates saline or alkali conditions in the subsoil which must be leached before using the land for farming.
Greasewood (Sarcobatus vermiculatus)
　　Indicates a saline or alkali soil which requires leaching.
Saltgrass (Distichlis stricta)
　　Usually grows on poorly drained saline soils which must be drained and leached.
Alkali sacaton (*tussockgrass*) (Sporobolus airoides)
　　In pure stands, it is a good indicator of wet, saline, or saline-alkali soils which need drainage and leaching.

Greasewood—An Accumulator of Salt

In arid regions, plants such as greasewood (Sarcobatus vermiculatus) have the ability to absorb large amounts of salt and to deposit it on the surface of the soil through the decomposition of the salt-laden leaves.[*] The United States Regional Salinity Laboratory at Riverside, California, made a study of the amounts of salts which have concentrated under greasewood bushes in comparison with that in the open. The results are presented in Table 22.1.

TABLE 22.1. The Amount of Soluble Sodium in the Soil Under a Greasewood Shrub Compared with That in a Nearby Open Area.[*]

| Depth (in.) | Soluble Sodium in the Soil [**] | |
	Under Greasewood Shrub %	In Open Area, 28 in. from Edge of Greasewood Shrub %
0-2	52.8	3.0
2-8	22.2	1.8
8-16	19.3	2.2
16-21	14.2	3.2
21-37	17.5	7.9

[*] Source: U. S. Salinity Laboratory data as reported on page 2 of *Soil Physical Conditions and Plant Growth,* edited by Byron Shaw, Academic Press, 1952.

[**] Soil was Antelope Springs silty clay loam at four locations in the Beryl Enterprise Area in Utah.

[*] R. C. Roberts, *Transactions of the 4th International Congress of Soil Science,* Amsterdam, Holland, 1950.

This table indicates that in the first two inches of soil, there is more than 17 times as much sodium under the greasewood shrub as in the nearby open area. Even at a depth of 21-37 inches, there is more than twice the sodium in the soil under the greasewood.

One explanation is that the salt in the deeper layers of the soil and over an extended area where the roots are growing is absorbed by the plant. The salt then goes into the leaves and is deposited on the surface of the soil when the leaves fall and decompose.

This concentration of salt is of extreme importance in the use of such land when irrigated. Soil areas where the greasewood originally grew contain so much sodium as to be toxic to plants. A patched appearance of the crops thus shows for several years, until excess salts are leached away from sites formerly occupied by clumps of greasewood.

Salt Tolerance of Crops

Under some circumstances, it may not be feasible to reduce the salt content of soils to permit the growth of sensitive crops. The alternative is to select crops which are tolerant of salt.

A classification of plants according to their salt tolerance has been made by the staff of the United States Salinity Laboratory at Riverside, California. Table 22.2 shows this list of plants in three degrees of tolerance and by four types of crops; namely, *field crops, forage crops, fruits,* and *vegetables*. In each group, the most tolerant crop is at the top of the list and the most sensitive crop is shown at the bottom.

Of the field crops, barley for grain, sugar beet, and cotton are the most tolerant to salt, while field beans are the most sensitive. Other crops, mainly the small grains, are intermediate in salt tolerance.

Many of the grasses, such as Bermuda-grass and western wheatgrass, are very tolerant of salt. Birdsfoot trefoil is the only legume in the group. Sweetclovers, alfalfa, and many common grasses are intermediate, while white clover, red clover, and Ladino clover are among the least tolerant of the forage crops.

Date palm is the only fruit known to be very tolerant of salty soils. Five fruits are shown in the table to be intermediate in tolerance; namely, pomegranate, fig, olive, grape, and cantaloupe. Most fruits are sensitive to salt concentrations in the soil.

Garden beet, kale, asparagus, and spinach are listed as very salt-tolerant, while radish, celery, and green beans are sensitive. Most vegetables are intermediate in tolerance.

The general salt tolerance of plants is shown in Figure 22.8 in relation to the scale of electrical conductivity. The conductivity of the soil saturation extract is measured in thousandths of reciprocal ohms at a standard temperature (25°C). According to this figure, salt concentra-

TABLE 22.2. Relative Tolerance of Crops to Salt *

High Salt Tolerance	Medium Salt Tolerance	Low Salt Tolerance
	Field Crops	
Barley (grain)	Rye (grain)	Bean (field)
Sugar beet	Wheat (grain)	
Cotton	Oats (grain)	
	Rice	
	Sorghum (grain)	
	Corn (field)	
	Flax	
	Sunflower	
	Castor bean	
	Forage Crops	
Alkali sacaton	Sweetclover, white	White clover
Bermuda-grass	Sweetclover, yellow	Meadow foxtail
Rhodesgrass	Perennial ryegrass	Alsike clover
Rescuegrass	Mountain bromegrass	Red clover
Canada Wildrye	Strawberry clover	Ladino clover
Western wheatgrass	Dallisgrass	
Barley (hay)	Sudangrass	
Birdsfoot trefoil	Sweetclover, Hubam	
	Alfalfa (Calif. common)	
	Tall fescuegrass	
	Rye (hay)	
	Wheat (hay)	
	Oats (hay)	
	Orchardgrass	
	Blue gramagrass	
	Meadow fescue	
	Reed canarygrass	
	Big trefoil	
	Smooth bromegrass	
	Sourclover	
	Fruits	
Date palm	Pomegranate	Pear
	Fig	Apple
	Olive	Orange
	Grape	Grapefruit
	Cantaloupe	Prune

* In each group, the plants named first are more tolerant and the plants named last are more sensitive to salt.

Source: *Diagnosis and Improvement of Saline and Alkali Soils,* U. S. Salinity Laboratory Staff, Agr. Handbook No. 60, U. S. Dept. of Agr., 1954.

TABLE 22.2. (Continued)

High Salt Tolerance	Medium Salt Tolerance	Low Salt Tolerance
		Plum
		Almond
		Apricot
		Strawberry
		Lemon
		Avocado
	Vegetables	
Beet, garden	Tomato	Radish
Kale	Broccoli	Celery
Asparagus	Cabbage	Green beans
Spinach	Cauliflower	
	Lettuce	
	Sweet corn	
	Potato (white rose)	
	Carrot	
	Onion	
	Peas	
	Squash	
	Cucumber	

tions represented by readings of 0-2 have no influence on crop growth, 2-4 restricts the growth of sensitive crops, 4-8 limits many crops, 8-16 restricts most crops, and salt concentrations represented by readings of 16-32 prevent the satisfactory growth of all but the most salt-tolerant of crops.

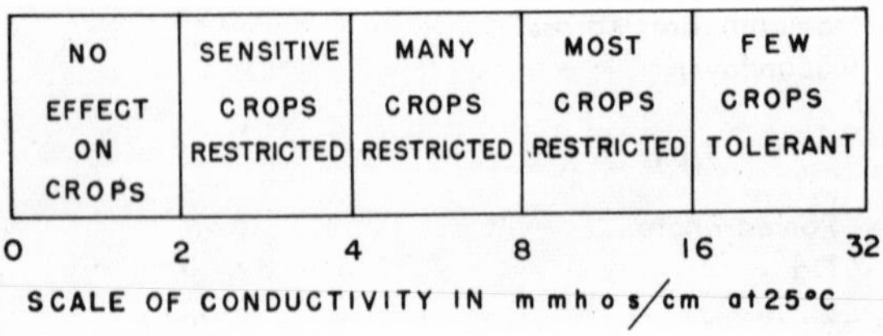

NO EFFECT ON CROPS	SENSITIVE CROPS RESTRICTED	MANY CROPS RESTRICTED	MOST CROPS RESTRICTED	FEW CROPS TOLERANT

0   2   4   8   16   32
SCALE OF CONDUCTIVITY IN mmhos/cm at 25°C

FIG. 22.8. The relationship between the salt content of soils and general crop response. (Source: "Diagnosis and Improvement of Saline and Alkali Soils," U. S. Salinity Laboratory Staff, **Agr. Handbook No. 60.** U. S. Dept. of Agr., 1954.)

Soil Moisture and Crop Response

In arid and semiarid regions, the total annual precipitation is not only small in amount, but it also comes occasionally in such intensity as to encourage runoff. To these factors must be added the high evaporation and transpiration losses which occur because of high summer temperatures, low relative humidities, and rapid wind movement. Water available for plant growth is therefore at a premium, and any management practice which makes better use of existing available water must be adopted.

One practice which is gaining wide acceptance is to determine the depth of water penetration at seeding time and to plant crops accordingly.

At wheat-planting time, in the fall, the soil should be moist to a depth of two to three feet to give satisfactory yields. If there is not this much moisture at that time, it is best not to plant wheat but to wait until spring before planting anything. In the spring, grain sorghum may be grown with a good chance for a successful crop if the soil is moist to a depth of one to two feet at the time that grain sorghum should be planted. If the soil is still too dry for grain sorghum, millet is often planted at a later time if the soil is moist to a depth of approximately one foot. If there is not enough moisture for millet, the field should be fallowed for the summer.

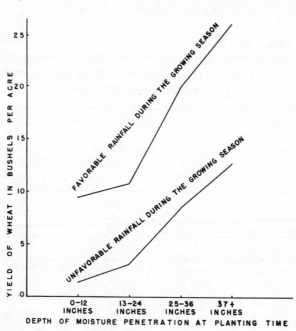

FIG. 22.9.   The yield of wheat in relation to the depth of soil moisture at sowing time (average of 1,107 soils). (H. E. Finnell, "Soil Moisture and Wheat Yields on the High Plains," U. S. D. A. Leaflet No. 247, 1948.)

The reationship between soil-moisture penetration and wheat yields in the 20-inch rainfall belt is shown in Figure 22.9. These data are averaged from 1,107 samples in the Great Plains.

During a growing season of unfavorable rainfall, the yield of wheat was 1.5 bushels per acre when the soil was moist to a depth of 0-12 inches at planting time. When the moisture was 13-24 inches deep, wheat yields averaged 3 bushels, 25-36 inches gave 8.5 bushels, and 37+ inches of soil moisture was responsible for a wheat yield of 12.5 bushels per acre.

Favorable growing-season precipitation gave these results: 0-12 inches of moisture, 9 bushels; 13-24 inches, 11 bushels; 25-36 inches, 20 bushels; and 37+ inches of soil moisture at seeding time, 26 bushels of wheat per acre.

The probability of obtaining specific yields of wheat in relation to the depth of moisture penetration at seeding time is given in Table 22.3. From these data it may be noted that, when the soil was dry at seeding time, a yield of 4 bushels or less of wheat per acre was obtained 71 per cent of the time, 10 bushels or more 18 per cent of the time, and yields of 20 bushels or more were never obtained. These data indicate that it is not a good practice to seed wheat on dry soil.

TABLE 22.3.   The Probability of Obtaining Specific Wheat Yields When the Soil Is Moist to Designated Depths at Seeding Time (Kansas. Av. Annual Precipitation, 18 inches; av. annual evaporation, 57 inches) *

Depth of Moisture Penetration at Time of Planting (feet)	Probability of Obtaining Specific Yields			
	4 bushels or less (%)	10 bushels or more (%)	20 bushels or more (%)	30 bushels or more (%)
0	71	18	0	0
1	34	43	19	0
2	15	62	29	9
3 or more	10	84	70	23

* Source: R. I. Throckmorton and H. E. Myers, *Summer Fallow in Kansas*, Kansas Agr. Exp. Sta. Bul. 293, 1941.

When the soil was moist to a depth of one foot, yields of wheat were 4 bushels or less 34 per cent of the time, 10 bushels or more 43 per cent of the time, and 20 bushels or more only 19 per cent of the time; while in no year was a yield of 30 bushels per acre obtained. This practice of seeding wheat when the soil is wet to only one foot probably does not pay over the years.

Wheat yields obtained when planted on soil which is moist to a depth of two feet probably are economical when the price of wheat is fairly high. During most years, however, wheat should be planted only when the soil at seeding time is moist to a depth of three feet or more.

Cropping Systems

Desirable cropping systems reduce soil and water losses, preserve and restore soil structure, and maintain or increase soil fertility. Deep-rooted crops such as alfalfa and sweetclover help to restore soil nitrogen and organic matter. Grasses such as bromegrass and crested wheatgrass are especially beneficial in improving soil structure.

Specific crop rotations are suggested for South Dakota as follows: *

CORN AREA
(25 inches of average annual precipitation)

First Year: Corn
Second Year: Small grains plus clover *
Third Year: Clover *

First Year: Corn
Second Year: Corn or soybeans
Third Year: Small grain plus clover *
Fourth Year: Clover *

First Year: Corn
Second Year: Small grains plus clover *
Third Year: Small grain
Fourth Year: Alfalfa-brome (2 to 4 years)

First Year: Corn
Second Year: Small grain plus clover *
Third Year: Corn
Fourth Year: Alfalfa-brome (2 to 4 years)
Fifth Year: Clover *

First Year: Corn
Second Year: Small grain plus clover *
Third Year: Corn
Fourth Year: Small grain
Fifth Year: Alfalfa-brome (2 to 4 years)

SMALL-GRAIN AREA
(20 inches of average annual precipitation)

First Year: Small grain
Second Year: Small grain plus sweetclover
Third Year: Row crop

* Leo F. Puhr and W. W. Worzella, *Fertility Maintenance and Management of South Dakota Soils.* South Dakota Agr. Exp. Sta. Cir. 92, 1952.

First Year: Small grain
Second Year: Row crop
Third Year: Small grain plus sweetclover
Fourth Year: Sweetclover °

First Year: Row crop
Second Year: Small grain plus sweetclover plus rye (planted in fall)
Third Year: Clover ° and rye pasture
Fourth Year: Small grain plus sweetclover
Fifth Year: Sweetclover °

First Year: Small grain
Second Year: Row crop
Third Year: Small grain plus sweetclover
Fourth Year: Sweetclover °
Fifth Year: Small grain or row crop

First Year: Small grain
Second Year: Row crop
Third Year: Small grain
Fourth Year: Small grain or row crop
Fifth Year: Small grain
Sixth Year: Alfalfa-brome (2 to 6 years)

RANGE AREA
(15 inches of average annual precipitation)

First Year: Row crop
Second Year: Small grain plus sweetclover
Third Year: Sweetclover-fallow

First Year: Row crop
Second Year: Small grain plus sweetclover
Third Year: Sweetclover-fallow
Fourth Year: Small grain

First Year: Row crop or fallow
Second Year: Small grain
Third Year: Small grain

First Year: Row crop
Second Year: Small grain
Third Year: Row crop
Fourth Year: Small grain plus sweetclover
Fifth Year: Sweetclover-fallow

° Refers to sweetclover or red clover for forage, pasture, green manure, or seed.

Fallow

In areas of 15 to 25 inches of average annual precipitation, it sometimes pays to grow a crop one year and no crop the next year, then back

to a crop the third year. The year no crop is grown the land is called *fallow.*

The main purpose of a fallow system of farming is to store moisture in the soil for use by the next year's crop. Certain soils are capable of storing adequate water in the soil during the fallow year and some are not. Sandy loams with a loam subsoil are capable of absorbing water quite rapidly and yet are able to store fairly large amounts within reach of plant roots. Such a soil should be able to store from one to two inches of available water per foot of soil depth, to at least a depth of three feet.

Figure 22.10 demonstrates the relative yields of wheat and grain sorghum when grown continuously as compared with a rotation of crop-fallow. This work was carried out during the years 1914 to 1939 in central and western Kansas, where the average annual precipitation is 18 inches and the annual evaporation averages 57 inches.

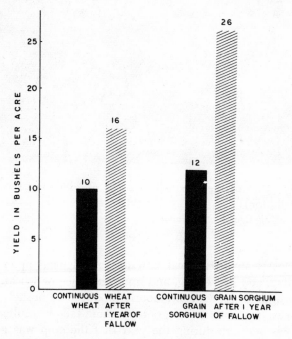

FIG. 22.10. Yields of wheat and grain sorghum when grown continuously as compared with a crop-fallow rotation. (R. I. Throckmorton and H. E. Myers, "Summer Fallow in Kansas," Kansas Agr. Exp. Sta. Bul. 293, 1941.)

Continuous wheat averaged 10 bushels per acre, while the wheat-fallow system yielded 16 bushels per acre the year the wheat was grown.

FIG. 22.11. One of the greatest hazards of fallowing land is erosion.
(Washington)
Courtesy Soil Conservation Service.

Whether this is an economical practice will depend upon the cost of labor, seeding, and harvesting, and upon the price of wheat.

Grain sorghum grown continuously produced 12 bushels of grain per acre per year. The rotation of grain sorghum-fallow resulted in a yield of 26 bushels per acre during the year that the crop was grown. Since more than twice as much grain sorghum was obtained every other year in the grain sorghum-fallow rotation, there is no doubt about the desirability of the practice. In a two-year period, continuous grain sorghum would average 24 bushels, while the grain sorghum-fallow rotation would yield 26 bushels per acre.

Grain sorghum-fallow is therefore a more desirable practice than a wheat-fallow rotation. (Figures 22.11, 22.12)

FIG. 22.12. Fallow land should be maintained in a stubble mulch whenever possible.
Courtesy Minneapolis-Moline Co.

Recent research has indicated that another primary aim of a fallow system, besides moisture accumulation, is an accumulation of available nitrogen.

Summary

Many soils in the West require only water to make them productive; others contain salts and need special treatment. Saline, Alkali, and Saline-Alkali are the names currently used to designate specific soils which need certain management practices before they produce satisfactory crops. Alkali soils are high in exchangeable sodium and need such treatment as gypsum to supply calcium for replacing the sodium.

Certain plants can be used as good indicators of saline, alkali, or saline-alkali soils.

Crops which are very tolerant of salt are barley, sugar beet, cotton, Bermuda-grass, birdsfoot trefoil, date palm, garden beet, and asparagus.

Soil moisture at planting time is a very good indication of crop yields at time of harvest. Cropping systems are restricted in areas with limited rainfall. One cropping system that is fairly common is grain sorghum one year and fallow (no crop) the next year.

Questions

1. Why does the rainfall vary along the Lime Line?
2. Characterize saline soils.

3. Describe alkali soils.
4. What are saline-alkali soils?
5. What kinds of soils can be successfully reclaimed with gypsum?
6. What kind of soil does mesquite land indicate?
7. What kind of land does saltgrass usually grow on?
8. Name five crops that are salt-tolerant.
9. Name five crops that are sensitive to salt.
10. When the soil is moist to a depth of three feet at wheat-seeding time, is it recommended to seed wheat?

References

Diagnosis and Improvement of Saline and Alkali Soils. United States Salinity Laboratory Staff. Agriculture Handbook No. 60. U. S. Department of Agriculture.

Donahue, Roy L., *Our Soils and Their Management.* The Interstate. Danville, Illinois. 1955.

Millar, C. E., and L. M. Turk, *Fundamentals of Soil Science.* John Wiley and Sons. New York. 1951.

Thorne, D. W., and H. B. Peterson, *Irrigated Soils.* The Blakiston Press. New York. 1954.

23

Soil and Plant Diagnosis

Continuously high crop yields are possible only when all essential elements are present in the soil in the right proportions and in adequate amounts. Such a balance between the nutrient needs of the crop and the ability of the soil to supply the nutrients at the right time is usually very difficult to maintain. Soil testing, tissue testing, and plant nutrient-deficiency symptoms aid in diagnosing the cause of low crop yields. Soil tests help to estimate the supply of available nutrients; tissue tests are an aid in finding the current limiting nutritional factor in plant growth; while plant-deficiency symptoms indicate extreme shortages of certain essential elements.

Valuable information can be obtained from soil tests and tissue tests, and from observing plant deficiency symptoms. But none of these diagnostic techniques can supply answers to unsatisfactory plant growth when the cause is dry weather, compacted soils, low temperatures, high temperatures, diseases, or insect damage.

How to Obtain a Soil Sample for Chemical Testing

Soil samples may be collected at any time of the year. If a single composite sample is to represent an entire field, it should be taken from at least ten places well distributed over the area. Composite samples should be used for testing, except that soils from different types should not be mixed. Samples from knolls, slopes, and low portions of the field will give entirely different results. Testing such samples separately may furnish information of much practical value.

Soil augers are suitable for obtaining soil samples, but a spade or trowel is more commonly used. With a spade or trowel, a vertical cut is made to a depth of from six to eight inches, and a thin slice down the face of this cut taken for the sample. Any grass or trash on the surface

FIG. 23.1. A spade, a soil auger, and a soil-sampling tube are desirable implements for collecting a soil sample for chemical testing.
Coutesy Farmstead News, The Stan-Steel Corporation.

should be removed before the sample is taken. The individual samples to be composited should be mixed, all soft clods and lumps broken, and stones, hard clods, and trash removed. A pint of soil is sufficient to keep for testing. Samples should be air-dried but not dried by means of artificial heat. (Figure 23.1)

Dust from gravel and limestone roads is known to materially affect the adjacent soil, especially its pH and available phosphorus content. This effect often extends 300 feet or more away from the road and should be taken into consideration in sampling. Areas adjacent to such roads should be sampled separately and not composited with other portions of the fields. In sampling pasture land and fields where stock have been kept, avoid locations near the entrance where the stock are likely to congregate.

The testing of the subsoil as well as surface soil may be desirable, especially for acidity. In general, subsoils tend to be much more deficient in available phosphorus than surface soils. Soil tests indicate whether available potash supply in subsoils is higher or lower than that in surface soils.

For each soil test made, a teaspoonful or less of soil is used. From this sample interpretations are made covering areas containing millions of pounds of soil. This fact emphasizes the necessity for a careful taking of the soil sample to be used for chemical testing.

Soil Testing

Each of the 48 states in the nation has a state-supported soil testing service. In addition, many states have county laboratories which operate as branch services for the central laboratory. In 1950 the total soil samples tested by these agencies numbered in excess of 1,200,000 yearly.

Many private commercial laboratories test soils. In 1951 more than 80 such laboratories existed in the United States.

Based upon the soil tests, lime and fertilizer recommendations are made in a variety of ways from state to state. In some states, one person at the central laboratory makes all of the recommendations; in another, the county agents make them.

Half of the states make no charge for soil testing, while in the other half the fee varies from approximately 50 cents to $2.00 per sample. Many fertilizer companies operate a soil testing laboratory, and the service is usually free.

Plant-Tissue Tests

Even though a soil test shows adequate amounts of essential elements, at any one time the plant may not have a balanced nutrition. Wet weather, dry weather, cool weather, or hot weather may cause poor plant growth even when the soil is fertile. A tissue test aids in plant diagnosis under these conditions.

Nitrogen enters the roots in the ammonium and the nitrate form. These nutrients are transported through the conducting tissue to all parts of the plants where they are needed as building materials for protein. Nitrate concentration is highest in the roots and the lower parts of the stalk and decreases toward the top of the plant and the tips of the leaves. During the daytime, when photosynthesis is active, less nitrate is in the plant because a large proportion is used in making protein. In testing a plant for nitrate, start with the lower stalk and work up until the test shows no more nitrate. Intensively fertilized crops, such as tobacco and tomatoes, have normally such a high nitrate content that no tests of the stem are necessary. Variations from field to field can be found only by testing the upper parts of the plant.

Phosphorus enters the plant mainly as $H_2PO_4^-$. While all parts of the plant contain some phosphorus, it is concentrated in the seed. It follows from this that phosphorus will be relatively abundant between the roots and the seed-bearing part and will be present in much smaller quantities elsewhere.

Potassium serves a different role in the plant from that of nitrogen and phosphorus. Besides aiding in the reduction of nitrates and in the formation of proteins, its main function is to stimulate the synthesis of carbohydrates and other compounds of which it is usually not a part. Potassium will concentrate, therefore, mostly in the parts where photosynthesis is most active, that is, in the leaves and the green parts of the stems. Very little of the potassium in the plant enters into insoluble compounds, and the majority of it remains in the mobile form and is detected by the plant-tissue test. This is in contrast to nitrogen and phosphate, of which only a fraction is in the mobile, detectable form at any one time.

Deficiency Symptoms in Corn *

Nitrogen. When young corn plants lack sufficient nitrogen, they are stunted and spindling in appearance. The leaves become greenish-yellow to orange-yellow in color, and the tip ends gradually die. When nitrogen deficiency occurs later in the growth of corn, yellowing of the tissues occurs first in the older leaves and follows the midribs from the tip. Later, the tip begins to dry and the whole leaf may become involved— a condition which is frequently referred to as "firing." Most people think "firing" is due directly to dry weather, but this is not true. Many times corn plants will "fire" to the ears without ever wilting. When corn plants

* N. D. Morgan, "Starved Plants Show Their Hunger," *Better Crops With Plant Food Magazine*, November, 1948.

need more moisture, they will be wilting from the top to the bottom, and not just "firing" on the lower leaves.

Phosphorus. When corn plants show no nitrogen deficiency and no potash deficiency but have a retarded rate of growth and slow maturity, the trouble is usually phosphorus deficiency. The plants are spindling and dark green in color. The leaves and stems may become purplish.

FIG. 23.2. **Left:** Normal apple leaf. **Right:** Magnesium - deficient leaf.
Courtesy Ed Rasmussen, New Hampshire Extension Service.

Potassium. The first symptom of potassium deficiency is a diminution in the rate of growth of the seedlings and young plants. The young leaves become yellowish-green to yellow. The edges and tips become dry and appear scorched. This marginal scorch is the outstanding leaf symptom. Ears produced on plants deficient in potash are usually nubbins, with the tip ends of the ears unfilled. The kernels that do form are poorly formed and poorly matured, becoming easily infected with ear-rot organisms.

Magnesium. The symptoms of magnesium deficiency are definite and easily recognized. With severe magnesium deficiency, a slight yellow streaking develops between the parallel veins in the older leaves. There is a definite and sharply defined series of yellowish-green, light-yellow, or even white streaks extending the entire length of the leaves. These streaked tissues may dry up and eventually die.

Deficiency Symptoms in Small Grains

Nitrogen. Oats and barley which need more nitrogen are usually erect and spindling, the leaves are yellowish-green to yellow, and the stems are purplish-green. In the case of wheat, the plants are stunted and yellowish-green in color. In nitrogen-starved leaves, the tissues dry out from the tip toward the base.

Phosphorus. Slow growth and lack of stooling are the common signs of phosphorus starvation, particularly when the plants are dark green in color and apparently otherwise healthy.

Potassium. The common symptoms of potassium deficiency in small grains is the "edge-scorch." In the early stages of growth, the tips and margins of the older leaves turn yellow and then brown, and finally die. A deficiency of potassium results in weak stem development in small-grain plants as they approach maturity.

Deficiency Symptoms in Cotton

Nitrogen. Nitrogen-deficiency symptoms in cotton are characterized by relatively little growth and a yellow-green color of the foliage. The older leaves are the most severely affected: they dry up and are shed prematurely.

Phosphorus. The most outstanding deficiency symptom for phosphorus is a dark green color of the foliage and a generally dwarfed type of plant.

Potassium. The most common symptom of potassium deficiency in cotton is what is commonly known as "cotton rust." The first symptom in the leaf is a yellowish-white mottling. The leaf color changes to light yellowish-green, and yellow spots appear between the veins. The centers of these spots die and numerous brown specks occur at the tip, around the margin, and between the veins. The tip and the margin of the leaf break down first and curl downward. As the trouble continues, the whole leaf finally becomes reddish-brown in color, dries, and is shed prematurely. As a result of this condition, the cotton bolls are dwarfed and immature.

Magnesium. The characteristic magnesium deficiency in cotton is a purplish-red leaf with green veins. Late in the season, magnesium deficiency is sometimes confused with age or maturity, although the latter is apt to be orange-red, rather than purplish-red. Magnesium-deficiency symptoms appear first on the lower leaves.

Boron. Boron-deficiency symptoms first appear in the terminal growth. The terminal buds often die and may produce dwarfed, many-branched plants. At a low boron level, cotton squares become chlorotic, the bracts flare open, and the buds drop from the plants.

Manganese. Manganese deficiency is characterized by a yellowish-gray or reddish-gray color in young leaves.

Deficiency Symptoms in Legumes

Nitrogen. A deficiency of nitrogen results in slow growth, a decrease in branching of the plant, and smaller plants at maturity. Severe deficiency often causes mild chlorosis, in which the leaves become pale green. The chlorosis generally spreads evenly over the entire leaf. The affected foliage usually appears first at the base of the plants, but it shows up almost simultaneously in other parts, usually toward the tips of branches or the main stem. Nitrogen-starved leaves remain chlorotic for a week or more, while the plant as a whole makes no apparent growth. The normal green color is immediately restored upon the addition of nitrogen.

It is generally assumed that the addition of nitrogen to legume plants is not advisable, but on soils very low in fertility a small application of nitrogen to young legume plants may be beneficial.

Phosphorus. Phosphorus deficiency in legume plants is usually exhibited by slow growth, with the plants remaining small and poorly developed. Flowering and seed production tend to be delayed and a bluish-green tinge may develop in the leaves, but there are no positive symptoms for phosphorus deficiency.

Potassium. Of all the symptoms observed in legumes, those of potassium deficiency are probably the most outstanding and most easily recognized.

Broad-leaved legumes, such as the soybean, quickly show evidence of insufficient potassium by irregular yellow mottling around the edges of the leaflets. The chlorotic areas soon merge, forming a continuous yellow border around the tip and along the sides, but rarely around the base. Death of the chlorotic area follows promptly, along with downward cupping of the leaf edges. Then the dead tissue falls out, giving the leaf a ragged appearance. The marginal firing often spreads to include half or more of the area of the leaf while the center and base are still green.

The other common legumes have symptoms similar to those of the soybean, especially in the latter stages of potassium starvation. In the early stages in alfalfa, sweetclover, white clover, Persian clover, and hop clover, the yellowing is preceded by the appearance of numerous very small white or yellowish dots arranged more or less in a crescent around the tips of the leaflets. Progress of potassium deficiency from this point on resembles that in the soybean, except that there is less tendency for the symptoms to start at the base of the plant and move upward. All parts of these plants are affected almost simultaneously.

Magnesium. Magnesium deficiency in legumes varies with the species. In the soybean and the cowpea, the areas between the main veins become pale green and then yellow, while the area along the veins remains green. Magnesium deficiency has not been observed on many legumes.

FIG. 23.3. Alfalfa plant on the left is normal, while the two on the right exhibit boron deficiency, a whitening of the terminal leaves. *Courtesy Pacific Coast Borax Co.*

Boron. Boron deficiency has been observed on a number of legumes. The symptoms are affected somewhat by external conditions. In the Central States, the most pronounced symptom is red coloration, sometimes with a purplish tint, affecting first the margins of the tip half of the leaf. The abnormal color extends to the entire leaf surface, including the veins; the leaf tips first affected usually die. In western and southern United States, boron deficiency in alfalfa is known as "white top."

Deficiency Symptoms in Truck Crops

Nitrogen. The major symptom of nitrogen deficiency in truck crops is very slow growth, followed by a change in color. The green color of the leaves becomes lighter than normal, fading through shades of green to pale yellow. From a yellowish green, the color of the veins may change to a deep purple, which is accentuated on the under sides of the leaves. The stems may become hard and fibrous, and they, too, may become deep purple in color with severe nitrogen deficiency.

Phosphorus. The symptoms of phosphorus deficiency in vegetable crops are slow growth and delayed maturity. An early symptom in tomatoes is the development of a reddish-purple color on the under side of the leaf. The color in the web of the leaf may first appear in spots and later spread over the entire leaf, with the veins finally becoming reddish-purple. The stems are slender and fibrous. The leaves are small and the plant is late in setting fruit.

Potassium. A deficiency of potassium is recognizable by a change of color in the vegetative parts as a whole and the occurrence of spots caused by the breaking down of the tissues. In soils extremely low in potassium, the symptoms may appear in the seedling stage; but in those with supplies that are moderate yet not sufficient to support normal growth to maturity, potassium deficiency may not appear until the fruiting stage. In soils with medium content of potassium and an abundant supply of nitrogen, potassium-deficiency symptoms may develop after a period of rapid growth. Where there is a moderate supply of potassium in the soil, potassium starvation may appear first at the middle of the plant and work upward; but in very deficient soils, the symptoms usually appear first in the older leaves at the base of the plants.

Potassium-starved tomato plants grow slowly, are stunted, and have a low yield. The young leaves become finely crinkled. Older leaves have an ashen grayish-green color at first, developing a yellowish-green color along the margins. The injury progresses from the margin toward the center of the leaflet, causing a bronzing of the tissue, which is followed by the development of large, light-colored spots between the larger veins. The affected areas often turn a bright orange color and frequently become brittle. The leaves turn brown and finally die. The stems become hard and woody and remain slender.

Bronzing along the margins of the leaves of most vegetable crops is a common potassium-deficiency symptom.

Boron. Boron deficiency in tomatoes is indicated by a yellowing of the tip of the leaflet, accompanied by a pinkness of the veins. The leaves later become orange and then die. In celery, a cracking of the stem occurs. An internal breakdown or rotting of the stem on cabbage and cauliflower usually develops when boron is deficient. In cauliflower, the curd becomes brown and watersoaked in appearance.

Magnesium and manganese. In tomatoes and most broad-leaved plants, magnesium deficiency is characterized by a yellowing of the tissue between the veins. The areas along the veins remain green, making them stand out in outline. The deficiency tends to show up first on the lower, older leaves. Manganese deficiency often shows a pattern similar to that of magnesium deficiency, but the former is more likely to appear on the upper, younger leaves.

Plant Symptoms on Saline and Alkali Soils

In semiarid regions, bare spots in a field planted to a crop may indicate the presence of a salt content of the soil sufficiently high to kill germinating seedlings. Plants that are growing adjacent to the bare spots may be normal if the salt content is not excessive, or they may exhibit unique symptoms typical of many plants on saline soils.

Plants stunted because of a high salt content in the soil are usually blue-green in color with a waxy coating on the leaves. The leaves of alfalfa, sugar beet, the cabbage family, and some grasses and clovers generally develop a blue-green appearance when growing on saline soils.

Chlorosis is common in plants growing in saline soils, but it is not a specific symptom of salinity. Soils high in calcium carbonate, or irrigation waters rich in bicarbonate, often cause chlorosis in plants.

The tips of some leaves of plants growing in saline and alkali soils exhibit a scorched or burned appearance. While the exact cause of the leaf-tip burn is not known, an analysis of the leaves usually shows a high content of chlorine or sodium or both. Some of this work is summarized in Table 23.1.

TABLE 23.1.   Approximate Concentrations of Chlorides and Sodium in Leaves Which Exhibit Leaf-Tip Burn *

Crop	Concentration in Leaves Showing Tip Burn Chlorides (Per Cent)	Sodium (Per Cent)
Plum	0.6	0.3
Pecan	0.6	——
Avocado	0.5 to 0.9	0.5
Grape	0.5 to 1.2	——
Peach	1.0	——
Grapefruit	1.0 to 1.5	——
Orange (Valencia)	1.0 to 1.5	——
Cotton	——	0.2
Almond	——	0.3 to 0.4

* *Diagnosis and Improvement of Saline and Alkali Soils*, U. S. Salinity Laboratory Staff, Agriculture Handbook No. 60, pp. 63-65, 1954, U.S.D.A.

Plum and pecan appear to show leaf-tip burn injury at chloride concentrations in the leaves as low as 0.6 per cent. The avocado, grape, and peach are less sensitive, in the order named. Leaves of citrus such as grapefruit and Valencia orange do not show tip-burn symptoms until the chloride content reaches from 1.0 to 1.5 per cent.

Not all leaves are sensitive to high chloride concentrations. Normal leaves of Irish potatoes have been observed that contain as much as 5 per cent chlorides.

Leaf-tip burn is exhibited in cotton when the sodium content of the leaves is only 0.2 per cent. Less sensitive to sodium injury are plum, almond, and avocado, in this order.

Correlation of Soil Tests, Plant-Tissue Tests, and Plant-Deficiency Symptoms

On the Jordan Soil Fertility Plots in Pennsylvania, a study was made of the soil tests, tissue tests, and plant-deficiency symptoms of corn, all in relation to each other.* The results of these correlations are summarized:

Nitrogen. An excellent correlation was found between tissue tests and deficiency symptoms. No soil test for nitrogen correlated with either tissue tests or deficiency symptoms.

Phosphorus. There was a highly significant correlation among soil tests, tissue tests, and deficiency symptoms.

Potassium. Significant correlations existed among all tests for potassium.

Portable Soil-Testing Kits

There are many soil-testing kits now on the market which are advertised as being useful for the backyard gardener as well as for the farmer. These kits range in price from a dollar or more for pH units to $100 for more elaborate apparatus for testing for most of the essential elements.

All kits have merit and should give desirable results if used on certain kinds of soils according to specific directions. Some of the more common soil-testing kits, together with the addresses of the manufacturers, are shown in Table 23.2.

TABLE 23.2. Common Soil-Testing Kits and Their Manufacturers

Name of Kit	Manufacturer
Hellige-Truog	Hellige, Inc., 3718 Northern Blvd., Long Island City, 1, N. Y.
La Motte	La Motte Chem. Products Co., Towson 4, Maryland
Simplex	The Edwards Laboratory, Box 2742, Cleveland, Ohio
Urbana	The Urbana Laboratories, 406 N. Lincoln Ave., Urbana, Illinois
Sudbury	Sudbury Laboratory, Box 765, South Sudbury, Mass.
Purdue	Agronomy Department, Purdue Univ., Lafayette, Indiana

Under controlled experimental conditions in Florida, all of the soil-testing kits listed in Table 23.2 were used on several soils and the adequacy of each type of kit was recorded.** Three soil types were used in the test: (Table 23.3)

* A .C. Richer and B. N. Driskell, *Correlation of Plant Tissue Tests of Corn Deficiency Symptoms and Soil Analyses on the Jordan Fertility Plots,* Pennsylvania Agr. Exp. Sta. Bul. 560, 1952.
** Ernest L. Spencer and J. R. Beckenbach, *The Value of Soil Testing Kits in Vegetable Crop Production,* Florida Agr. Exp. Sta. Cir. S-48, 1952.

TABLE 23.3. Sensitivity of Each of Six Soil-Testing Kits to Specified Levels of Nitrates and Exchangeable Potassium, in Pounds Per Acre 6 inches [1]

Kit	Nitrate Nitrogen			Exchangeable Potassium		
	between 10 and 25 *	between 25 and 40 **	between 10 and 40	between 50 and 100 *	between 100 and 150 **	between 50 and 150
Hellige-Truog	Adequate	Adequate	Adequate	Adequate	Adequate	Adequate
Lamotte	Inadequate	Inadequate	Inadequate	Adequate	Adequate	Adequate
Simplex	Inadequate	Adequate	Adequate	Inadequate	Adequate	Adequate
Urbana	Inadequate	Adequate	Adequate	Inadequate	Adequate	Adequate
Sudbury	Inadequate	Inadequate	Inadequate	Inadequate	Inadequate	Inadequate
Purdue	——	——	——	Inadequate	Adequate	Adequate

* Sensitivity desired.
** Sensitivity necessary for satisfactory performance.
[1] Ernest L. Spencer and J. R. Beckenbach, *The Value of Soil Testing Kits in Vegetable Crop Production,* Florida Agr. Exp. Sta. Cir. S-48, 1952.

1. Leon fine sand, pH 6.0.
2. Bradenton fine sandy loam, pH 5.8.
3. Parkwood fine sandy loam, pH 7.3.

The sensitivity of each of the six soil-testing kits for differentiating between specified fertility levels of nitrates and exchangeable potassium is seen in Table 23.3. From Table 23.3 it is readily seen that, under the conditions of this experiment, the Hellige-Truog soil-testing kit appears the most sensitive. No other kit was sufficiently sensitive to differentiate between 10 and 25 pounds of nitrate nitrogen per acre-6 inches. For the exchangeable potassium, the Hellige-Truog and the Lamotte kits were the most sensitive.

All soil-testing kits have inherent weaknesses which must be recognized before they can be used successfully. These weaknesses are:

1. The difficulty of keeping the glassware chemically clean
2. The problem of contamination and deterioration of the reagents
3. The hazard of properly interpreting the results in terms of necessary lime and fertilizer

Summary

Soil testing, tissue testing, and plant nutrient-deficiency symptoms are fairly well correlated and aid in diagnosing the cause of low crop yields. Directions must be carefully followed for taking a soil sample for chemical testing. All states now offer a soil-testing service either at no charge or at a charge not to exceed $2.00 per sample.

Plant-tissue tests are frequently necessary even though a soil test has been made. Weather conditions may be abnormal, resulting in slow plant growth, and the difficulty can be readily diagnosed with the aid of tissue tests.

Each group of plants has specific deficiency symptoms which are caused by a shortage of an essential element. There are also characteristic plant symptoms that indicate the presence of saline and alkali soils.

Portable soil-testing kits have different degrees of sensitivity and hazards in their satisfactory use.

Questions

1. Under what conditions will soil tests, tissue tests, and plant-deficiency symptoms *not* supply satisfactory answers?
2. Briefly describe how to take a sample of soil for chemical testing.
3. How common is soil testing?
4. Under what conditions will a tissue test greatly supplement soil-test information?
5. In corn, compare the deficiency symptoms of nitrogen and potassium.

6. Describe a plant that is stunted because of a high salt content in the soil.
7. What crop is injured least by a high chloride content of the leaves?
8. Why would you expect a soil test for nitrogen to correlate very poorly with either a tissue test or nitrogen-deficiency symptoms?
9. What soil testing kit would you recommend for use on sandy soils in Florida?
10. Name the main hazards of using a portable soil-testing kit.

References

Bear, Firman E., et al., *Hunger Signs in Crops.* The American Society of Agronomy and the National Fertilizer Association. Washington, D.C. 1949.

Donahue, Roy L., *Our Soils and Their Management.* The Interstate. Danville, Illinois. 1955.

Kitchen, Herminie B., ed., *Diagnostic Techniques for Crops and Soils.* The American Potash Institute. Washington 6, D.C. 1948.

Peterson, J. B., et. al., *Soil Testing in the United States.* Prepared by the Soil Test Work Group of the National Soil and Fertilizer Research Committee. U.S.D.A. 1951.

Richards, L. A., ed., *Diagnosis and Improvement of Saline and Alkali Soils.* U.S.D.A. Agr. Handbook No. 60. 1954.

APPENDICES

A

Glossary *

ABC Soil. A soil with a distinctly developed profile, including A, B, and C horizons.

AC Soil. A soil having a profile containing only A and C horizons and no clearly developed B horizon.

Absorption. The process by which a substance is taken into and included within another substance, such as the intake of water or nutrients by plants.

Accelerated Erosion. Erosion more rapid than natural, normal, or geological erosion, resulting from the activities of man or animals.

Acidity, Active. The activity of hydrogen ion in the aqueous phase of a soil. Its activity is measured and expressed as a pH value.

Acidity, Potential. The amount of exchangeable hydrogen ion in a soil that can be rendered free or active in the soil solution by cationic exchange.

Acid Soil. A soil with an acid reaction (below pH 7.0).

Actinomycetes. A general term applied to a group of organisms intermediate between the bacteria and the true fungi, usually producing a branched mycelium and which sporulate by segmentation of the entire mycelium or, more commonly, by segmentation of special terminal hyphae.

Adsorption. The increased concentration of ions or molecules on a surface, including exchangeable cations and anions on the surface of soil practices.

Aerate. To impregnate with a gas, usually air.

Aeration, Soil. The process by which air and other gases in the soil are renewed. The rate of soil aeration depends largely on the size and number of soil pores and on the amount of water clogging the pores.

* Sources: (1) *Preliminary Report of Definitions Approved by Committee on Terminology*, Soil Science Society of America, 1954. (2) Official Publication of the Association of American Fertilizer Control Officials. No. 9, 1955. (3) *Diagnosis and Improvement of Saline and Alkali Soils*. U. S. Salinity Laboratory Staff. Agr. Handbook No. 60. U.S.D.A., 1954.

Note: Also useful is: *Soil and Water Conservation Glossary*, The Soil Conservation Society of America, Des Moines, Iowa.

Aerobic. (1) Living or active only in the presence of molecular oxygen.
(2) Pertaining to or induced by aerobic organisms, as aerobic decomposition.

Aggregate. A group of soil particles cohering so as to behave mechanically as a unit.

Aggregation. The process of forming aggregates.

A Horizons. *See* Soil horizons.

Alkaline Soil. Any soil that is alkaline in reaction (above pH 7).

Alkali Soil. An alkali soil has either so high a degree of alkalinity (pH 8.5 or higher) or so high a percentage of exchangeable sodium (15 per cent or higher) or both that the growth of most crop plants is reduced. Thus, alkali soils, as a group, have a wide range of exchangeable sodium and of pH.

Alkalization. A process whereby the exchangeable sodium content of the soil is increased.

Ammonification. Production of ammonia as a result of the biological decomposition of organic nitrogen compounds.

Anaerobic. (1) Living or active in the absence of molecular oxygen. An obligately anaerobic organism thrives only in the absence of air or free oxygen, while a facultatively anaerobic organism is capable of living in either the absence or presence of air or free oxygen.
(2) Pertaining to, or induced by anaerobic organisms, as anaerobic decomposition.

Antibiotic. An organic compound produced by microorganisms or higher plants which in sufficient concentration will kill or inhibit growth of certain other organisms.

Apparent Density. *Obsolete: See* Bulk density.

Apparent Specific Gravity. *Obsolete: See* Bulk density.

Artificial Manure. *See* Compost. In European and Asiatic usage, may denote commercial fertilizers.

Atmosphere, Standard. A unit of pressure defined as follows:
1 atmosphere at sea level (20°C) =
1.013×10^6 dynes per sq. cm.
14.71 pounds per square inch
76.39 cm. of mercury column
1,036 cm. of water column
34.01 ft. of water column

Autotrophic. Capable of utilizing carbon dioxide as a source of carbon and of obtaining energy for the reduction of carbon dioxide and other life processes from the oxidation of inorganic elements or compounds, e.g. sulfur, hydrogen, ammonium, and nitrite salts, or from light. Contrast with *heterotrophic*.

Azonal Soils. Soils without distinct genetic horizons.

BC Soil. A soil with a profile having no A horizon.

Bedrock. Solid rock either underlying soils or exposed at the surface.

Bench Terrace. Terrace with steep drop on the downhill side; used on very steep slopes.

B Horizons. *See* Soil horizons.

Biological Interchange. The interchange of elements between organic and inorganic states in a soil or other substrate through the agency of biological activity. It results from biological decomposition of organic compounds and the liberation of inorganic materials on the one hand (mineralization) and the utilization of inorganic materials in the synthesis of microbial tissue on the other (immobilization). Both processes commonly proceed continuously in normal soils.

Biological Mineralization. The conversion of an element occurring in organic compounds to the inorganic form as a result of biological decomposition.

Bleicherde. The light-colored, leached, A_2 horizon of Podzol soils.

Bog Iron Ore. Impure ferruginous deposits developed in bogs or swamps by the oxidizing action of algae, bacteria, or the atmosphere on iron carried in solution.

Bottomland. *See* Flood plain.

Broad-Base Terrace. A low, wide terrace used on gentle slopes.

Buffer Compounds, Soil. The clay, organic matter, and such compounds as carbonates and phosphates, which enable the soil to resist appreciable change in pH value.

Bulk Density, Soil. Mass per unit bulk volume of soil that has been dried to constant weight at $105°C$. When expressed as grams per cubic centimeter, bulk density is numerically equal to these terms which are now largely obsolete: *Apparent density, apparent specific gravity,* and *volume weight.*

Buried Soil. Soil usually covered by a deposit of considerable depth.

Calcareous Soil. Soil containing sufficient calcium carbonate (often with magnesium carbonate) to effervesce visibly when treated with cold 0.1 N hydrochloric acid.

Caliche. Layers near the surface, more or less cemented by secondary carbonates of calcium or magnesium precipitated from the soil solution. It may be soft, thin soil horizons or hard, thick beds just beneath the solum or exposed at the surface by erosion.

Canopy (Forestry). In a forest, the cover of green leaves and branches formed by crowns of all the individual trees. Its density is ordinarily expressed as the amount (or percentage) of the ground that would be completely shaded by the forest if the sun were straight overhead.

Carbon Cycle. The sequence of transformation of carbon which is used by one organism, later liberated upon the death and decomposition of the organism, and returned to its original state to be reused by another organism.

Carbon-Nitrogen Ratio. The ratio of the weight of organic carbon to the weight of total nitrogen in a soil, or in organic material.

Catena. A sequence of soils from similar parent material and of similar age in areas of similar climate but whose characteristics differ owing to variations in relief and internal drainage.

Cation Exchange. The interchange between a cation in solution and another cation on the surface of a colloidal or other surface-active material.

Cation Exchange Capacity. The sum total of exchangeable cations adsorbed by a soil, expressed in milliequivalents per 100 gm. of soil.

Chiseling. Breaking or loosening compact soil or subsoil with a chisel cultivator.

C Horizon. *See* Soil horizons.

Chroma. One of the three variables of color. The relative purity of strength (sometimes called *saturation*) of the spectral color. The chroma increases with increasing purity of the dominant wave length of light or decreasing grayness. *See* Munsell notation, Hue, *and* Value.

Classification. The assignment of objects or units to groups within a system of categories distinguished by their properties. In the classification of soils, the fundamental unit is a soil type. Similar soil types are grouped to form a series. Series are grouped into families, families into Great Soil Groups, these into suborders, and suborders into orders (of which there are three: the Zonal, Azonal, and Intrazonal).

Clay. (1) A soil separate. *See* Soil Separates.

(2) A textural class. *See* Soil Texture.

Clayey. Includes all clay textural classes, *i. e.*, sandy clay, silty clay, and clay.

Clay Loam. A textural class. *See* Soil texture.

Clay Pan. Dense subsoil horizon high in clay content, having a sharply defined upper boundary, and formed by downward movement of clay or by synthesis of clay in place during soil formation.

Climax. A plant community of the most advanced type that is capable of development under the prevailing climatic conditions.

Coarse Fragments. Masses of mineral or rock material greater than 2 mm. in diameter.

Coarse Sand. *See* Soil Separates *and* Soil Textures.

Coarse Texture. In the United States, includes the sands, loamy sands, and sandy loams, except the very fine sandy loam, textural classes. Sometimes subdivided into sandy and moderately coarse-textured.

Cobbles. Rounded mineral or rock fragments between 3 and 10 inches in diameter.

Cobbly. Soils having rounded or partially rounded fragments of rocks ranging from 3 to 10 inches in diameter; **angular cobbly,** formerly included as stony, is similar to **cobbly,** except that fragments are not rounded. A single piece of either is a **cobblestone,** or small stone.

Colluvium. Deposit of rock fragments and soil material accumulated at the base of steep slopes by gravitational action.

Color. *See* Munsell notation.

Columnar (Soil Structure). Similar to **prismatic structure,** except that the tops of the blocks are rounded.

Compost. (1) Organic residues, or a mixture of organic residues and soil, which have been piled, moistened, and allowed to undergo biological decomposition. Mineral fertilizers are sometimes added. Often called **artificial** or **synthetic manure** when produced primarily from plant residues.

(2) A potting mixture. Usually consists of a mixture of soil with varying proportions of one or more of the following: manure, peat moss, leaf mold, composted plant residues, and sand.

Concretion. Hardened local concentrations of certain chemical compounds, as calcium carbonate or iron oxides, in the form of indurated grains or nodules of various sizes, shapes, and colors.

Consistence. (1) Resistance to deformation of material.

(2) The degree of cohesion or adhesion of the soil mass or its resistance to deformation or rupture. Separate terms used for describing these properties at three moisture contents follow:

(a) **Consistence when dry**—loose, slightly hard, hard, very hard, and extremely hard.

(b) **Consistence when moist**—loose, very friable, friable, firm, very firm, and extremely firm.

(c) **Consistence when wet (stickiness)**—non-sticky, slightly sticky, sticky, and very sticky.

(d) **Consistence when wet (plasticity)**—non-plastic, slightly plastic, plastic, very plastic.

Consumptive Use. The water used by plants in transpiration and growth, plus water vapor lost from adjacent soil. Usually expressed as inches of free water per unit of time and equal in numerical value to rainfall. For example: consumptive use of alfalfa may be 0.2 inches of water per day.

Coppice Mounds. Small mounds of soil material stabilized around desert shrubs.

Cradle Knoll. The earth raised and left in a knoll by an uprooted tree.

Creep. Mass movement of soil and soil material slowly down steep slopes primarily by gravity, but facilitated by saturation with water and alternate freezing and thawing.

Crust. A hard or brittle layer formed on the surface of many soils when dry.

Crystal. A homogeneous substance bounded by plane surfaces having definite angles with each other and with a definite chemical composition. *See* Mineral.

Decalcification. Removal of calcium carbonate or calcium ions from the soil by leaching.

Denitrification. The biological reduction of nitrate or nitrite to gaseous nitrogen (molecular nitrogen or the oxides of nitrogen). The process results in the escape of nitrogen into the air, and hence is undesirable in agriculture.

Desert Crust. A hard layer, containing calcium carbonate, gypsum, or other binding material exposed at the surface in desert regions.

Diatomaceous Earth. A geological deposit derived chiefly from the remains of diatoms.

Diatoms. Algae having a siliceous cell wall which persists as a skeleton after death. Any of the microscopic unicellular or colonial algae. They occur abundantly in fresh and salt waters and are widely distributed in soils.

Dispersed Soil. Soil in which the clay readily forms a colloidal sol, usually with low permeability. Upon drying, it shrinks, cracks, and becomes hard; upon wetting, it slakes readily and is plastic.

D Layer. *See* Soil horizons.

Drag. The retarding force to flowing water or wind over the surface of the ground.

Drain (verb). (1) To provide outlet channels so that excess water can be removed by surface flow or by downward internal flow through the soil.
(2) To lose water by percolation.

Drainage. Internal: The removal of excess water from within the soil by downward movement through the soil.
External: The discharge of water over the surface of a sloping soil.

Drainage Terrace. Constructed channel for conducting surplus surface water from land with minimum erosion.

Drain Tile. Concrete or pottery pipe for water outlets from soil.

Dry Land Farming. The practice of crop production without irrigation where rainfall is usually deficient.

Dust Mulch. An induced loose, fine, granular, or powdery condition in the surface soil.

Dynamometer. An instrument for measuring draft of tillage implements and for measuring resistance of soil to penetration by tillage implements.

Ecology. The science that deals with the study of the interrelationships of organisms in and to their environment.

Edaphology. The scientific study of the relationships between soils and living things, including man's use of the land.

Eluvial Horizon. Soil horizon from which some fine material has been removed either in solution or in water suspension.

Eluviation. Removal of soil material from the upper to the lower horizon in solution or in colloidal suspension.

Energy Source. The source from which an organism derives the energy for metabolic activities, *e. g.*, sunlight, sulfur, cellulose, hydrogen, *etc.*

Equivalent Weight. The weight in grams of an ion or compound that combines with or replaces 1 gr. of hydrogen. The atomic weight, or formula weight divided by its valence.

Erode. To take away exposed soil by wind, water, or other agents.

Erodible. Susceptible to erosion. A soil, for example, that is quite susceptible to erosion is referred to as erodible, while one that is resistant to erosion is said to be relatively non-erodible.

Erosion. (1) The wearing away of the land surface by running water, wind, or other geological agents, including such processes as gravitational creep.
(2) All processes by which earthly materials or rocks are loosened and moved from place to place.
(3) Detachment and movement of soil or rock material by water, wind, ice, or gravity.

Evapo-Transpiration. The sum of water transpired by vegetation and that lost by evaporation, for a particular area during a specified time.

Exchangeable Potassium. The potassium which is held mainly by the colloidal portion of the soil and which is easily exchanged with the cations of neutral salt solutions. It is readily available to growing plants.

Fertilizer. Any organic or inorganic material of natural or synthetic origin which is added to a soil in an attempt to provide plant nutrients.

Fertilizer Terms. **Acid-forming fertilizer.** One that is capable of increasing the residual acidity of soil.

> **Analysis.** As applied to fertilizers, designates the actual percentage composition of the product as determined by a laboratory analysis.

> **Brand.** A term, design, or trademark used in connection with one or several grades of fertilizers.

> **Brand name.** A specific designation applied to an individual fertilizer.

> **Bulk fertilizer.** Commercial fertilizer delivered to the purchaser, either in the solid or the liquid state, in a non-packaged form.

> **Formula.** The amount and grade of fertilizer materials used in making a mixed fertilizer. For example 600 pounds of 33.5 per cent ammonium nitrate, 1,000 pounds of 20 per cent superphosphate, and 300 pounds of 60 per cent muriate of potash.

> **Grade.** The minimum guaranty of its plant-nutrient content expressed as whole numbers in terms of total nitrogen (N), available phosphoric acid (P_2O_5), and water-soluble potash (K_2O).

> **Non-acid forming fertilizer.** One that is not capable of increasing the residual acidity of the soil.

> **Organic.** Organic materials that are not soluble in water.

> **Unit of plant nutrient.** Twenty pounds or 1 per cent of a ton.

Field Capacity. The moisture content of soil in the field, two or three days after a thorough wetting of a well-drained soil by rain or irrigation water. It is expressed as a percentage by weight of oven-dry soil.

> **Fifteen-atmosphere percentage.** The moisture percentage, on an oven-dry basis, of a wetted sample in equilibrium with a pressure of 221 pounds per square inch. Approximately equal to the wilting percentage. Sometimes called the *lower limit of readily available water.*

Fine Texture. (1) Predominating in fine fractions, as clay.

> (2) Includes clay loam, sandy clay loam, silty clay loam, sandy clay, silty clay, and clay.

Fire, Ground (Forestry). A fire that not only consumes all the organic materials of the forest floor, but also burns into the underlying soil itself, as, for example, a peat fire. (Usually combined with, but not to be confused with, a surface fire.)

Firm. A consistence term used in describing moist soil which crushes under moderate pressure between thumb and forefinger, but with a resistance distinctly noticeable. *See* Consistence.

First Bottom. The normal flood plain of a stream.

Flagstone. A relatively thin fragment 6 to 15 inches long, of sandstone, limestone, slate, shale, or schist.

Flood Plain. Land bordering a stream, built of sediments from the stream and subject to flooding in times of high water unless protected artificially.

Forest Floor. All dead vegetable matter on the mineral soil surface. Includes litter and unincorporated humus.

Forest Soils. (1) Any soil developed under trees.
(2) Soils found under temperate forest (*European usage*).

Friability. The ease of crumbling of soils.

Frost, Concrete. That type of frost in the soil which is so filled with ice as to be virtually a solid block, such as that found in plowed ground.

Frost, Honeycomb. Frost in the soil of a crystalline nature, giving it a loose structure and permitting the ready entrance of water, such as that on the forest floor.

Genetic. Resulting from soil-formation processes, such as a genetic soil profile or a genetic horizon.

Geological Erosion. *See* Natural erosion.

Glacial Drift. A general term for the rock debris that has been transported by glaciers and is deposited, either directly from the ice or from the meltwater, or melting, of the glacier. It may be heterogeneous or it may be assorted.

Glacial Soil. *Obsolete:* Soil formed from glacial drift.

Glacial Till. *See* Till.

Glaciofluvial Deposits. Material moved by glaciers and subsequently sorted and deposited by streams flowing from the melting ice. These deposits are stratified and may be in the form of outwash plains, deltas, kames, and eskers.

Gleization. The soil-formation processes leading to the development of a glei soil.

Gravelly. A coarse-fragment class used in soil-textural class names.

Green Manure. A crop grown for the purpose of being turned under while green, or soon after maturity, for improving the soil.

Gully. A large, intermittent water course with steep sides—usually an obstacle to agricultural machinery.

Gully Erosion. Erosion that results in gullies.

Halophytic. Able to grow in salty soil.

Heavy Soil. *Obsolete in scientific use: See* Fine-textured soil. A soil which has a high draw-bar pull; a soil difficult to cultivate.

Heterotrophic. Capable of deriving energy for life processes only from the breakdown of organic carbon compounds, and incapable of using carbon dioxide as the sole carbon source for cell synthesis. Contrast with **autotrophic.**

Horizon. *See* Soil horizons.

Hue. One of the three variables of color. The dominant spectral color. The hue changes with the dominant wave length of the light. *See* Munsell notation, Chroma, *and* Value.

Humus. Colloidal organic matter.

Hydromorphic Soils. Soils developed in the presence of excess water.

Illuvial Horizon. Horizon that has received material in solution or suspension from some other part of the soil.

Illuviation. The process of deposition of soil material removed from one horizon to another horizon of the soil, usually from an upper horizon to a lower horizon in the profile.

Immature Soil. Lacking a well-developed profile.

Immobilization. The conversion of an element from inorganic to organic combination in microbial or plant tissues. This has the effect of rendering unavailable (and usually not readily soluble) an element that previously was leachable or directly available to plants.

Impeded Drainage. Condition in which downward movement of gravitational water is hindered.

Impervious. Resistant to penetration by fluid or roots.

Indicator Plants. Plants characteristic of specific soil or site conditions.

Infiltration. The downward entry of water into soil.

Infiltration Rate. The maximum rate at which a soil, in a given condition at a given time, can absorb water. Also, the maximum rate at which a soil will absorb water impounded on the surface at a shallow depth when adequate precautions are taken regarding border or fringe effects. Defined as the volume of water passing into the soil per unit of area per unit of time.

Infiltration Velocity. The volume of water moving downward into the soil surface per unit of area per unit of time. The maximum infiltration velocity is the infiltration rate.

Infiltrometer. A device for measuring the rate of entry of a fluid into a porous body (*e. g.,* water into soil).

Intergrade. Soils which possess moderately well-developed distinguishing characteristics of two or more genetically related Great Soil Groups.

Ion. Acids, bases, and salts (electrolytes) when dissolved in certain solvents are more or less dissociated into electrically charged units, called *ions*. Positively charged ions are called *cations;* negatively charged ions are called *anions*.

Irrigation Methods. **Border-strip.** Water applied at the upper end of a strip with earth borders to confine the water to the strip.
   Check (basin). Water applied rapidly to relatively level plots surrounded by levees. The basin is a small check.
   Corrugation. Water applied to small, closely placed furrows, frequently in grain and forage crops, to confine the flow of irrigation water to one direction.
   Flooding. Water released from field ditches and allowed to flood over the land.
   Furrow. Water applied in small ditches made by cultivation implements for tree and row crops.

Sprinkler. Water sprayed over the soil surface through nozzles from a pressure system.

Subirrigation. Water applied in open ditches or tile lines until the water table is raised sufficiently to wet the soil.

Wild flooding. Irrigation water is released at high points in the field without controlled distribution.

Kame. An irregular ridge or hill of stratified glacial drift.

Lacustrine. Refers to deposits formed on the bottom of lakes.

Land Classification. The classification of units of land for the purpose of showing their relative suitability for some specific use.

Landscape. All the features that distinguish one part of the earth's surface from another part.

Land Slide. (1) Rapid movement downslope of a mass of soil, rock, and debris.

(2) Mass of material that has slipped down hill.

Leached Saline Soils. (1) Soils which have had the soluble salts removed by leaching.

(2) Soils which have been saline and which still possess the major physical characteristics of saline soils but from which the soluble salts have been leached, generally as a result of reclamation.

Leaching. The process of removal of soluble material by the passage of water through a substance.

Light Soil. *Obsolete in scientific use: See* Coarse-textured. A soil which has a low drawbar pull; a soil easy to cultivate.

Lime. Most agricultural lime is calcium carbonate or a mixture of calcium and magnesium carbonate. Chemically speaking, lime is CaO.

Air-slaked lime. A product composed of varying proportions of the oxide, hydroxide, and carbonate of calcium, or of calcium and magnesium, and derived from the exposure of quicklime to the weather.

Agricultural liming material. A material whose calcium and magnesium content is capable of neutralizing soil acidity.

Dolomite. A material composed chiefly of carbonates of calcium and magnesium.

Ground limestone. The product obtained by grinding either calcitic or dolomitic limestone so that all the material will pass a 10-mesh sieve and at least 50 per cent will pass a 100-mesh sieve.

Ground shell marl. The product obtained by grinding natural deposits of shell marl so that at least 75 per cent passes a 100-mesh sieve.

Ground shells. The product obtained by grinding the shells of mollusks so that not less than 50 per cent passes a 100-mesh sieve. The product also carries the name of the mollusk from which the product is made, such as *oyster shell lime.*

Gypsum, land plaster, or crude calcium sulfate. A product consisting chiefly of calcium sulfate. It does not neutralize soil acidity.

High-calcic products. Materials of which 90 per cent or more of the total calcium and magnesium oxide content consists of calcium oxide.

High-magnesic products. Materials in which more than 10 per cent of the total calcium and magnesium oxide consists of magnesium oxide.

Hydrated or air-slaked lime. A dry product consisting chiefly of the hydroxide of calcium and the oxide and hydroxide of magnesium.

Magnesia (magnesium oxide). A product consisting chiefly of the oxide of magnesium. Its grade is stipulated, for example, Magnesia—75 per cent MgO.

Pulverized limestone (fine-ground limestone). The product obtained by grinding either calcitic or dolomitic limestone so that all the materials will pass a 20-mesh sieve and at least 75 per cent will pass a 100-mesh sieve.

Quicklime, Burned lime, Caustic lime, Lump lime, Unslaked lime. Calcined materials, the major part of which is calcium oxide, in natural association with a lesser amount of magnesium oxide, and which is capable of slaking with water.

Waste lime, By-product lime. Any industrial waste or by-product containing calcium or calcium and magnesium in forms that will neutralize soil acidity. It may be designated by prefixing the name of the industry or process by which it is produced, *i. e., gashouse lime, tanners' lime, acetylene lime-waste, lime-kiln ashes,* or *calcium silicate.*

Lime Concretion. An aggregate cemented by precipitation of $CaCO_3$.

Lime Pan. A hardened layer cemented by calcium carbonate.

Lime Requirement. The number of pounds of limestone or other specified liming material required to raise the pH of one acre-six inches (or 2,000,-000 lb.) of an acid soil to any desired pH value.

Lithosols. An azonal group of soils having an incomplete solum or no clearly expressed soil morphology and consisting of a freshly and imperfectly weathered mass of rock.

Loamy. A broad grouping of texture classes; includes all sandy loams, clay loams, loam, silt, and silt-loam textures.

Loess. A fine-grained eolian deposit dominantly of silt-sized particles.

Made-land. Areas filled artificially with earth or trash.

Manure. (1) The excreta of animals, with or without the admixture of bedding or litter, and of varying stages of decomposition. Also referred to as **barnyard,** or **stable manure.** (*The usual meaning of the term as used in the U.S.*)

(2) Any material which fertilizes land; a fertilizer of either organic or inorganic origin. (*Seldom used in this sense in the U.S., but frequently so used elsewhere.*)

Marl. Earthy deposit of $CaCO_3$.

Metamorphic Rocks. Rocks derived from pre-existing rocks by mineralogical, chemical, and structural alterations due to geologic processes originating within the earth. Igneous and sedimentary rocks may be changed to metamorphic rock, or one metamorphic rock may be changed into another metamorphic rock.

Microclimate. (1) A modification of the general climate produced by the local environment.

(2) The sequence of atmospheric changes within a very small region.

Microfauna. The part of an animal population comprised of individuals so small that they cannot be clearly distinguished without the use of a microscope. Usually applied to protozoa, nematodes, and similar organisms.

Microflora. The part of a plant population comprised of individuals so small that they cannot be distinguished without the use of a microscope. Usually applied to algae, fungi, bacteria, actinomycetes, and similar organisms.

Microrelief. Small-scale differences in relief, including mounds, swales, or pits that are a few feet across and have differences in elevation up to about 6 feet.

Mineral, Soil. A natural inorganic compound usually having definite physical properties, crystalline structure, and chemical composition.

Mineralization. The conversion of an element that is immobilized in some organic combination to an available form as a result of microbial decomposition.

Mineralogical Analysis. Estimation of the kinds or amounts of minerals in soil or rock.

Mineral Soil. A soil whose properties are dominated by the mineral matter, usually containing less than 20 per cent organic matter, or with only a thin surface organic layer less than one foot thick.

Moisture Tension. The equivalent negative gauge pressure, or suction, in the soil moisture. Soil-moisture tension is equal to the equivalent negative or gauge pressure to which matter must be subjected in order to be in hydraulic equilibrium, through a porous permeable wall or membrane, with the water in the soil.

Mottled Zone. Soil layer that is marked with spots or blotches of different color or shades of color.

Mottling. Patches or spots of colors different from those of the general soil mass.

Mulch. A loose covering on the surface of the soil. Usually consists of organic residues but may be loose soil produced by cultivation or other inorganic materials.

Mulch Farming. A system of farming in which the organic residues are not plowed into the ground but are left on the surface.

Munsell Notation. A color-designation system that specifies the relative degrees of the three simple variables of color: hue, value, and chroma. For example: 10 YR 6/4 is a color of soil with a hue of 10 YR, a value of 6, and a chroma of 4. These notations can be translated into several different systems of color names as desired. *See* Hue, Value, Chroma.

Mycorrhiza. The morphological association, usually symbiotic, of fungi with the roots of plants.

Natural Erosion. (Geological erosion.) Erosion of the natural landscape undisturbed by man or domestic animals.

Nitrate Reduction. The biological reduction of nitrates to the nitrite form.

Nitrification. The biological oxidation of ammonium salts to nitrites and the further oxidation of nitrites to nitrates.

Nitrogen Assimilation. The incorporation of nitrogen compounds into cell substances by living organisms.

Nitrogen Cycle. The sequences of transformation undergone by nitrogen wherein it is used by one organism, later liberated upon the death and decomposition of the organism, and converted by biological means to its original state of oxidation to be re-used by another organism.

Nitrogen Fertilizers (Inorganic). Ammoniated superphosphate. (*See* Phosphorus fertilizers.)

Ammonium nitrate. The ammonium salt of nitric acid. It contains not less than 33 per cent nitrogen, one-half of which is in the ammonium form and one-half in the nitrate form.

Ammonium sulfate nitrate. A double salt of ammonium sulfate and ammonium nitrate in equal molecular proportions. It contains not less than 26 per cent nitrogen, one-fourth of which is in the nitrate form and three-fourths in the ammonium form.

Calcium nitrate. The calcium salt of nitric acid. It contains not less than 15 per cent nitrate nitrogen.

Nitrate of potash (potassium nitrate). The potassium salt of nitric acid. It contains not less than 12 per cent nitrogen and 44 per cent potash (K_2O).

Nitrate of soda (sodium nitrate). The sodium salt of nitric acid. It contains not less than 16 per cent nitrate nitrogen and 26 per cent sodium.

Sulfate of ammonia (ammonium sulfate). The ammonium salt of sulfuric acid. It contains not less than 20.5 per cent nitrogen.

Nitrogen Fertilizers (Natural Organic). Acidulated fish tankage, acidulated fish scrap. The rendered product derived from fish and treated with sulfuric acid.

Activated sewage products. Made from sewage that has been aerated and inoculated with microorganisms. The resulting flocculated organic matter is filtered, dried, ground, screened, bagged, and sold as a fertilizer.

Bat guano. Partially decomposed bat manure of variable composition.

Dried blood. The collected blood of slaughtered animals that has been dried and ground. It contains not less than 12 per cent nitrogen in several organic forms.

Dried, pulverized, or shredded manures. These are what the names indicate, and not mixtures of manures and other materials.

Fish tankage, fish scrap, dry ground fish, fish meal. The dried, ground products derived from rendered or unrendered fish.

Garbage tankage. The rendered, dried, and ground product derived from waste household food materials.

Hoof and horn meal. Processed, dried, and ground hoofs and horns.

Peat. Partly decayed organic matter of natural occurrence.

Process tankage. Products made under steam pressure from crude, inert nitrogenous materials, with or without the use of acids, for the purpose of increasing the activity of the nitrogen.

Sheep manure-wool waste. The by-product from wool-carding establishments, consisting chiefly of sheep manure, trash from dirty wool, and wool waste.

Tankage. The rendered, dried, and ground by-products, largely consisting of the meat and bones of slaughtered animals.

Nitrogen Fertilizers (Synthetic Organic). Cyanamid. A commercial product consisting principally of calcium cyanamid ($CaCN_2$) and carbon. It contains not less than 20 per cent nitrogen and 54 per cent calcium oxide.

Urea. The commercial synthetic acid amide of carbonic acid. It contains not less than 42 per cent nitrogen.

Urea-formaldehyde fertilizer materials. Reaction products of urea and formaldehyde containing at least 35 per cent nitrogen, largely in an insoluble but slowly available form.

Nitrogen Fixation. The conversion of elemental nitrogen to organic combinations, or to forms readily utilizable in biological processes, by nitrogen-fixing microorganisms. When brought about by bacteria in the root nodules of leguminous plants, it is spoken of as *symbiotic;* if by free-living microorganisms acting independently, it is referred to as *nonsymbiotic fixation.*

Nodule Bacteria. *See* Rhizobia.

Nonsaline-Alkali Soils. A soil that contains sufficient exchangeable sodium to interfere with the growth of most crop plants but does not contain appreciable quantities of soluble salts. The percentage of exchangeable sodium is more than 15 and the pH of the saturated soil paste is usually above 8.5.

One-Third-Atmosphere Percentage. The moisture percentage on an oven-dry basis of a soil in equilibrium with a tension of 4.9 pounds per square inch (345 cm. of water). This value closely approximates the moisture equivalent and the field capacity. Sometimes called the *upper limit of readily available water.*

Organic Phosphorus. Phosphorus present as a constituent of an organic compound.

Oven-Dry Soil. A soil dried at 105° to 110° centigrade until it loses no more moisture at that temperature.

Pans. Horizons or layers in soils that are strongly compacted, indurated, or very high in clay content.

Particle Density. The average density of the soil particles. Particle density is usually expressed in grams per cubic centimeter and is sometimes referred to as "real density or grain density" in soils. The term *particle density* has now replaced *specific gravity.*

Parts Per Million (PPM). Weight units per million weight units of soil, oven-dry basis. *Parts per million* expresses grams per million grams of soil, or pounds per million pounds of soil; or, in the case of soil solution or other solution, it expresses weight units per million weight units of solution.

Penetrability. The work required to push a probe a unit distance into the soil.

Percolation (Soil Water). A qualitative term applying to the downward movement of water through soil. Especially, the downward flow of water in saturated or nearly saturated soil at hydraulic gradients equal to the pull of gravity.

Permafrost. Permanently frozen soil.

Permafrost Table. The upper boundary of the permafrost, coincident with the lower limits of seasonal thaws.

Permanent Wilting Percentage. The moisture percentage of soil at which plants wilt and fail to overcome wilting even though placed in a saturated atmosphere. Usually determined with dwarf sunflowers as the test plant.

Permeability. (1) (*Soil*) Permeability as used in describing soils refers to the readiness with which air, water, or plant roots penetrate into or pass through its pores. The portion of the soil being discussed should be designated, *e. g.*, "the permeability of the A horizon."

(2) (*Qualitative*) The quality or state of a porous medium relating to the readiness with which it conducts or transmits fluids.

(3) (*Quantitative*) The specific property designating the rate or readiness with which a porous medium transmits fluids under standard conditions.

pH (Soil). The negative logarithm of the hydrogen-ion activity of a soil.

Phosphorous Fertilizers. Acidulated bone. Ground bone or bone meal that has been treated with sulfuric acid.

Ammoniated superphosphate. A product obtained when superphosphate is treated with ammonia or with solutions which contain ammonia or other compounds of nitrogen..

Ammonium phosphate. A product obtained when phosphoric acid is treated with ammonia; it consists principally of mono-ammonium phosphate, di-ammonium phosphate, or a mixture of these two salts.

Ammonium phosphate sulfate. A product obtained when a mixture of phosphoric acid and sulfuric acid is treated with ammonia. It consists principally of a mixture of ammonium phosphate and ammonium sulfate.

Available phosphoric acid. The sum of the water-soluble phosphoric acid ((monocalcium phosphate) and citrate-soluble phosphoric acid (dicalcium phosphate).

Basic phosphate slag. A by-product of the manufacture of steel from phosphatic iron ores. It contains not less than 12 per cent total phosphoric acid of which at least 80 per cent is available (citrate-soluble). It is ground so that not less than 70 per cent of the material passes through a 100-mesh sieve and 90 per cent passes through a 50-mesh sieve.

Calcium metaphosphate. A vitreous product resulting from the treatment of phosphorous rock with gaseous phosphorous pentoxide (P_2O_5) at high temperatures.

Citrate-soluble (reverted) phosphoric acid. That part of the total phosphoric acid in a fertilizer that is insoluble in water but soluble in a neutral solution of citrate of ammonia. Mostly in the form of dicalcium phosphate, $Ca_2H_2 (PO_4)_2$.

Dicalcium phosphate. A manufactured product consisting chiefly of the dicalcic salt of phosphoric acid, $Ca_2H_2 (PO_4)_2$.

Fused calcium-magnesium phosphate. A vitreous product resulting from the fusion of phosphate rock with magnesium silicate.

Fused tricalcium phosphate. A product resulting from the fusion of phosphate rock to produce the alpha form of tricalcium phosphate.

Ground raw bone. Ground animal bones that have not been steamed under pressure.

Ground steamed bone. Ground animal bones that have been steamed under pressure.

Phosphate rock. A natural rock containing one or more calcium phosphate minerals of sufficient purity to permit its use, either directly or after concentration, in the manufacture of commercial phosphorous fertilizers. The phosphorus is mostly in the form of tricalcium phosphate, $Ca_3 (PO_4)_2$.

Phosphoric acid. Designates phosphorus pentoxide (P_2O_5).

Precipitated phosphate. A product consisting mainly of dicalcium phosphate obtained by neutralizing, with calcium hydroxide, the acid solution of either phosphate rock or processed bone.

Soft phosphate with colloidal clay. A very finely divided low-analysis by-product from mining Florida rock phosphate by an hydraulic process in which the colloidal materials settle in artificial ponds.

Superphosphate. A product obtained when rock phosphate is treated with either sulfuric acid, phosphoric acid, or a mixture of those acids. The guaranteed percentage of available phosphoric acid is stated as a part of the name, such as "20 per cent superphosphate."

Physical Weathering. The breakdown of rock and mineral soil into smaller fragments by physical forces such as frost action.

Phytogenic Soils. Soils developed under the dominant influence of the natural vegetation, mainly in temperate regions.

Phytometer. A plant or plants used to measure the physical factors of the habitat in terms of physiological activities.

Pitchy Peat. Dense and hard when dry, breaking with smooth, somewhat lustrous fracture into sharp-angled (conchoidal) fragments. Wet pitchy peat is very plastic, and if squeezed in the hand, oozes out between the fingers.

Plastic. Capable of undergoing deformation without rupture.

Plate Count. A method for estimating the number of microorganisms in a given weight of soil which will form colonies on semi-solid nutrient media.

Platy. Soil aggregates predominantly developed along the horizontal axes, *i. e.*, laminated.

Plow Pan. A compacted layer at a depth usually of 6 to 8 inches below the surface caused by compression at the bottom of a plow.

Pore Space. Total space not occupied by solid soil particles.

Porosity. The fraction of the soil volume not occupied by soil particles. Expressed as an equation, porosity is:

$$\frac{\text{The sum of the volumes of liquids and gases}}{\text{The sum of the volumes of liquids, gases, and solids}}$$

Potassium Fertilizers. Double sulfate of potash-magnesia (langbeinite). The double sulfate of potash magnesium ($K_2SO_4 \cdot 2MgSO_4$) is a commercial product containing 22 per cent potash (K_2O), and 18 per cent MgO. It is usually sold under the trade name of Sul-Po-Mag.

Kainit. A potash salt containing potassium and sodium chlorides and sometimes sulfate of magnesia, with not less than 12 per cent potash (K_2O).

Mine-run potash salts. Potash salts containing a high percentage of chloride and from 20 to 30 per cent potash (K_2O).

Muriate of potash (commercial potassium chloride). A potash salt containing 48 to 62 per cent potash (K_2O), chiefly in the chloride form.

Potassium metaphosphate. A product composed of phosphoric acid (P_2O_5) and potash (K_2O). Example: Potassium metaphosphate, 55 per cent available phosphoric acid (P_2O_5), and 37 per cent water-soluble potash (K_2O).

Sulfate of potash (commercial potassium sulfate). A potash salt containing not less than 48 per cent potash (K_2O), chiefly as sulfate and not more than 2.5 per cent chlorine.

Wood ashes, leached. Ashes that have been exposed to or digested in water or other liquid solvents, as in the extraction of dyes, so that part of the plant nutrients have been dissolved and removed.

Wood ashes, unleached. Ashes that have had no part of their plant nutrients removed. They contain 4 per cent or more of water-soluble potash (K_2O) and 50 per cent or more CaO.

Potassium Fixation. The process of converting water-soluble or exchangeable potassium to less available forms.

Potassium-Supplying Power of Soils. The capacity of the soil to supply potassium to growing plants from the water-soluble, the exchangeable, and some of the less available forms.

Pressure Membrane. A membrane, permeable to water and only very slightly permeable to gas when wet, through which water can escape from a soil sample in response to pressure gradients.

Prismatic Soil Structure. Prism-like structure with the vertical axis of the aggregates longer than the horizontal axis.

Productive Soil. A soil in which the chemical, physical, and biological conditions are favorable for the economic production of the crops suited to a particular area.

Pure Culture. The growth of a single species or strain of an organism without contact or association with other living species or strains.

Rainfall Interception. Interception of raindrops by a canopy of vegetation or by a vegetative residue.

Reaction, Soil. The degree of acidity or alkalinity of a soil, usually expressed in terms of pH value. Descriptive terms commonly used are as follows: extremely acid, below 4.5; very strongly acid, 4.5-5.0; strongly acid, 5.1-5.5; medium acid, 5.6-6.0; slightly acid, 6.1-6.5; neutral, 6.6-7.3; mildly alkaline, 7.4-7.8; moderately alkaline, 7.9-8.4; strongly alkaline, 8.5-9.0; very strongly alkaline, 9.1 and higher.

Reclamation. The process of removing from the soil excess soluble salts or excess exchangeable sodium.

Regolith. The unconsolidated mantle of weathered rock and soil material on the earth's surface; loose earth materials above solid rock. This is approximately equivalent to the term *soil*, as used by many engineers.

Regosols. An azonal group of soils lacking definite genetic horizons and derived from deep, soft mineral deposits, such as loess or glacial drift.

Rendzina Soils. (1) (*U.S.*) An intrazonal group of soils with brown or black friable surface horizons underlain by light gray to pale yellow calcareous material; developed from soft, highly calcareous parent material under grass vegetation or mixed grasses and trees in humid and semiarid climates.

(2) (*Europe*) A group of calcareous soils with dark gray to nearly white surface horizons that are usually stony and that grade into partially disintegrated limestone at shallow depths. These would be called Lithosols in the U. S.

Residual Material. Unconsolidated and partly weathered mineral materials accumulated by disintegration of consolidated rock in place.

Residual Soil. *Obsolete:* Soil resting on consolidated rock of the same kind as that from which it was formed. The proper term is "soil developed from residual material."

Reticulate Mottling. A network of streaks of different colors, most commonly found in the deeper horizons of latosolic tropical soils.

Reversion. The interaction of a soluble plant nutrient with the soil which causes a precipitation of the nutrient in a less soluble form. The term is usually restricted to the conversion of monocalcium phosphate to the less soluble dicalcium or tricalcium phosphate.

Rhizobia. The bacteria capable of living in symbiotic relationship with leguminous plants in nodules on the roots, the association usually being capable of fixing nitrogen (from the generic name *Rhizobium*).

Rhizosphere. The soil region in the immediate vicinity of the plant roots in which the abundance or composition of the microbial population is affected by the presence of the roots. The microflora of the rhizosphere is that found in this region.

Rill. A small, intermittent watercourse with steep sides but usually presenting no obstacle to agricultural machinery; usually a few inches in depth.

Rill Erosion. Formation of small channels, or rills, by the uneven removal of surface soil by running water.

River-Wash. Barren alluvial land, usually coarse-textured, exposed along streams at low water level and subject to shifting during normal high water.

Rock-Land. Areas containing frequent rock outcrops and shallow soils. Rock outcrops usually occupy from 25 to 90 per cent of the area.

Rolling. Having moderately steep, complex slopes; intermediate between undulating and hilly.

Rough-Broken Land. Very steep land, ordinarily not stony, broken by numerous intermittent drainage channels but having a vegetative cover.

Rubble-Land. Areas with 90 per cent or more of the surface covered by stones and boulders.

Saline-Alkali Soil. (1) A soil containing sufficient exchangeable sodium to interfere with the growth of most crop plants and containing appreciable quantities of soluble salts. The exchangeable sodium is greater than 15 per cent. The pH of the saturated soil is usually less than 8.5.

(2) A saline-alkali soil has a combination of harmful quantities of salts and either a high alkalinity or high exchangeable sodium or both so distributed in the profile that the growth of most crop plants is reduced.

Saline Soil. A nonalkali soil containing sufficient soluble salts to impair its productivity. The pH of the soil is usually less than 8.5.

Salinization. The process of accumulation in the soil of soluble salts.

Saturate. (1) To fill with a liquid all of the voids among soil particles.

(2) To form the most concentrated solution possible under a given set of physical conditions.

Second Bottom. The first terrace above the normal flood plain of a stream.

Sedimentary Rock. A rock largely composed of sediments more or less consolidated; the chief sedimentary rocks are sandstones, shales, limestones, and conglomerates.

Self-Mulching Soil. (1) A soil that cracks deeply and becomes so granular at the surface when very dry that the granular mulch washes into the cracks when rains begin, the whole soil swelling enough as it becomes moist to force material upward between the former cracks.
(2) A soil in which the surface layer becomes so well aggregated that it does not crust and seal under the impact of rain.

Shaly. A coarse fragment class used in soil-texture class names.

Shear. Force, as of a tillage implement, acting at right angles to the direction of movement.

Sheet Erosion. The gradual, uniform removal by water of the earth's surface, without the formation of rills or gullies.

Silting. The deposition of water-borne sediments, chiefly silt, in lakes, reservoirs, stream channels, or overflow areas.

Site. (1) The combination of biotic, climatic, and soil conditions of an area.
(2) An area sufficiently uniform in soil, climate, and natural biotic conditions to produce a particular climax vegetation.

Slaty. A coarse fragment class used in soil-texture class names.

Slick Spots. Small areas in a field that are slick when wet, owing to alkali or high exchangeable sodium.

Soil Air. The combination of gases occurring in the soil.

Soil Association. (1) A group of defined and named taxonomic soil units occurring together in an individual and characteristic pattern over a geographic region; comparable in many ways to plant associations.
(2) A mapping unit used on general soil maps, composed of two or more defined taxonomic units geographically associated, where the scale and purpose of the map do not permit or require the delineation of the individual soils. A soil association is described in terms of the taxonomic units included, their relative proportions, and their pattern of association if one exists in the area. Sometimes called "natural land type."

Soil Auger. A tool for boring into the soil and withdrawing a small sample for field or laboratory observations; augers are of two general types: those with worm-type bits and those with a hollow cylinder.

Soil Classification. Study of soils and their interrelationships, describing their properties and naming and grouping them systematically. The taxonomic units are frequently regrouped for various purposes, such as drainage requirements, crop adaptations, and highway construction, or for forestry purposes.

Soil Complex. A mapping unit used in detailed soil surveys where two or more defined taxonomic units are so intimately associated geographically that they cannot be separated by boundaries at the scale used.

Soil Extract. The solution separated from a soil suspension or a soil at a particular moisture content by filtration, centrifugation, or displacement.

Soil-Formation Factors. The independent variables that define the soil system. Five main groups of soil-formation factors are generally recognized by soil scientists: parent material, climate, organisms (plants and animals), topography, and time.

Soil Horizon. A layer of soil material approximately parallel to the land surface and differing from adjacent genetically related layers in properties such as color, structure, texture, and consistence and in biological and chemical characteristics.

Soil-Management Groups. Groups of taxonomic soil units with similar soil properties and similar adaptations or management requirements for one or more specific purposes, such as: adapted crops, crop rotations, drainage practices, fertilization, forestry, and highway engineering.

Soil Map. A map designed to show the distribution of soil types or other soil-mapping units in relation to the prominent physical and cultural features of the earth's surface. The following kinds of soil maps are recognized in the United States:

    Detailed reconnaissance soil map. In a detailed reconnaissance map, some portions satisfy the specifications for detailed soil maps, while other portions are reconnaissance soil maps.

    Detailed soil map. A soil map on which the boundaries between all soil types that are significant to potential use (generally, field-management systems) are shown. The scale of the map depends upon the purpose to be served, the intensity of land use, the pattern of soils, and the scale of other cartographic materials available. Traverses are usually made at one-quarter mile or more frequent intervals. Commonly, a scale of 4 inches equals 1 mile (1:15,840) is now used for field mapping in the U.S.

    Generalized soil map. Small-scale maps made to bring out the contrasts within large areas by generalization of more detailed maps. They vary from soil association maps of a county on a scale of 1 inch equals 1 mile (1:63,360) to maps of larger regions showing associations dominated by one or more Great Soil Groups.

    Reconnaissance soil maps. Maps made by observation of the area at intervals such that the complete land area is not examined as in the case with detailed surveys. The intervals of traversing vary from about one-half mile to several miles. The units shown are soil associations. The maps are usually made for exploratory purposes to outline areas of soil suitable for more intensive development. The scale is usually smaller than for detailed maps; sometimes ½ inch equals 1 mile.

    Schematic soil maps. Maps of very small scale (1:1,000,000 or smaller) compiled from the scant existing knowledge of new and undeveloped regions by the application of existing information about the relationship of soil properties to the soil-formation factors of the area, such as climate, living organisms, relief, parent material, and time.

Soil Monolith. A vertical section taken out of a soil profile and mounted for display or study.

Soil Morphology. (1) The constitution of the soil body, as expressed in the kinds, thicknesses, and arrangement of the horizons in the profile, and in the texture, structure, consistence, porosity, and color of each horizon.

(2) The properties, collectively, of the soil body or any of its parts. (Includes physical, chemical, mineralogical, and biological properties.)

Soil Organic Matter. The organic fraction of the soil. Includes plant and animal residues at various stages of decomposition, cells and tissues of soil organisms, and substances synthesized by the soil population. Commonly determined as those organic materials which accompany the soil when the soil is screened through a 2-mm. sieve.

Soil Piping or Tunneling. Accelerated erosion which results in subterranean voids and tunnels.

Soil Population. All of the organisms living in the soil; the combined soil fauna and flora.

Soil Pores. Interstices (voids) between soil particles.

Soil Salinity. The amount of soluble salts in a soil, expressed in terms of percentage, parts per million, or other convenient unit.

Soil Separate. Mineral particles, less than 2 mm. in equivalent diameter ranging between specified sized limits. The names and sizes of separates recognized in the U. S. are: very coarse sand (2.0-1.0 mm.), coarse sand (1.0-0.5 mm.), medium sand (0.5-0.25 mm.), fine sand (0.25-0.10 mm.), very fine sand (0.10-0.05 mm.), silt (0.05-0.002 mm.), and clay (< 0.002 mm.). The separates recognized by the International Society of Soil Science are: I (2.0-0.2 mm.), II (0.2-0.02 mm.), III (0.02-0.002 mm.), and IV (< 0.002 mm.).

Soil Solution. The aqueous solution existing in equilibrium with a soil at a particular moisture tension.

Soil Survey. The systematic examination, description, classification, and mapping of soils in an area.

Soil Variant. A soil whose properties are believed sufficiently different from other known soils to justify a new series name but whose geographic area is so limited that creation of a new series is not believed to be justified.

Solum (*plural:* **Sola**). The upper, most weathered part of the soil profile; includes the A and B horizons.

Specific Gravity. *See* Particle density.

Splash Erosion. The removal of soil particles from their position by the beating effect of raindrops.

Step Terrace. Terrace with vertical drop on the downhill side, with the flat part suitable for cultivation.

Stones. Rock fragments greater than 10 inches in diameter if rounded, and greater than 15 inches along the longer axis if flat.

Stoniness. The relative proportion of stones present; used in the classification of soils.

Stony. Soils containing sufficient stones to interfere with or prevent tillage. Stones usually occupy more than 0.01 per cent of the surface.

Stony Land. Areas containing so many stones that use of machinery is impractical; usually 15 to 90 per cent of the surface is covered with stones.

Stratified. Deposited in layers.

Strip Cropping. Practice of growing different types of crops, such as row crops and sod crops, in alternate strips along contours or across the prevailing direction of the wind.

Stubble Mulch. The stubble of crops or crop residues left essentially in place on the land as a surface cover before and during the preparation of the seed bed and at least partly during the growing of a succeeding crop.

Subsoiling. Breaking of compact subsoils without inverting them, with a special narrow cultivator shovel or chisel, which is pulled through the soil at a depth usually of from 12 to 24 inches and at spacings of from 2 to 5 feet.

Subsurface Tillage. Tillage with a special sweep-like plow or blade which does not turn the surface cover but instead leaves the crop residues on the surface.

Surface Sealing. The packing of dispersed soil particles in the immediate surface layer whereby it becomes almost impermeable to water and air.

Surface Soil. The upper part of the soil ordinarily moved in tillage, or its equivalent in uncultivated soils, about 4 to 10 inches in thickness.

Swamp. Any area, such as a marsh or bog, where the ground is saturated with water throughout much of the year, but where during most of the year the surface of the soil is not deeply submerged.

Symbiosis. The living together in more or less intimate association of two dissimilar organisms, with a resulting mutual benefit. Common examples are lichens (algae and fungi), leguminous plants living in association with rhizobia, and pine trees in association with mycorrhizae.

Taluds. Short, steep escarpments formed gradually at the downslope margins of fields by deposition against hedges or stone walls.

Talus. Fragments of rocks and other soil material accumulated by force of gravity at the foot of cliffs or steep slopes.

Threshold Moisture Content. Biological. The minimum moisture condition, measured either in terms of moisture content or moisture stress, at which biological activity just becomes measurable.

Tidal Flats. Areas of nearly flat, barren mud, periodically covered by tidal waters. Normally these materials have an excess of soluble salt; a miscellaneous land type.

Tight Soil. Compact, impervious and tenacious, usually plastic soil.

Tile Drain. Concrete or pottery pipe placed at suitable spacings and depths in the soil or subsoil to provide water outlets from the soil.

Till. Unstratified, glacial deposits.

Tillage Pan. A compacted zone in the soil at a depth usually of from 6 to 10 inches beneath the surface, caused by the packing action of heavy farm implements.

Tilth. The physical conditions of soil relative to its response to tillage machinery and its mechanical impedance to root penetration.

Top Soil. (1) The layer of soil moved in cultivation.

(2) The A horizons.

(3) The A_1 horizons.

(4) Presumably fertile soil material used to top-dress roadbanks, gardens, and lawns. Usually inaccurately called "loam."

Transitional Soils. Soils somewhat resembling two different soils and genetically related to them.

Transported Soil. *Obsolete:* Soil formed from unconsolidated sedimentary rocks.

Truncated. Having lost all or part of the upper soil horizon or horizons.

Tundra Soils. A zonal group of soils having dark-brown, highly organic surface horizons over grayish or brownish horizons which rest on cold or ever-frozen substrata; developed under shrubs and mosses in cold, semi-arid to humid climates, *e. g.,* in arctic regions.

Ultimate Particles. Soil particles after a standard dispersing treatment, with all aggregates broken down.

Underground Runoff. (*Seepage*) Water flowing toward stream channels after infiltration into the ground.

Value, Color. One of three variables of color. The relative intensity of the reflected light increases as the value increases. *See* Munsell notation.

Varves. Distinctly marked annual deposits of sediment, regardless of their origin.

Volume Weight. *See* Bulk density.

Waterlogged. State of being saturated with water.

Water-Stable Aggregate. A soil aggregate not broken down by agitation in water, usually by wet sieving.

Water Table. The upper surface of ground water.

Water Table, Perched. The upper surface of a body of free ground water in a zone of saturation separated, by unsaturated material, from an underlying body of ground water.

Weathering. All physical and chemical changes produced in rocks, minerals, and soil materials at or near the earth's surface by atmospheric agents and which result in disintegration and decomposition.

Windbreak. A strip of trees or shrubs serving to reduce the force of wind; any protective shelter from the wind.

Xerophytes. Plants that grow in dry sites (soils).

B

Conversion Factors

---

1 standard atmosphere = 1.013 × 10⁶ dynes per sq. cm.
                               = 14.71 lb. per square inch
                               = 76.39 cm. of mercury column, at 20°C.
                               = 1,036 cm. of water column, at 20°C.
                               = 34.01 feet of water column

1 mile
                               = 5,280 feet
                               = 1,760 yards
                               = 1,609 meters
                               = 1.61 kilometers
                               = 320 rods

1 inch   = 2.54 cm.
1 foot   = 30.48 cm.
1 pound   = 453.59 gm.

1 acre   = 43,560 square feet

1 U.S. gallon   = 231 cubic inches
                               = 8.345 pounds of water
                               = 0.1337 cubic feet
1 cubic foot   = 7.48 gallons
1 cubic foot of water weighs 62.43 pounds.

C

Atomic Weight and Valence
of Common Elements

Name	Symbol	Atomic Weight	Valence
Barium	Ba	137.36	2
Boron	B	10.82	3
Calcium	Ca	40.08	2
Carbon	C	12.00	2,4
Chlorine	Cl	35.46	1,3,5,7
Cobalt	Co	58.94	2,3
Copper	Cu	63.57	1,2
Fluorine	F	19.00	1
Hydrogen	H	1.01	1
Iodine	I	126.92	1,3,5,7
Iron	Fe	55.84	2,3
Magnesium	Mg	24.32	2
Manganese	Mn	54.93	2,4,6,7
Molybdenum	Mo	96.00	3,4,6
Nitrogen	N	14.01	3,5
Oxygen	O	16.00	2
Phosphorus	P	31.02	3,5
Potassium	K	39.10	1
Silicon	Si	28.06	4
Sodium	Na	23.00	1
Sulfur	S	32.06	2,4,6
Zinc	Zn	65.38	2

Author Index

A

Albert, A. R., 279
Aldrich, Daniel G., 283
Alexander, L. T., 17
Allaway, W. H., 190
Allison, F. E., 258
Allison, R. V., 279
Anderson, M. S., 257, 258
Andrews, W. B., 164
Arnon, Daniel I., 130

B

Baldwin, Ira L., 96
Bauer, F. C., 268
Baver, L. D., 28
Beale, O. W., 204
Bear, Firman E., 78, 105, 248, 252, 312
Beckenbach, J. R., 309, 310
Beeson, Kenneth C., 10-15
Bender, Carl B., 248
Bertramson, B. R., 78
Bizzell, J. A., 116
Bloodworth, Morris, 81
Blow, Frank E., 196
Bouyoucos, G. J., 17
Boynton, Damon, 122
Brady, N. C., 37, 78, 96, 260, 279
Broadbent, F. E., 74
Broadfoot, W. M., 243, 246
Brown, B. A., 252
Buckman, H. O., 37, 78, 96, 260, 279
Burnett, Earl, 198, 205
Burton, Glenn W., 227

C

Cady, John G., 70, 71
Carter, W. T., 31, 41
Cato, 5, 237
Chandler, Robert F., Jr., 96
Chucka, Joseph A., 266
Clark, Francis E., 88
Clark, Noble, 216
Clayton, B. S., 277, 279
Code, W. E., 229
Collings, Gilbearth, 163, 176
Columella, 5
Corrow, Henry, 7, 111

D

Davidson, F. E., 265
de Roo, Henry, 82
De Vane, E. H., 227
Dimick, Niel A., 226
Donahue, Roy L., 15, 83, 105, 176, 209, 298, 312
Doyle, J. J., 80, 255
Dreibelbis, F. R., 114
Driskell, B. N., 309
Dumm, L. E., 254
Dunklee, D. E., 145, 251
Dunn, Drue W., 232

E

Eaton, Theodore H., Jr., 96
Edminster, T. W., 190
Ellis, Roscoe, Jr., 136
Elmendorf, Harold B., 201, 202
Erie, Leonard J., 226
Evans, Everett F., 209

F

Finnell, H. E., 291
Fisher, C. E., 198, 205
Fletcher, Herbert C., 201, 202
Flint, R. F., 37
Fraps, G. S., 73
Fred, Edwin B., 96
Fudge, J. F., 73

G

Gilbert, J. H., 6
Gilluly, James, 37
Gilman, Joseph C., 96
Gooding, T. H., 96
Goodman, A. M., 244, 246

H

Hamilton, W. J., 84
Hamman, A. J., 229
Harrold, Lloyd L., 203
Hawkins, Arthur, 266
Hays, Orville E., 216
Hilgard, E. W., 8, 9, 15, 286

Holben, F. J., 252
Houston, Clyde E., 284, 285
Hubbell, D. S., 80

I

Ignatieff, Vladimir, 105, 176

J

Jackson, M. L., 213
Jacob, K. D., 163
Jacobson, H. G., 86
Jamison, Vernon C., 185
Jefferson, Thomas, 198
Jones, Harold E., 255
Jones, L. I., 209
Jones, Lewis A., 240, 246, 279

K

Kelley, W. P., 78
Kellogg, C. E., 53, 105
King, Willis A., 248
Kitchen, Herminie B., 312
Klingebiel, A. A., 134, 263

L

Lawes, J. B., 6
Lawrence, George A., 232
Lewis, R. D., 101
Liebig, 6
Linsley, C. M., 247, 249, 252
Locke, L. F., 187
Longnecker, E. D., 139, 145
Longwell, C. R., 37
Lunt, H. A., 86
Lyon, T. L., 37, 78, 96, 116, 260, 279

M

Machlis, Leonard, 130
MacKenzie, A. J., 266
Marbut, C. F., 53, 281
Massey, H. F., 213
McCalla, T. M., 96
McCoy, Elizabeth, 96
McVickar, Malcolm, 176
Melsted, S .W., 103
Midgley, A. R., 48, 76, 145, 251
Millar, C. E., 260, 270, 298
Miller, M. F., 215, 264
Morgan, N. D., 302
Musgrave, R. B., 180, 181
Myers, H. E., 184, 292, 295

N

Neller, J. R., 279
Nelson, A. L., 179
Nelson, L. B., 113, 115
Nikiforoff, C. C., 51

O

Osborn, Ben, 125

P

Page, H. J., 176
Papanos, Stanley, 252
Peech, Michael, 73
Peele, T. C., 204
Peterson, H. B., 236, 298
Peterson, J. B., 312
Peterson, V. H., 265
Plate, Henry, 159
Porter, J. A., 139, 145
Prine, Gordon M., 227
Puhr, Leo F., 104, 293

R

Raney, W. A., 182, 190, 243, 246
Rasmussen, Ed, 303
Richards, L. A., 312
Richardson, T. C., 31
Richer, A. C., 252, 309
Roberts, R. C., 287
Rogers, Howard T., 133
Rood, P. J., 145
Russell, E. John, 15, 96, 130
Russell, E. Walter, 15, 96, 130

S

Salter, Robert M., 101
Sauchelli, Vincent, 163
Schoonover, W. R., 283
Shaw, Byron T., 28, 118, 190, 287
Slipher, J. A., 101
Smith, Dwight D., 172, 215
Smith, F. W., 265
Spencer, Ernest L., 309, 310
Stallings, J. H., 199, 219
Stanley, William R., 234
Staten, Glen, 80
Stauffer, R. S., 188
Stockton, Dale, 103
Strickling, Edward, 262

T

Templeton, George S., 253
Thaxton, E. L., Jr., 227
Thompson, D. O., 85
Thompson, Louis M., 15
Thorne, D. W., 236, 298
Throckmorton, R. I., 184, 292, 295
Truog, Emil, 130, 141
Tull, Jethro, 6
Turk, L. M., 254, 260, 298
Turner, E. C., 135, 145

U

Uhland, R. E., 113, 115
Uyl, Daniel Den, 279

V

Van Doren, C. A., 134, 263
Van Helmont, 5

W

Waksman, Selman A., 96, 279

Washington, George, 237, 245
Wasley, Yushok, 252
Waters, Aaron C., 37
Weidemann, A. G., 254
Weir, W. W., 15
Wheeting, L. C., 254
White, J. L., 78, 252
Whitt, Darnell M., 215
Wilson, H. G., 200
Woodford, A. O., 37
Woodle, H. A., 135, 145
Worzella, W. W., 104, 293

X

Xenophon, 5

Y

Young, T. W., 73, 112

Z

Zeasman, A. R., 279
Zeasman, O. R., 279

Subject Index

_____

A

Acid soil, 133, 134
Acid soils, reasons for, 133, 134
Actinomycetes, 88, 94
A horizon, 44-46, 59
Air-dry weight, 110
Alfalfa hay, composition of, 258
Algae, 88, 94, 95
Alkaline soil, 74, 75
Alkali soil, 281-285
Alkali soils:
  plants as indicators of, 286, 287
  plant symptoms on, 307, 308
Ammonia, 152-153
Ammoniation, 153
Ammonium nitrate, 150, 151
Ammonium sulfate, 150, 151
Analysis, soil:
  Bouyoucos hydrometer method of, 17,
    18
  how to sample for, 299-301
  mechanical, 16, 17
  pipette method of, 17
Animals, essential elements for, 119, 120
Anionic exchange, 73, 74
Anthropic pans, 183-186
Antibiotics, 94
Apparent specific gravity, 24
Arid regions, management of soils in,
    280-298
Arthropods, 87
Artificial manure, 255, 256
Autotrophic bacteria, 88, 89
Availability, nutrient, influence of soil
    pH on, 141, 142
Available water, 112, 113
Azonal soil, 52

B

Bacteria:
  autotrophic, 88, 89
  classification of, 88, 89
  heterotrophic, 89, 90
  nodule, 90-92
  nonnitrogen-fixing heterotrophic, 93
  nonsymbiotic nitrogen-fixing, 92, 93
  symbiotic, 90-92
B horizon, 44-46, 59

Blast-furnace slag, 137
Bog soils, 50, 51
Border irrigation, 234, 235
Boron, 122, 124, 156, 157, 306, 307
  foliar application of, 122-124
Bulk density, 24

C

Calcium, 127, 128, 156
  foliar application of, 123, 127, 128
  function of, in plants, 123
Carbonation, 36
Carbon-nitrogen ratio, 100, 101
Cation exchange capacity, 72-74
Cationic exchange, 71-74
Chalk, 137
Chelation, 77
Chemical properties of soils, 69-78
Chemical testing, how to take sample for,
    299-301
Chemical weathering, 35, 36
Chernozem soils, 49, 50
Chiseling, 181, 182
C horizon, 44-46, 59
Clay crystals, 69-71
Clay pans, 184
Climate, soil formation in relation to, 38-
    42
Coarse fragments, 22, 23
Colloidal clay, 69-78
Colloidal properties of soils, 69-78
Colloids, organic, 71-74
Colluvium, 34
Compact horizons, restriction of root
    growth in, 188, 189
Compaction:
  effect of tillage, on peat, 276, 277
  effect of tractor tire on, 185, 186
Compost, 255, 256
Conservation, soil, 210-222
Conservation, water, 191-209
  contour tillage for, 198, 199
  forests as factor in, 199-201
  frozen soils in relation to, 204-208
  land-use in relation to, 203, 204
  terracing for, 196-198
Consumptive use, 226, 227
Contour tillage, 198, 199

Copper, 156
  foliar application of, 122, 124
Corn:
  deficiency symptoms in, 302, 303
  manure as a mulch on, 253
Corrugation irrigation, 233, 234
Cotton, deficiency symptoms in, 304
Cow manure, 247, 248
Cropping systems:
  examples of, 293, 294
  influence on soil structure by, 187, 188
  losses of nitrogen as influenced by, 264
  relation of soil erosion to, 215, 216
  soil conditions influenced by, 262-264
Crops:
  irrigation depth for, 228
  lime requirement of, 139, 140
  nutrients removed by, 166
  salt tolerance of, 288-290
  soil moisture in relation to, 290-293
Crop yields:
  depth of topsoil in relation to, 214, 215
  manure in relation to, 254
Crusts, surface, 184
Cyanamid, 150, 151
Cycle, hydrologic, 191-194

D

Deficiency, areas of mineral, 9-13
Deficiency symptoms, 302-307
  corn, 302, 303
  cotton, 304
  legume, 305, 306
  small grain, 304
  truck crop, 306, 307
Density, bulk, 24
Density, particle, 22-24
Desert soils, 50
D horizon, 44-46, 59
Drain, tile, 245
Drainage, 237-246
  benefits of, 239
  capacity, 242-244
  history of, 237, 238
  land classification for, 67
  soils that require, 239-242
  surface, 243, 244
  tile, 245
Dry land farming, 280-298
Dry sands, 52

E

Earthworms, 85, 86
Erosion:
  control, relation of terracing to, 216
    217

Erosion (Cont.)
  gully, 212, 213
  rainfall in relation to, 213, 214
  rill, 212, 213
  soil, cropping systems to reduce, 215,
    216
  splash, 211, 212
  surface, 211-214
  water:
    nature of, 210-214
    types of, 211-213
  wind:
    practices to control, 219-221
    problems of, 217, 218
    selective process of, 218, 219
Essential elements:
  for animals, 119, 120
  for plants, 119, 120
Everglades, Florida, organic soils in, 272,
    273
Exchange:
  anionic, 73, 74
  cationic, 71-74
Exchange capacity, 72-74

F

Fallow, 294-297
Feed, nutrients from, in manure, 251,
    252
Fertility, soil, long-time studies of, 267-
    269
Fertilization, crop increases from, 169
Fertilizer:
  acid-forming, 150, 151
  consumption, 164, 165
  formula, 157-160
    open, 158-161
  formulations, 157-160
  non-acid-forming, 150, 151
  placement of, 168, 169, 173-175
  profit from using, 169-171
Fertilizer industry, 146-149
  important dates in, 147, 148
Fertilizers:
  acidity of, 161, 162
  basicity of, 161, 162
  characteristics of, 150-163
  consumption of, 164, 165
  mixed, problems of manufacturing,
    161
  requirement of potatoes for, 265-267
  soil moisture efficiency increased by,
    171-173
  time of applying, 166, 168
  use of, 164-176
    on peat, 275

Field capacity, 110
Fixation:
    of phosphorus, 77
    of potassium, 76
Florida Everglades, soil of, 272, 273
Foliar nutrition of plants, 122-124
Forests and water conservation, 199-201
Forest site classification, 65
Formulas, fertilizer, open, 158-160
Formulations, fertilizer, 157-160
Fragments, coarse, 22, 23
Frost:
    concrete, 206
    granular, 208
    honeycomb, 206, 207
    stalactite, 206, 207
Fungi, 88, 93, 94
Furrow irrigation, 231-233

G

Gastropods, 87
Glacial till, 33, 34
Greasewood, 287, 288
Gully erosion, 212, 213
Gypsum, 282-285

H

Hay, alfalfa, composition of, 258
Heterotrophic bacteria, 88, 89
Horizon, 44-46
    A, 44-46
    B, 44-46
    C, 44-46
    D, 44-46
Horizons:
    compacted, 184
    dispersed, 184
    indurated, 184
Hydrated lime, 136
Hydration, 36
Hydrologic cycle, 191-194
Hydrolysis, 36
Hygroscopic coefficient, 110

I

Igneous rocks, 30, 31
Indicator plants, 286, 287
Indicators, plant:
    alkali soils in relation to, 286, 287
    saline soils as indicators of, 286, 287
Indurated horizons, 184
Infiltration, 106-108, 186
    effect of plow pans on, 186
Intrazonal soils, 50-52

Iron, foliar application of, 124
Irrigation, 223-236
    border, 234, 235
    corrugation, 233, 234
    depth of, for crops, 228, 229
    frequency of, 228-230
    furrow, 231-233
    land classification for, 66, 67
    sprinkler, 230-231
    water quality in relation to, 224-226

K

Kaolinite, 70, 71

L

Land-capability classification, 62-64
Land classification:
    for drainage, 67
    for irrigation, 66, 67
Leaching, loss of nutrients by, 115, 116
Leaf-tip burn, salts in relation to, 308
Legumes:
    deficiency symptoms in, 305, 306
    rotation with, 264, 265
Lime, 132-145
    air slaked, 136
    balance sheet for, 144
    chemical guarantees of, 138, 139
    crop response to, 135, 136, 139, 140,
        265-267
    dolomitic, 136
    function of, in soil, 134, 135
    hydrated, 136
    methods of applying, 142, 143
    physical guarantees of, 139
    use of, on peat, 275
Lime Line, 132, 280, 281
Lime pan, 184
Lime requirement:
    of crops, 139, 140
    of soil, 139, 140
Limestone:
    calcic, 136
    dolomitic, 136
    oyster shell, 137
Liming materials, 136, 137
Liming practices, 142-144
Lithosols, 52

M

Magnesium, 128, 156
    foliar application of, 128
    function of, in plants, 123
Mammals, soil-inhabiting, 83-85

Manganese, 156
Manure, 247-255
    artificial, 255, 256
    available water in relation to use of,
        253, 254
    care of, 248, 249
    cow, 247, 248
    crop yields influenced by, 253, 254
    nutrients from feed in, 251, 252
    poultry, 252, 253
    rabbit, 253
    reinforcing, 250, 251
    value of, 254, 255
Marl, 136
Mechanical analysis:
    Bouyoucos hydrometer method of, 17,
        18
    pipette method of, 17
Metamorphic rock, 30, 31
Microflora, 79-81, 88-95
Micronutrients, 128, 129, 156
    foliar application of, 128, 129
    function of, in plants, 128, 129
Mineral deficiency, areas of, 9-13
Mineral toxicity, areas of, 9-13
Minor elements, materials supplying, 156
Moisture, soil, crop response in relation
    to, 290-293
Moisture tension, 111
Molybdenum, 156
    foliar application of, 156
Montmorillonite, 70, 71
Muck, origin of, 34
Mulch, 219-221, 253
    stubble, 219-221
    use of manure as, 253
Muriate of potash, 155, 156

N

National Cooperative Soil Survey, 57, 61
Nematodes, 87, 88
Nitrate of soda, 150, 151
Nitrogen:
    fixation, 90-92
    foliar application of, 125, 126
    function of, in plants, 125, 126
    losses of, cropping systems in relation
        to, 264
    materials, solid, 150-152
    solutions, 153, 154
Nitrogen fertilizers:
    ammonia, 152, 153
    ammonium nitrate, 150, 151
    cyanamid, 150, 151
    nitrate of soda, 150, 151
    sulfate of ammonia, 150, 151
    urea, 150, 151

Nodule bacteria, 90-92
Nutrients:
    availability, influence of soil pH on,
        141, 142
    crop removal of, 166
    losses of, by leaching, 115, 116
    uptake:
        chemical forms of, 119, 120
        mechanism of, 120-122
Nutrition:
    foliar, of plants, 122-124
    plant, soil physical conditions influ-
        encing, 124, 125
Nutritional predictions, 65, 66

O

Organic matter, 97-105, 255
    biological properties of, 100, 101
    carbon-nitrogen ratio of, 100, 101
    chemical properties of, 98-100
    effect of tillage on, 183
    function of, 97, 98
    maintenance of, 101-104
    soil structure in relation to, 255
Organic soils, 22, 271-279
Oven-dry soil, 110, 111
Oven-dry weight, 110, 111
Overliming, 143
Oxidation, 35

P

Pan formations, 183, 184
    anthropic, 183-186
    clay, 184
    compacted horizon, 184
    dispersed horizon, 184
    indurated horizon, 184
    natural, 183, 184
    silt, 184
Pans, 183, 184
    clay, 184
    lime, 184
    pasture, 184
    plow, 183-186
    tillage, 183-186
Parent material:
    alluvial, 32
    classification of, 29, 30
    colluvial, 34
    cumulose, 34
    eolian, 32-34
    igneous, 30, 31
    lacustrine, 32
    loess, 33
    marine, 32

Parent material (*Cont.*)
  metamorphic, 30, 31
  moraine, 30, 33, 34
  outwash plain, 30, 33, 34
  residual, 30-32
  sedimentary, 30, 31
  till plain, 30, 33, 34
  transported, 32-34
Particle density, 22-24
Peat, 34, 271-279
  classification of, 272
  crops adapted to, 274, 275
  fertilization of, 275
  liming of, 275
  origin of, 271, 272
  special problems in management of, 277, 278
  subsidence of, 275, 276
  tillage compaction of, 276, 277
  uses of, 273, 274
  water control of, 240-242, 275
Percolation, 113-115
Permanent wilting percentage, 110-112
Permeability, 108, 109
pH, 74, 75
  soil, influence of lime on, 140, 141
Phosphate:
  dicalcium, 154, 155
  monocalcium, 154, 155
  tricalcium, 154, 155
Phosphoric acid, 154, 155
Phosphorous fertilizer:
  phosphate rock as a, 154, 155
  superphosphate as a, 154, 155
Phosphorus:
  application of, to manure, 250, 251
  fixation, 77
  foliar application of, 126, 127
  function of, in plants, 123
  materials supplying, 154, 155
Physical weathering, 35
Pipette method of analysis, 17
Planosol soils, 51
Plant-deficiency symptoms, correlation of, 309
Plant growth:
  early concepts of, 5
  essential elements for, 119, 120
  modern concepts of, 6
  soil factors influencing, 4
  tillage in relation to, 178-181
Plant nutrition, soil physical conditions influencing, 124, 125
Plant roots, 81-83
Plants:
  consumption of water by, 201-203
  essential elements for, 119, 120

Plants (*Cont.*)
  foliar nutrition of, 122-124
  indicator, 286, 287
Plant symptoms:
  alkali soils in relation to, 307, 308
  saline soils in relation to, 307, 308
Plant-tissue tests, 301, 302, 309
  correlation of, 309
Plow pan, 183-187
  influence on rate of infiltration of, 186
Podzol soils, 49
Pore space, 24, 25
Potassium:
  fixation of, 76
  foliar application of, 127
  materials supplying, 155, 156
Potassium fertilizer:
  muriate of potash as a, 155, 156
  potassium sulfate as a, 155, 156
  sulfate of potash as a, 155, 156
Potassium sulfate, 155, 156
Potato soils, fertilizer and lime needs of, 265-267
Poultry manure, 252, 253
Precipitation, 194-196
Productivity rating, 64
Protozoa, 87, 88

R

Rabbit manure, 253
Rainfall, erosion in relation to, 213
Reduction, 35
Rendzina soils, 51
Rhizobia, 90-92
Rhizobium, 90-92
Rock:
  igneous, 30, 31
  metamorphic, 30, 31
  sedimentary, 30, 31
Root growth, factors restricting, 188, 189
Roots, plant, 81-83
Rotations, legumes in, 264, 265
Runoff, 195, 196

S

Saline-alkali soil, 281-285
Saline soil, 281-285
Saline soils, 281-285
  plants as indicators of, 286, 287
  plant symptoms on, 307, 308
  reclamation of, 282-285
Salinity, soil, 281-285
Salt accumulation, greasewood in relation to, 287, 288

Salts, leaf-tip burn in relation to, 308
Salt tolerance:
  crops in relation to, 288-290
  rating of crops in relation to, 288-290
Sands, dry, 52
Sawdust, 256, 258
  composition of, 258
Secondary elements, materials supplying,
      156, 258
Sedimentary rocks, 30, 31
Separates, soil, 18, 19
Sewage sludge, 256, 257
Silt pans, 184
Slag, blast-furnace, 137
Sludge, sewage, 256, 257
Small grains, deficiency symptoms in,
      304
Sodium nitrate, 150, 151
Soil:
  associations, 47
  classification of, 38-53
  conservation, 210-222
  Dry Sand, 52
  erosion:
    cropping systems to reduce, 215, 216
    terraces to control, 216, 217
  fertility, relation of native vegetation
      to, 8
  formation of, 38-53
    factors of, 38
      biosphere as, 43-46
      climate as, 38-42
      parent material as, 42
      relief as, 43
      time as, 44, 45
  horizons, 44-46, 59
  management, 261-298
  microflora, 79-81, 88-95
  moisture:
    crop response in relation to, 290-293
    effect of tillage on, 183
    fertilizers to increase efficiency of,
      171-173
  organic matter, 97-105
  pans, 183-189
  pH of, 74, 75
    influence of lime on, 140, 141
  phases, 57, 58
  profile, 60, 61
    description of, 60, 61
  salinity, 281-285
  sample, how to take a, 299-301
  sampling, 299-301
  separates, 18, 19
  series, 57, 58
  structure:
    class of, 26, 27

Soil (Cont.)
  frozen soils in relation to, 204-208
  grade of, 27
  organic matter in relation to, 255
  type of, 26
  survey, 54, 55
    National Cooperative, 57
    report, 61, 62
    use of, 56, 57
  testing, 299-311
    kits:
      accuracy of, 309-311
      manufacturers of, 309-311
      portable, 309-311
    obtaining samples for, 299-301
  tests, correlation of, 309-311
  texture, 19-22
  types, 57, 58
  water, 106-118, 196, 228
    classification of, 109, 110
    measurement of, 110, 111
    storage of, 196
    tillage in relation to, 183
Soils:
  acid, reasons for, 133, 134
  alkali, 281-285
    reclamation of, 282-285
  azonal, 52
  bog, 50, 51
  chemical properties of, 69-78
  Chernozem, 49, 50
  colloidal properties of, 69-78
  Desert, 50
  drainage, 237-246
  drainage capacity of, 242, 243
  frozen water in relation to, 205-208
  intrazonal, 50-52
  lithosols, 52
  organic, 22
  planosol, 51
  Podzol, 49
  potato:
    fertilizer needs of, 265-267
    lime needs of, 265-267
  Rendzina, 51
  saline, 281-285
    reclamation of, 282-285
  saline-alkali, 281-285
  water-holding capacity of, 228
  Zonal, 20-48
Solution, 36
Solutions, nitrogen, 153, 154
South Dakota, cropping systems for, 293,
      294
Specific gravity, 22-24
Sprinkler irrigation, 230, 231
Straw, wheat, composition of, 258

Structure:
  class of, 26, 27
  frozen soils in relation to, 205-208
  grade of, 27
  soil, 25-27, 79-81, 187, 188
    influence of cropping systems on, 187, 188, 262-264
    organic matter in relation to, 79-81, 255
  type of, 26
Stubble mulch, 219-221
Subsoiling, 181, 182
Subsurface tillage, 219-221
Sulfate:
  of ammonia, 150, 151
  of potash, 155, 156
  of potash-magnesia, 156
Sulfur, 128, 156
  foliar application of, 129
  function of, in plants, 128
Superphosphate, ammoniated, 153
Surface drainage, 243, 244
Survey report, soil, 61, 62
Symbiosis, 90-92
Symbiotic bacteria, 90-92
Symptoms, deficiency, 302-307

T

Terracing for water conservation, 196-198, 216, 217
Testing, soil, 299-312
Textural triangle, 20
Texture, soil, 19-22
Tile drainage, 245
Tillage, 177-190, 276, 277
  and organic matter, 183
  and plant growth, 178, 181
  and soil moisture, 183
  contour, 198, 199
  deep, 181, 182
  insects controlled by, 183
Topsoil, 214, 215
Toxicity, areas of mineral, 9-13
Tractor-tire compaction, 185, 186, 276, 277
Triangle, textural, 20
Truck crops, deficiency symptoms in, 306, 307

U

Urea, 123, 151
  foliar application of, 123

V

Vegetation, native, and soil fertility, 8
Volume weight, 24

W

Water:
  available, 112, 113, 253, 254
  conservation, 191-209
    contour tillage in relation to, 198, 199
    forests in relation to, 199-201
    frozen soils in relation to, 204-208
    land-use in relation to, 203, 204
    terracing for, 196-198
  consumptive use of, 226, 227
  control, peat soils in relation to, 275, 276
  erosion:
    nature of, 211-214
    types of, 211-213
  -holding capacity, 228
  land-use to conserve, 203, 204
  luxury consumption of, 201-203
  quality, 224-226
  soil, 106-118, 183, 196
  storage of, in soil, 196
  table, 275, 276
Weathering:
  chemical, 35, 36
  physical, 35
Weight:
  air-dry, 110
  oven-dry, 110, 111
Wheat straw, composition of, 258
Wheat yields, soil moisture in relation to, 292, 293
Wind erosion:
  practices to control, 219-221
  problems of, 217, 218
  selective process of, 218, 219
Wood chips, 258, 259

Y

Yields, wheat, soil moisture in relation to, 292, 293

Z

Zinc, 124, 156
  foliar application of, 124
Zonal soils, 48-50

C